CONTENTS

CHAPTER ONE   The Sentence   1
Lesson   1   What Is a Sentence?   1
         2   Subject and Predicate   3
         3   Finding the Verb   5
         4   Complete Subject and Simple Subject   7
         5   Sentences with Compound Verbs and Compound Subjects   9
         6   Simple and Compound Sentences   11
         7   Chapter Review   13
         8   Building Vocabulary: Words and Experience   15
         9   Spelling: Do You Add *s* or *es*?   17

CHAPTER TWO   Words That Build Sentences   19
Lesson 10   Nouns   19
        11   Pronouns   21
        12   Adjectives   23
        13   Verbs   25
        14   Adverbs   27
        15   Kinds of Modifiers   29
        16   Prepositions   31
        17   Conjunctions and Interjections   33
        18   Which Part of Speech?   34
        19   Chapter Review   35
        20   Cumulative Review   37
        21   Building Vocabulary: More About Context   39
        22   Spelling: Choosing Between *ie* and *ei*   41

CHAPTER THREE   The Sentence Base   43
Lesson 23   The Sentence: A Framework for Ideas   43
        24   Action Verbs and Linking Verbs   45
        25   Finding the Direct Object   47
        26   A Linking Verb Needs a Subject Complement   49
        27   Adverb or Adjective?   51
        28   Chapter Review   53
        29   Cumulative Review   55
        30   Building Vocabulary: Getting Meaning from Context   57
        31   Spelling: Three Sounds of *ea*   59

CHAPTER FOUR   Building with Prepositional Phrases   61
Lesson 32   What Is a Prepositional Phrase?   61
        33   The Adjective Phrase   63
        34   The Adverb Phrase   65

i

35	Placing Modifying Phrases Correctly	67
36	Chapter Review	69
37	Cumulative Review	71
38	Building Vocabulary: Using the Dictionary	73
39	Spelling: A Trio of Confusing Prefixes: *pre-, pro-, per-*	75

CHAPTER FIVE   Commas Are for Clarity — 77

Lesson	40	How to Punctuate a Series	77
	41	A Compound Sentence Needs a Comma	79
	42	Commas for Interrupters	81
	43	Commas in Dates and Addresses	83
	44	Chapter Review	85
	45	Cumulative Review	87
	46	Building Vocabulary: Dictionary Meanings	89
	47	Spelling: Words Containing the Prefixes *mis-, dis-,* and *un-*	91

CHAPTERS ONE TO FIVE   Review — 93

CHAPTER SIX   Sentence Fragments and Run-on Sentences — 97

Lesson	48	Spotting Sentence Fragments	97
	49	Phrase Fragments	99
	50	The Participial Phrase Fragment	101
	51	What Makes a Sentence Complete?	103
	52	Avoiding Run-on Sentences	105
	53	Chapter Review	107
	54	Cumulative Review	109
	55	Building Vocabulary: Explaining What Words Mean	111
	56	Spelling: Adding *-ing* to Words Ending in Silent *e*	113

CHAPTER SEVEN   Understanding Capital Letters — 115

Lesson	57	Capitals for Proper Nouns	115
	58	More Capitals for Proper Nouns	117
	59	Capitals for Proper Adjectives	119
	60	Capitals for Titles	121
	61	Chapter Review	123
	62	Cumulative Review	125
	63	Building Vocabulary: Synonyms	127
	64	Spelling: Words Containing the Suffixes *-ly* and *-ness*	129

CHAPTER EIGHT   A Verb Agrees with Its Subject — 131

Lesson	65	Singular and Plural	131
	66	Matching the Verb to Its Subject	133
	67	Watch Out for Phrases!	135
	68	Problems with Pronouns	137

69	Reversed Word Order in Sentences	139
70	*Don't* and *Doesn't*	141
71	What About Compound Subjects?	143
72	Chapter Review	145
73	Cumulative Review	147
74	Building Vocabulary: Antonyms	149
75	Spelling: Does It End with *-cle* or *-cal?*	151

CHAPTER NINE   Using Verbs Correctly 153

Lesson 76	How Verbs Show Time	153
77	*See* and *Come, Do* and *Go*	155
78	Sorting Out the Problem Verbs	157
79	Nine Problem Verbs	159
80	More Problem Verbs	161
81	Using *Sit* and *Set* Correctly	163
82	Using *Lie* and *Lay* Correctly	165
83	Chapter Review	167
84	Cumulative Review	169
85	Building Vocabulary: Choosing the Precise Word	171
86	Spelling: Homophones	173

CHAPTER TEN   Getting Your Pronouns Straight 175

Lesson 87	Pronouns as Subjects	175
88	Pronouns as Subject Complements	177
89	Pronouns as Direct Objects	179
90	Pronouns After Prepositions	181
91	Pronoun-Antecedent Agreement	183
92	Chapter Review	185
93	Cumulative Review	187
94	Building Vocabulary: Choosing the Appropriate Word	189
95	Spelling: Silent Consonants	191

CHAPTER ELEVEN   Apostrophes and Quotation Marks 193

Lesson 96	Apostrophes Show Possession	193
97	Apostrophes for Contractions	195
98	Apostrophes: Some Don'ts	197
99	Punctuating Quotations	199
100	Working with Longer Quotations	201
101	Chapter Review	203
102	Cumulative Review	205
103	Spelling: Review	207

CHAPTERS SIX TO ELEVEN   Review 209

CHAPTER TWELVE Sentence Combining 213

Lesson 104 Combining with Adjectives and Adverbs 213
105 Combining with Prepositional Phrases 217
106 Combining with Compound Subjects and Compound Verbs 219
107 Combining Sentences into Compound Sentences 221
108 Combining Sentences with Other Conjunctions 223
109 More Conjunctions 225
110 Review of Sentence Combining 227

CHAPTER THIRTEEN Composition 229

Lesson 111 What Is a Paragraph? 230
112 The Topic Sentence 232
113 Choosing a Subject 234
114 Selecting Your Ideas 239
115 Writing a Good Beginning 243
116 Supporting Your Ideas 246
117 Coherence in Paragraphs 250
118 Using Transitional Expressions 253
119 Effective Conclusions 256
120 Writing a Narrative Paragraph 260
121 Writing a Descriptive Paragraph 262
122 Writing an Expository Paragraph 265
123 Writing a Persuasive Paragraph 267
124 Writing Friendly Letters 269
125 Writing Letters of Appreciation 272
126 Writing Business Letters 274

Index 277
Index of Vocabulary Words 279
A Note on Spelling 279
Consonant Sounds and Their Common Spellings 281
Vowel Sounds and Their Common Spellings 282
Key to ENGLISH GRAMMAR AND COMPOSITION 283

The Sentence

When you say something or write something, you want to be understood by other people. You want your words to make sense. When you put words together and they do not make sense, you have written (or spoken) nonsense, and other people will not understand you.

In this chapter, you will study some of the basic rules for making sentences that people will understand.

What Is a Sentence?

Look first at three different groups of words:

EXAMPLES   from the shelf with a loud crash (Something must have fallen. What was it? A flower vase? A lamp? A large book?)

melted from the heat (What melted?)

the well-trained horse (What did the horse do?)

If you said any of these groups of words, listeners might complain that they did not understand you, or might ask you what you meant. That is because none of these groups of words say anything by themselves. They leave the listeners dangling. They are not sentences. But look at these groups of words:

EXAMPLES   *A box of nails* fell from the shelf with a loud crash.
The ice sculpture melted from the heat.
The well-trained horse *stopped at its master's command*.

Anyone who heard (or read) these groups of words would know what they mean. They are complete in themselves. They are sentences.

A <u>sentence</u> is a group of words expressing a complete thought.

Note that when you write a sentence, you show where the sentence begins by using a capital letter. You show where it ends by using a punctuation mark—a period, a question mark, or an exclamation point.

EXAMPLES   My new toothbrush is green.
When will the parade pass in front of us?
That noise scared him!

1

AX

100

EXERCISE A. Half of the groups of words that follow are sentences, but the beginning capital letters and the end punctuation have been left out. In the space at the left of each, write *S* if the group of words is a sentence and *NS* if it is not. (Add 10 points for each correct answer.)

S. 1. three business leaders organized a fund-raising drive

S 2. she drove to Mexico City with her parents

NS 3. saying that custard was her favorite dessert

S 4. the road made a hairpin turn

NS 5. before doing any of the extra-credit problems

NS 6. the cost of a new car when you trade it in every year

NS 7. stayed up watching television until after midnight

NS 8. a red light blinking on and off at the top of the tower

S 9. we got lost on the new express highway

S 10. her shouts echoed against the steep canyon walls

100

EXERCISE B. Complete the following sentences by writing in each blank the word or words in parentheses that complete the thought. (Add 10 points for each correct sentence.)

1. Michelle and Sara ...run.... long distances. (run, running)

2. ..They.....practice on an indoor track. (And, They)

3. They must .stretch..their muscles before running. (stretch, stretching)

4. ..Warm-ups..limber them up. (Because warm-ups, Warm-ups)

5. .They both.will run in the race next week. (They both, Since they)

6. The race .takes... place at Longwood Track Club. (taking, takes)

7. A gold medal .....is...... the first prize. (is, being)

8. .Someone.might break the track record. (And, Someone)

9. Sara ..has..... never raced before. (has, having)

10. .She says. that she is very excited about the race. (She says, Saying)

2

Subject and Predicate

There are all sorts of sentences, some long and some short. All of them, however, have two necessary parts: a *subject* and a *predicate*.

The subject of a sentence is the part about which something is being said.

The predicate of a sentence is the part that says something about the subject.

EXAMPLE $\overset{\text{Sup}}{\text{Carmen}}$ $\overset{\text{Pred}}{\text{moved}}$ here from Cuba.

The sentence is *about* Carmen. *Carmen* is the subject of the sentence. What is being said about Carmen? Carmen moved here from Cuba; *moved here from Cuba* is the predicate of the sentence.

In the following examples, the subject is separated from the predicate by a red line. The part of the sentence before the line is the *subject*. The part after the line is the *predicate*. As you read each sentence, ask yourself about whom or what something is being said (the subject) and what is being said about the subject (the predicate).

EXAMPLES   The skier | glided safely between two trees on the narrow trail.
The price of a movie ticket at the local theater | has just gone up.

Notice that the subject of a sentence may be quite long and the predicate quite short—or the other way around. The important thing, of course, is not length at all, but the job the words do in each part of the sentence. In the first example, the words that tell what or whom the sentence is about are *the skier*, which is therefore the *subject*. Every other word tells what the *skier* did, and belongs, therefore, to the *predicate*. The second example uses several words to say what or whom the sentence is about. The subject is *The price of a movie ticket at the local theater*. The four remaining words say something about this subject and are the *predicate* of the sentence.

EXERCISE A. Use a vertical line to separate the subject and the predicate in each of these sentences. (Add 5 points for each correct answer.)

EX. Dad | bought a new car last week.   100

1. This new car | is blue and white.

2. He | goes to work in it.

3. We | take the bus to school.

4. We | will ask him for a ride next week.

5. My sister and I are interested in cars.

6. The family's new car is a small one.

7. Only four people can fit in the car.

8. Both my mother and father are happy with the car.

9. Half of the cars on our block are painted red.

10. Most of the people in our neighborhood must like red especially.

11. Several families on our block have small cars.

12. Almost all of the small cars are new.

13. Many of these small cars are made in Europe.

14. The cars are shipped to this country by boat.

15. This method of shipping can take a long time.

16. American car companies are also making small cars today.

17. Consumers are paying more money for gasoline.

18. Small cars use less gasoline than large cars.

19. Some owners of large cars have traded them for smaller models.

20. Car owners suffer during a gasoline shortage.

EXERCISE B. In the following sentences, underline the subject once and the predicate twice. If you are not sure what the subject is, ask yourself about whom or what something is being said (the subject) and what is being said about it (the predicate). (Add 10 points for each correctly marked sentence.)

EX. The frightened men ran across the street into the police station.

1. One passenger wanted a glass of water.

2. Some people can speak both French and English.

3. The cut on Harry's foot kept him out of the game.

4. The famous movie actress sat at a nearby table.

5. Hardly any news reporters were present.

6. The lights in the houses along the shore came on one by one.

7. The lighthouse could be seen from the boat.

8. Two detectives questioned him.

9. A goose with six goslings waddled down to the pond.

10. Ruth left her scarf on the bus.

Finding the Verb

The predicates you studied in Lesson 2 are called *complete predicates*. Most complete predicates contain a main word (or group of words) known as the *simple predicate*. The simple predicate is the most important part of the predicate—it is the *verb* of the sentence.

In many sentences, you can leave out all of the predicate except the verb and the sentence will still more or less make sense. This is because the verb is the most active and informative part of the predicate. It does the basic job of *telling something about the subject*.

The simple predicate, or verb, is the main word or group of words in the complete predicate.

EXAMPLE   The train | **moved**.

This is a complete sentence with a one-word predicate, *moved,* which is the verb. The predicate always contains a verb, but it often contains more.

EXAMPLE   The train | **moved** slowly across the bridge to the other shore.

This time, *the train* is still the subject, and the predicate is the rest of the sentence. But the verb is still *moved*. It gives the basic information about the train.

The verb in a sentence may be a group of words. The added words that make up a complete verb are called *helping verbs*—they help the main verb make a statement. In the following examples, the verbs are printed in red and the helping verbs are underlined.

EXAMPLES   The train | **was blowing** its whistle.

He | **had heard** the rumor before.

I | **will have left** before dawn.

The examples illustrate two of the commonest helping verbs. *Was* is a form of the helping verb *to be,* whose other forms are *am, is, are, were,* and *been. Had* is a form of the helping verb *to have,* which also includes *has*. These two important helping verbs are often combined with other helping verbs, such as *shall, will, can, could, should, would, will have, can be, should have been*.

The words *not* and *never* are frequently used with verbs, but they are not verbs themselves. They are never part of the complete verb.

EXERCISE A. Draw a line between the subject and the predicate. Then underline the verb, including any helping verbs. (Add 10 points for each correctly marked sentence.)

1. An artist from our town gave our school a picture.

2. She came into the school one day with the picture under her arm.

3. She asked one of the students the way to the principal's office.

4. The principal's office had been moved.

5. The busy student forgot this.

6. He gave the artist the wrong directions.

7. The artist lost her way.

8. The principal was going past her old office just then.

9. She noticed a confused stranger.

10. The students should be happy with the new picture.

EXERCISE B. Underline the verbs, including the helping verbs, in the paragraph below. (Add 4 points for each correct answer.)

SMOKE EATERS

1   Just before noon, the siren in the fire station sounded. The fire

2 department had received news of a major forest fire. The fire had been

3 raging for two hours already. It was out of control. The people at the

4 scene called for help from our fire department. They knew it would

5 respond quickly. Our fire department always helps in such emergencies.

6 The firefighters drove their trucks fifteen miles. At the scene of the fire,

7 they rushed their equipment into action. They put their hoses into the

8 river. With the pumps on the trucks, they sprayed water on the fire. They

9 coughed because of the smoke. They could not breathe easily. The smoke

10 also made their eyes red. No one would envy firefighters at times like this.

11 Everyone would respect their bravery. Despite all their efforts, the fire

12 raged for hours. The heat forced the firefighters back. Anyone would have

13 felt discouraged. Slowly, however, a change came over the sky. Then

14 suddenly the rain was pouring down on them. Torrents of rain quickly

15 dampened the fire. Without the rain, this forest fire could have been a

16 great disaster. Instead, it came under control.

100%

92%

6

Complete Subject and Simple Subject

Like the predicate of a sentence, the subject often consists of several words.

EXAMPLE   The dark-haired girl from Omaha swam across the lake.

About whom or what is something being said? (the dark-haired girl from Omaha) *The dark-haired girl from Omaha* is called the *complete subject* of the sentence. There is a main word in this, and in every complete subject. The main word in this complete subject is *girl*. The other words merely tell us *which particular* girl swam across the lake. *Girl* is called the *simple subject*.

The simple subject is the main word in the complete subject.

In this book, the *simple subject* will be referred to simply as the *subject*. You will have no trouble locating the subject of a sentence if you find the verb first. When you have found the verb, ask the question *who?* or *what?* before the verb. The answer will always be the subject of the sentence.

EXAMPLES   A tall, old oak tree fell on the house. (*What* fell? *Tree* fell. *Tree* is the subject.)

The angry fan in front of us leaped out of his seat. (*Who* leaped? *Fan* leaped. *Fan* is the subject.)

In an imperative sentence (a request or a command), the subject is usually not stated. In these sentences the person spoken to is understood to be the subject.

EXAMPLES   Open the window!
Wait your turn, please.

The subject *you* is the understood subject of each of the above sentences.

EXERCISE A. Underline the complete subject once and the verb (including helping verbs) twice. Two of the sentences are imperatives (commands or requests) with no expressed subject to underline. For these sentences, write the understood subject in parentheses after the appropriate sentence. (Add 10 points for each correctly marked sentence.)

EX. The whole basketball team will stay for dinner.

1. Any well-behaved person would have known better.

2. This car is powered by a solar battery.

3. I must have dropped our tickets for the movie.

4. Give them to your father right away.

5. George will have left for the movies already.

6. The television star appeared last week at the shopping mall.

7. The first cars in the parade passed near us.

8. Basketball is one of our favorite sports.

9. We can sleep out in our tents tonight.

10. Please send the package to me by parcel post.

EXERCISE B. Underline the complete subject, and then write the simple subject in the blank at the right. (Add 5 points for each correctly marked sentence.)

1. Seven bearded miners appeared without warning.   *miners*

2. The townspeople watched them with interest.   *townspeople*

3. This isolated desert town had never seen such a sight.   *town*

4. No passing traveler had mentioned seeing them.   *traveler*

5. Nobody knew anything about the miners.   *nobody*

6. The exhausted strangers trudged down the street.   *stranger*

7. They went straight to the county clerk's office.   *They*

8. Nothing could stop the hungry, thirsty men.   *nothing*

9. Each miner filed a claim.   *miner*

10. These new claims lay together on Bald Mountain.   *claims*

11. Several curious townspeople questioned the miners.   *townspeople*

12. The miners politely refused to answer.   *miners*

13. The exact location of their claims remained a secret.   *location*

14. The silent, secretive group stayed around town.   *group*

15. An ambitious young reporter tried to interview the miners.   *reporter*

16. The local newspaper wanted their story.   *newspaper*

17. The editor of the paper promised the reporter a large bonus.   *editor*

18. The miners agreed to remain silent.   *miners*

19. None would talk to the reporter.   *none*

20. The secret of the seven miners was kept.   *secret*

8

Sentences with Compound Verbs and Compound Subjects

Many sentences have subjects with more than one part or verbs with more than one part (or both). We call these more complicated sentence parts *compound subjects* and *compound verbs*.

A compound verb consists of two or more connected verbs that have the same subject.

EXAMPLES Joe **intercepted** a pass and **ran** for a touchdown.
Dorothy **jumped** the hurdle and **ran** to the finish line.
Olga **played** the piano and **sang** Swedish songs.

Subjects can be compound, too.

A compound subject consists of two or more connected subjects that have the same verb.

EXAMPLES An **atlas** or an **almanac** can answer your question.
June, July, and **August** are summer months.

There are also sentences with both compound subjects and compound verbs.

EXAMPLES <u>Rita</u> and <u>Herman</u> <u>hated</u> skiing but <u>loved</u> skating.

    <u>Mom,</u><u>Dad</u>, and my <u>brother</u> <u>flew</u> to Chicago and <u>drove</u> back.

Notice that compound subjects are usually connected by *and* or *or*. Compound verbs may be connected by *and, or,* or *but*. These connecting words are called *conjunctions*. Commas are used to separate the parts of a compound verb or subject having more than two parts.

COMPOUND SUBJECT <u>Willis, Ethel, and Paula</u> <u>have been nominated</u> for class president.

COMPOUND VERB The <u>rocket</u> <u>lifted</u> from the pad, <u>soared</u> upward, and <u>went</u> out of sight.

EXERCISE A. Draw two lines under the verbs in the following sentences. Then write *CV* (for compound verb) in the blank to the left of any sentence that contains a compound verb. (Add 10 points for each correctly marked sentence.)

CV EX. The hurricane <u>shook</u> houses and <u>blew</u> down trees.

.... 1. Branches and broken glass <u>littered</u> the streets.

.... 2. One family found their automatic washer two blocks away and brought it home in a wheelbarrow.

.... 3. Some parts were missing and never were found.

.... 4. Repairs to the washer would cost over one hundred and fifty dollars.

.... 5. They decided against the repairs and bought a new washer.

.... 6. A damaged painting was thrown away.

.... 7. They rehung curtains and washed the floors.

.... 8. A plumber came and pumped sand out of the cellar.

.... 9. Damage to the foundation and the walls was repaired.

.... 10. Most of the furniture was broken but could be saved.

EXERCISE B. Draw one line under the subjects in the following sentences. Write *CS* (for compound subject) in the blank to the left of any sentence that contains a compound subject. (Add 10 points for each correctly marked sentence.)

CS EX. A dog and a girl with a leash got out of the car.

.... 1. Tourists and sightseers visit the skyscraper.

.... 2. The overfilled pitcher promptly spilled.

.... 3. The lights on the neon sign flashed brightly.

.... 4. The headlights of the oncoming cars were blinding.

.... 5. Tables and chairs were turned upside down.

.... 6. Jagged rocks and pieces of dirt fell on the roof.

.... 7. A clown and a juggler rode at the head of the parade.

.... 8. The wallpaper and the gold paint were peeling off.

.... 9. Two hawks soared above the valley.

.... 10. A firefighter leaned out the window and dropped a small dog into the net below.

Simple and Compound Sentences

A *simple sentence* has only one subject and only one verb, although both may be compound. All of the sentences you have studied so far have been simple sentences.

A *compound sentence,* on the other hand, has two (or more) subjects and each subject has its own verb. It is really two (or more) simple sentences joined together, usually by a conjunction.

A compound sentence consists of two or more simple sentences usually joined by a conjunction.

SIMPLE SENTENCES	Roxanne <u>caught</u> a three-pound trout . We <u>cooked</u> it over an open fire.
COMPOUND SENTENCE	Roxanne caught a three-pound trout **, and** we cooked it over an open fire.

Notice the conjunction *and* which connects the two parts of the compound sentence. The conjunctions *but, or,* and *nor* may also be used to join the parts of a compound sentence. A comma is placed before the conjunction.

The big difference between a simple sentence and a compound sentence is not that one is long and the other short. A simple sentence may be quite long. A compound sentence may be quite short. But a compound sentence can always be broken up into its parts and the parts will still be sentences—they will make sense by themselves.

EXAMPLES   Frances Willard and Mary Lyon taught school and founded seminaries for girls in the nineteenth century. (simple sentence with compound subject—*Frances Willard* and *Mary Lyon*—and compound verb—*taught* and *founded*)

Fish swim **, but** birds fly. (compound sentence: *Fish swim* and *birds fly* make sense by themselves and can be written as two separate simple sentences)

EXERCISE A. Underline each subject once and each verb twice. Circle *C* if the sentence is compound, or *S* if the sentence is simple. Remember that a simple sentence may have compound parts. (Add 10 points for each correctly marked sentence.)

C (S)   1. Christopher Columbus was born in Italy and became a sailor at fourteen.

C S 2. Marie studied astronomy, geometry, and geography in school, and she read books about computers at home.

C S 3. Some people have warned me about the dangers of sky diving, but I am not afraid.

C S 4. For our early ancestors, the world was a flat plane, and the sky was a very deep bowl.

C S 5. The winner was brave, intelligent, and lucky.

C S 6. The knight asked for the king's help, but the evil monarch refused.

C S 7. My sister traveled to Europe and visited six countries.

C S 8. Before the American Revolution, the British had fought a costly war against the French.

C S 9. After the concert my date and I hurried toward the bus.

C S 10. Mercury was the messenger of the gods.

EXERCISE B. Insert the conjunction *and, but,* or *or,* depending on which makes the best sense in the sentence. Notice the example. (Add 10 points for each correctly marked sentence.)

EX. The pond was frozen, . *and* . we decided to go ice-skating.

1. Pat lives next door to me, ... we never walk to school together.

2. Our house is painted yellow, ... the shutters are painted white.

3. Ann Boston is the class president, ... she is also the yearbook editor.

4. You can rake the lawn, ... you can do the dishes.

5. Pearl must be sick, ... she would be in school today.

6. The oak was struck by lightning, ... it is still alive.

7. Rosalie worked in a lumberyard, ... Mario delivered newspapers.

8. I washed the car on Saturday, ... today I am going on a picnic.

9. Paul studied for three hours, ... he forgot to memorize the poetry.

10. Bart promised to pay me back, ... he never did.

Chapter Review

EXERCISE A. Some of the following items are sentences, and some are not. Circle *S* before the items that are sentences and *NS* before the items that are not sentences. (Add 20 points for each correct answer.)

S NS 1. You can often buy tacos from pushcart vendors.

S NS 2. We bought some tacos when we visited New York City.

S NS 3. Standing in Central Park.

S NS 4. Vendors selling tacos and tamales from pushcarts.

S NS 5. The tamales and tacos were delicious.

EXERCISE B. Some of the following sentences are simple, and some are compound. In each sentence, underline the *subject* (or *subjects*) once and the *verb* (or *verbs*) twice, including helping verbs. Watch out for compound subjects and verbs. (Add 5 points for each correct sentence.)

EX. After the fall of Rome, life and property were unsafe.

1. In A.D. 374 the Huns crossed the Volga River and entered Europe.

2. They were a nomadic and warlike tribe from Asia.

3. In 451 Attila and the Huns swept across Europe.

4. Attila spared the city of Rome, and his army withdrew from Italy.

5. In 476 the Germans fought and defeated the Roman army.

6. The defeat of the Roman army was a disaster for the Roman Empire.

7. The Romans had built a great civilization, but after the defeat of Rome this society fell apart.

8. Historians study the collapse of the Roman Empire, and they write articles about the people and customs of those years.

9. Poor Roman farmers would sell their lands and work for wealthy landowners.

10. In time these farmers became serfs and lost their private property.

11. Serfs were bound to the land and were sold with it.

12. The serfs would work much of the time in the noble's castle and would farm the noble's lands.

13. Cities often had walls around them, and large churches were built inside the walls.

14. People wove colorful tapestries, and these hung on the city walls.

15. Some of these tapestries have survived and are hanging in museums.

16. Small wars and invasions were common.

17. The markets and fairs spread new ideas.

18. Food shortages and diseases were frequent, and thousands of people died.

19. Later in the Middle Ages, strong rulers gathered armies and stopped the frequent wars between feudal lords.

20. Nations grew up with kings or queens as rulers, and the lords became their vassals.

EXERCISE C. Write the appropriate letter (*a, b, c,* etc.) in front of each sentence to explain what kind of sentence it is according to the following code. (Add 10 points for each correct answer.)

a—simple sentence with one subject and one verb
b—simple sentence with compound subject
c—simple sentence with compound verb
d—simple sentence with compound subject and compound verb
e—compound sentence

.... 1. Many famous speakers and writers blunder in their speech and make errors in their writing.

.... 2. W. A. Spooner was an English clergyman.

.... 3. He made many blunders during his sermons, and these blunders are called *spoonerisms*.

.... 4. Spooner would switch the first consonants of two words and would accidentally form two new words.

.... 5. He said the *bl*ushing *cr*ow for the *cr*ushing *bl*ow and a half-*w*armed *f*ish for a half-*f*ormed *w*ish.

.... 6. Spooner said *k*inquering *c*ongs, but we study *c*onquering *k*ings.

.... 7. Sometimes blunders and errors are humorous.

.... 8. Often television announcers and hosts will blunder and confuse a guest's name.

.... 9. A blunder in writing or speaking may result in a pun.

.... 10. Puns are plays on words and can be hilarious.

Building Vocabulary: Words and Experience

Language provides a number of ways of discovering the meanings of words and of adding them to your vocabulary. In these vocabulary lessons, you will learn to use these methods systematically. As a start, let us consider what is meant by *context* and how it can help you learn new words.

The context, or situation, in which a word is used shows what it means in that instance.

The first time you go bowling, you know the words *strike* and *spare* already, but you probably do not know what they mean in bowling. You learn in a variety of ways: from seeing someone make a strike or a spare, from hearing someone explain how it is done, and from observing how it affects the score.

These experiences teach you the meanings of the special words that go with bowling. When you use the words again, you will remember the *situations* in which you first learned them. In the same way, you learned the baseball meaning of *strike* and perhaps its meaning in fishing and in labor-management relations. Each of these situations adds something to the meaning that the word *strike* has for you. The situation in which a word is used—everything that you and others do and say—is called its *context*.

Study the meanings and examples given for the words below. Try to think of contexts in which you might use each word. Then complete the following exercise. The two charts (on pages 281 and 282) contain the symbols for the pronunciations given after each vocabulary word.

aristocrat /ə rís tə krat/, *n.* A member of a class that enjoys certain privileges and responsibilities by birth; a leader in society because of wealth, talent, or intelligence: *Many of the leaders of the American Revolution were aristocrats.*— aristocracy/ár is tók rə sē/, *n.*

balmy/bá mē/, *adj.* Mild, soft, soothing: *I enjoyed the balmy spring weather.*

blemish/blém ish/, *n.* Any mark of imperfection; a surface flaw: *This tomato is perfect, without a blemish. A spiteful tongue is a blemish on one's character.*

farce/fars/, *n.* A short, broadly comic play; a ridiculous affair or action, an absurd failure: *Slapstick comedy is the kind of play called farce. The baseball game was a farce—we lost 20 to nothing.*

gaudy /gáu dē/, *adj.* Brightly colored and showy but in bad taste: *The man's hand-painted tie, which was orange and green, was rather gaudy.*

mimic/mím ik/, *v.* To imitate closely, usually with a comic effect: *Small children often mimic their parents. Everyone mimicked Ellen's British accent.*

protrude/prō trūd/, *v.* To stick out from the surface of something: *Only a little of an iceberg protrudes above the water.*

ravenous /ráv ən əs/, *adj.* Frantically hungry: *After two days without food, the dog was ravenous.*

replica/rép lə kə/, *n.* An exact copy: *That painting in our living room is not an original but a replica of it.*

submerge /səb múrj/, *v.* To go or to put under water: *The alligator submerged in the river until only its head was showing.*

EXERCISE. Each of the numbered items below describes a situation, or context, in which you could use one of the words defined in this lesson. Decide which of the ten words would be most appropriate in each situation, and write the word in the space provided. (Add 10 points for each correct answer.)

1. *Situation:* A submarine dives to escape the enemy.

   Word: ....

2. *Situation:* A house is painted in red and yellow stripes.

   Word: ....

3. *Situation:* At Independence Hall in Philadelphia, where the Declaration of Independence was signed, you can buy a copy that looks exactly like the original document.

   Word: ....

4. *Situation:* It is a beautiful spring day, warm and pleasant, neither too hot nor too cold.

   Word: ....

5. *Situation:* Your father notices a nail sticking up from a board on the front porch and asks you to hammer it back in.

   Word: ....

6. *Situation:* The head of the British government is often a wealthy person whose family has been important in public life for generations.

   Word: ....

7. *Situation:* You laugh at an old movie on television in which two men chase each other around a roller-skating rink.

   Word: ....

8. *Situation:* Your mother is nailing a toolshed together, and your little sister gets her toy hammer and starts hammering too.

   Word: ....

9. *Situation:* After an all-day hike, the children come back to the camp for dinner, quickly gulp down all the food at their table, and immediately ask for seconds.

   Word: ....

10. *Situation:* You have been helping your parents paint the living room, and after finishing, you discover a patch that you forgot, where the original color shows through.

    Word: ....

Spelling: Do You Add s or es?

Before you begin this first spelling lesson, read the section "A Note on Spelling," on page 280, and become familiar with the two charts that follow it.

These charts will be referred to in many of the spelling lessons in this book. You will find them useful in learning to spell the *majority* of English words. Remember: When a letter appears between a pair of slanted lines, it is the *sound* that is being referred to; a letter alone refers to that *letter* itself.

Why does English add *-s* to some words and *-es* to others when forming the plural of a noun or changing the form of a verb? Why can't our language just add *-s*? As you examine the words below, notice which ones add just *-s* and which add *-es*.

1	2
chair—chair**s**	glass—glass**es**
brag—brag**s**	furnish—furnish**es**
youth—youth**s**	witch—witch**es**
succeed—succeed**s**	tax—tax**es**
gallop—gallop**s**	buzz—buzz**es**

Why do you suppose the words in list *1* need add only *-s,* and yet those in list *2* require *-es?* Pronounce the words in the left-hand column of list *2,* paying special attention to the final sound of each word. Notice that the endings all sound like some form of a hiss. Such hissing sounds are known as *sibilants.* The final sounds in these words can be found in the chart "Consonant Sounds and Their Common Spellings" on page 282 listed under /s/, /sh/, /ch/, and /z/. (The letter *x* is not listed on the chart because it usually represents two separate sounds: /k/ and /s/. Nevertheless, words that end in *x* have a final *sound* of /s/.)

Now, attempt to add still another sibilant, /s/, to these words that already end in a sibilant. Try saying *furnishs, taxs,* etc. The words become unpronounceable. To say these words and others with a sibilant at the end, you must add another *syllable, es,* to the original word.

Add -es to form the plural of a noun or change the form of a verb if the word ends in s, sh, ch, x, or z.

EXERCISE A. Pronounce the following words. Decide whether you must add *-s* or *-es* to each to form the plural of the noun or to change the verb. Then write the words in the blanks, adding *-s* or *-es*. (Add 10 points for each correct answer.)

1. villain ....
2. progress ....
3. highway ....
4. panic ....

5. accomplish .... 8. brick ...brick*s*.........

6. waltz ...*waltzes*............ 9. relax ...*relaxes*...........

7. approach .... 10. gas ...*gases*.............

EXERCISE B. Write *s* or *es* at the end of each italicized word in the sentences below. Again, use the "sound" test before deciding. (Add 10 points for each correct answer.)

1. Many college *campus* .... are less crowded these days.

2. Our dog *cough* .... whenever it smells dust.

3. Pam's little brother *follow* .... her everywhere.

4. Soda water *fizz* .... when you open the bottle.

5. There are two *church* .... at the north end of town.

6. Please put those books into two separate *box* ....

7. In the distance we saw two bright *flash* .... of light.

8. Most large cities have many *problem* .... to solve.

9. Jan broke her leg and must use *crutch* .... for a while.

10. Laura certainly *express* .... herself clearly.

EXERCISE C. Complete each italicized word in the paragraph below by writing *s* or *es* in the blank. Pronounce the words before deciding on the endings. (Add 10 points for each correct answer.)

1   The pelican *catch* .... fish with its pouch. The pouch is also used to

2   store fish while the bird *search* .... for more prey. The pelican *pass*

3   .... over the water. When it *sight* .... a fish, it *fix* .... the

4   point in its mind and *whizz* .... to the water. The *splash* ....

5   made by the pelican's body as it repeatedly *hit* .... the water can be

6   heard for almost half a mile. The pouch *stretch* .... to make room for

7   the fish and water. A greedy pelican often *fall* .... on its face because

8   of the weight of its pouch.

CHAPTER 2

Words That Build Sentences

Words are the tools used to build sentences. There are many words, but only a few *kinds* of words. Being familiar with these various kinds of words and knowing how they are used help you to build strong sentences. This chapter is about eight basic kinds of words. As a group, they are called the *parts of speech*.

Nouns

The subject of a sentence is usually the kind of word called a *noun*. When you write or talk, you are writing and talking about things, and nouns are the words that name these things.

> A <u>noun</u> is a word that names a person, place, thing, or idea.

In the following sentences, the words printed in red are all nouns. Notice which nouns name persons and which name places, things, or ideas.

EXAMPLES   Eudora Welty writes stories about the South.
San Diego is a city in California.
This table needs another coat of shellac.
Honesty wins respect from friends.

Here are some nouns of each of the four types:

PERSONS   Ann, Mr. Smedley, mother, children, painter, teacher
PLACES   Egypt, street, park, school, West Virginia, continent, home
THINGS   chair, clock, money, cobra, bicycle, dog, car, robin
IDEAS   charity, freedom, power, happiness, curiosity, wisdom

Usually there are several nouns in every sentence.

EXAMPLES   My parents heard Martina Arroyo sing *Aïda* at the Metropolitan Opera House.
Some drugstores sell appliances and stationery as well as medicine.
Some people value power above freedom.
A plane flying from Boston to Seattle crosses the continent.

EXERCISE A. In each line, write three nouns that name persons, places, things, or ideas, as indicated by the italicized word at the beginning of the line. Notice the examples. (Add 5 points for each correct answer.)

Persons   EX. ...*child*... 1............ 2............ 3....*Hedgehog*

Places   EX. ...*city*... 4............ 5....*country*... 6....*Planet*

Things   EX. *umbrella* 7....*donkey*... 8............ 9....*tree*....

Ideas   EX. ...*truth*... 10............ 11............ 12....*calmness*

Fill in the blanks in the following sentences with appropriate nouns. Do not use any noun twice.

13. My .... is painted red and green.

14. Marion likes .... better than ....

15. Geoffrey stood on a .... to hang the ....*picture*....

16. .... and .... are much bigger than ....*Lucy*......

17. ....*Brazil*.... and ....*a place*.... are both in South America.

18. We used the .... while the .... was broken.

19. Kay bought a silver .... instead of a ....*plate*....

20. She made .... with her new ....

EXERCISE B. Underline all the nouns in the following sentences. The words *we, us,* and *you* are *not* nouns. (Add 4 points for each correct answer.)

EX. For <u>weeks</u> my <u>family</u> had planned a <u>trip</u>.

1. One <u>day</u> we got into the <u>car</u> and drove to a <u>lake</u>.

2. Because the <u>road</u> was uncrowded, the <u>drive</u> took only thirty minutes.

3. The <u>water</u> at the <u>lake</u> was just the right <u>temperature</u>.

4. We dived in and had a good <u>time</u> for about an <u>hour</u>.

5. The swimming <u>place</u> has a <u>pier</u> and a <u>raft</u> with a diving <u>board</u>.

6. You can imagine our <u>disappointment</u> when <u>clouds</u> blew up.

7. A <u>storm</u> was beginning.

8. The first <u>drops</u> of <u>rain</u> fell on us.

9. Before we got to the <u>car</u>, the <u>rain</u> was coming down in <u>torrents</u>.

10. That <u>storm</u> certainly ruined our <u>outing</u>.

Pronouns

A <u>pronoun</u> is a word used in place of one or more than one noun. It may stand for a person, place, thing, or idea.

All of these words are pronouns:

COMMON PRONOUNS

I, me, my,* mine	we, us, our,* ours	anybody	one
you, your,* yours	they, them, their,* theirs	both	several
he, him, his*	myself	either	someone
she, her,* hers	ourselves	nobody	others
it, its*		none	

We can think of pronouns as noun substitutes. We use them in certain situations to make our meaning clear. Compare these two conversations.

WITHOUT PRONOUNS   Al and Sue were talking. "*Al* thought *Sue* would take that job," Al remarked.
"How did *Al* know that *Sue* had been offered a job?" Sue asked.
"*Al* was there when *Sue's* name came up," Al said.

WITH PRONOUNS   Al and Sue were talking. "I thought **you** would take that job," Al remarked.
"How did **you** know that I had been offered a job?" Sue asked.
"I was there when **your** name came up," Al said.

Notice how useful pronouns can be. In the first sentence, *I* replaces *Al* and *you* replaces *Sue;* in the second sentence, *you* replaces *Al* and *I* replaces *Sue;* and in the third, *I* replaces *Al* and *your* replaces *Sue's.*

EXERCISE A. Underline the pronouns. Notice the first line, which has been done for you. (Add 2 points for each correct answer.)

1   Mother saw Dawn and <u>me</u> at the door and asked <u>us</u> where <u>we</u> were

2   going. I had on my hiking boots, and Dawn was carrying a knapsack on

3   her back. "We are going on a hike," I told her. "Our science teacher is

4   going to show us how to build a tepee."

5   "It sounds like an interesting project," she said. "Be sure to stay near

6   the group. I don't want either of you getting lost."

7   We told her we would be careful.

8   Dawn and I and Mrs. Rogers headed for Bailey's Woods. When we got

9   there, we found a whole troop of scouts camping out.

*The starred words are called pronouns in this book but are sometimes treated as adjectives. Use the term your teacher prefers.

10   "We can't do much as long as they are here," I said.

11   "We can ask how long they will be here," Dawn suggested.

12   "Too long," I thought to myself.

13   We decided the scoutmaster would be able to tell us, but none of the

14   scouts could tell us where he was. They were by themselves. Several

15   suggested that he must have gone for water. Others thought he might be

16   searching for a good trail. One believed he was foraging for berries.

17   Then someone said that the scoutmaster was coming back. We saw him

18   bringing a large pail of water. They all filled their canteens from it. As

19   soon as their canteens were filled, they were ready to go. The whole troop

20   picked up their packs and hiked off. At last we had the woods entirely to

21   ourselves.

EXERCISE B. Cross out each noun in italics, and write a suitable pronoun above it. Sometimes one pronoun will substitute for two or more words, for example, *they* for *Ginny and Percy*. (Add 5 points for each correct answer.)

1   Ginny Patterson is the smartest person in our class. ~~*Ginny*~~ *She* plans to be a

2   physicist. *Ginny* is the only member of the class who knows what *the*

3   *member* wants to be. The rest of *the members* haven't decided yet. Ginny

4   is already doing algebra. *Ginny* gets special tutoring from other teachers.

5   Everyone in *Ginny's* family is remarkable. *Ginny's* older brother is a

6   champion wrestler and halfback on the high school football team. *Ginny's*

7   *older brother's* name is Percy, but nobody calls *Percy* that, because *Percy*

8   doesn't like it. Everyone calls *Percy* "Perce." *Ginny and Percy's* mother

9   is a famous singer. *Ginny and Percy's mother* was performing when *the*

10   *mother* met *Ginny and Percy's* father. *Ginny and Percy's* father is the state

11   champion chess player. *The father* is teaching Ginny how to play chess.

12   Perce already knows. Perce and Ginny play each other almost every day.

13   *Chess* is different from any other game, *Perce and Ginny* say. *Perce and*

14   *Ginny* also know how to play bridge, but *Perce and Ginny* prefer chess.

Adjectives

An <u>adjective</u> is a word that modifies a noun or pronoun.

Modify means *to limit.* An adjective modifies, or limits, a noun or pronoun by making its meaning more specific. Instead of saying that Cicely lives in a house, we can say that she lives in a *brick* house, a *red* house, a *square* house, or even a *square red brick* house. The adjectives *square, red,* and *brick* make the meaning of *house* more specific. They set Cicely's house apart from all the other houses that do not have these qualities.

In the following sentences, the adjectives are printed in red and the words they modify are underlined.

EXAMPLES   The new car is in the driveway. (modifies a noun)

Hand me that big book on the top shelf. (modify nouns)

Hand me that big one. (modify a pronoun)

Most adjectives answer one of these questions: *What kind? Which one? How many?* or *How much?*

WHAT KIND?	WHICH ONE?	HOW MANY?
an **easy** answer	**that** apple	**no** questions
the **large** apartment	**those** peaches	**thirty-two** helicopters
canned new peas	the **third** line	a **dozen** excuses
the **open** door	the **next** time	**many** friends

WHAT KIND?	WHICH ONE?	HOW MANY?
a **thin, round** cookie	the **oldest** show	**one** operation
a **funny** answer	the **highest** cloud	a **few** peanuts
heavy, yellow metal		
Portland cement		
smiling eyes		

Notice that several of the expressions above include the words *a, an,* or *the.* These three common little words are also adjectives. They form a special category all their own and are called *articles.* Although you will find many articles in this book, you may disregard them in any exercises on identifying adjectives.

EXERCISE A.   Underline the adjectives in the following sentences, and draw an arrow from each adjective to the word it modifies. Do not underline the articles *a, an,* or *the.* (Add 10 points for each correctly marked sentence.)

EX. Despite the terrible heat, everyone had a good time.

1. A hot, dry wind blew over the parched prairie town.

2. The temperature rose to ninety-nine degrees.

3. The weary citizens sought out the shadiest spots.

4. Huge, black thunderheads piled up on the horizon.

5. Panting dogs hid under the thickest bushes.

6. Vendors sold cold drinks to thirsty children.

7. Some fortunate people with air conditioners stayed in their cool and comfortable homes.

8. The long, hot day drew to a close in a fiery sunset.

9. Thunder rolled from the storm clouds, and a delightful cool wind stirred the dusty elms along the main street of the town.

10. Soon a heavy rainstorm brought an end to the hot weather.

EXERCISE B. Underline each adjective. Write the letter *a, b,* or *c* above the adjective to show which question it answers about the word it modifies. (Add 4 points for each correct answer.)

Write *a* if the adjective answers the question *what kind?*
b if the adjective answers the question *which one?*
c if the adjective answers the question *how many? (how much?)*

RUBBER

1   Natural rubber, which comes from trees in dense tropical forests, is an
2   important and useful product. There were few ways to use rubber in
3   everyday living until the twentieth century. It did not even get an ordinary
4   name until a famous scientist discovered that it could rub out pencil
5   marks. The first practical use of rubber was as an eraser. It was also used
6   to make waterproof coats. These early rubber coats melted in hot weather.
7   An American inventor named Charles Goodyear found ways to keep
8   rubber from melting. The discovery led to many new uses of rubber.
9   Today, rubber is used for electrical insulation, elastic bands, all kinds of
10 tires, and numerous other items.

Verbs

A <u>verb</u> is a word that expresses action or otherwise helps to make a statement.

A verb is a necessary part of every sentence. It has the job of telling something about the subject. When a verb expresses action, the action may be physical (*jump*), or it may be mental (*believe*). Verbs that express physical or mental action are called *action verbs*.

ACTION VERBS   move, run, hit, jump, whirl, eat, talk, sleep, think, understand, speculate, wonder, prefer

Some verbs do not show action of *any* kind. They help to make a statement by linking the subject to a word in the predicate that describes or explains it. These verbs are called *linking verbs*. The linking verbs include various forms of *to be* (*am, is, are, was, were, been*).

Besides *to be*, other common linking verbs are *appear, become, feel, grow, look, taste, remain, seem, smell, sound*.

LINKING VERBS   Ms. Byrne **is** the mayor of Chicago. (*Is* links *Ms. Byrne* and *mayor*.)
I **became** sad at the sight. (*Became* links *I* and *sad*.)
This sport **looks** easy. (*Looks* links *sport* and *easy*.)

EXERCISE A. Underline the verbs in the following sentences. (Add 10 points for each correct answer.)

EX. Toni <u>played</u> the bass guitar.

1. Amanda accompanied her on rhythm guitar.

2. They formed a musical group with two other friends.

3. There were many rehearsals.

4. After several months of practice, the group sounded very professional.

5. Suddenly the vocalist moved to another city.

6. Janet took the place of the original singer.

7. Everyone in the group liked her style of singing.

8. Carla became the manager for the quartet.

9. They performed for an enthusiastic audience at the summer concert.

10. This marked the beginning of a successful career for the band.

Helping Verbs   Often, the exact meaning of a main verb cannot be made clear without the help of a special kind of verb—a helping verb. In the following examples, the main verbs are printed in red and the helping verbs are underlined.

EXAMPLES   Mike **has** never **been** there.

Leroy's mother **has returned** from her trip.

The baby **should** not **be** hungry yet.

They **will** always **remain** friends.

Notice that words like *not, always,* and *never* may come between a main verb and the helping verb. Such words are modifiers and are *not* part of the verb. Learn to recognize these common helping verbs:

HELPING VERBS   be (am, is, are—was, were—been)
have (has, had)   will, would
do (does, did)   may, might, can, could
shall, should   must, ought (to)

EXERCISE B. Underline all the verbs, including helping verbs, in the following paragraph. Circle the helping verbs as well as underlining them. Do *not* mark any modifiers that come between a main verb and the helping verb. (Add 10 points for each correct answer.)

FRENCH BORDERS

1   Natural barriers (have) always separated France from neighboring coun-

2   tries. On the north, west, and south, it is protected by the sea. The

3   Pyrenees Mountains form the rest of France's southern border and divide

4   France from Spain. The Alps rise in the southeast. Only in the northeast

5   has there ever been any danger from invaders. There, France and Germany

6   meet along the banks of the Rhine River. Between France and Belgium, the

7   land boundary crosses flat, open country. As a result of its natural

8   frontiers, France is larger than any other European country except the

9   Soviet Union.

Adverbs

An adjective modifies a noun or a pronoun. An adverb is another type of modifier.

An <u>adverb</u> is a word that modifies a verb, an adjective, or another adverb.

EXAMPLES My father spoke **sharply** to me. (*Sharply* modifies the verb *spoke*.)

That pencil is **too** soft. (*Too* modifies the adjective *soft*.)

The game ended **rather** suddenly. (*Rather* modifies the adverb *suddenly*.)

We can sort out the various adverbs by the kinds of questions they answer about verbs, adjectives, and adverbs.

EXAMPLES Arlene went **out**. (*Where* did Arlene go? She went *out*.)

They left **yesterday**. (*When* did they leave? They left *yesterday*.)

We **seldom** hurry. (*How often* do we hurry? We *seldom* hurry.)

Jane dresses **neatly**. (*How* does Jane dress? Jane dresses *neatly*.)

Most adverbs answer the question *where? when?* (or *how often?*) or *how?* The *how?* adverbs, most of which end in *-ly*, form by far the largest group. Here are some of the most frequently used adverbs of each kind.

WHERE?	away, around, back, elsewhere, here, nowhere, out, outdoors, somewhere, there, upstairs
WHEN? (HOW OFTEN?)	always, finally, later, monthly, never, now, once, often, promptly, seldom, sometimes, soon, then, today, twice, usually, weekly, yearly
HOW?	badly, boldly, brightly, coldly, coyly, happily, loudly, lovingly, patiently, quickly, sadly, shyly, slowly, somehow, thoroughly, well

A few adverbs are often used with adjectives and adverbs to answer the question *to what extent?*

EXAMPLES He came home **very** soon. This is **more** important.

Constance is **unusually** intelligent.

TO WHAT EXTENT?	almost, more, much, only, quite, somewhat, too, very, especially, exceptionally, hardly, largely, nearly, particularly, really, scarcely, so, surprisingly

EXERCISE A. Circle the adverb in each of the sentences below, and draw an arrow from the adverb to the word it modifies. Watch out for adverbs which are separated from the words they modify, especially from verbs, as in the example. (Add 10 points for each correctly marked sentence.)

EX. (Often) at our house we start do-it-yourself projects.

1. (Yesterday) I decided on a special project.

2. I (carefully) shortened the legs of an old dresser.

3. (Next) I placed a piece of plywood on top of the dresser.

4. (Awkwardly,) I nailed the plywood onto the top of the dresser.

5. I (proudly) showed my parents this new desk.

6. They (then) suggested a new coat of paint.

7. I looked (around) for a brush.

8. Dad had left a can of paint (somewhere).

9. (Finally) we found the paint in the garage.

10. I painted the desk (completely.)

EXERCISE B. Fill in the blanks in the paragraph below with adverbs chosen from the lists of adverbs on page 27. Try to vary the adverbs you choose. (Add 5 points for each correct answer.)

1   I arrive . . . . at my piano teacher's house for my lesson. My

2   piano teacher . . . . delays my lesson by keeping another pupil

3   overtime. I . . . . sit for a long time waiting. I . . . . sit

4   in the waiting room. Sometimes I pace . . . . around the room. I

5   take the time to look . . . . The student who comes before me

6   plays . . . . I listen to him . . . . I never play

7   . . . ., but I do not always play . . . . well, either. I

8   . . . . enjoy waiting for my lesson. I . . . . enjoy

9   listening to other students. When they . . . . finish, I am waiting

10   . . . . My teacher . . . . comes out to say hel-

11   lo. I return her greeting . . . . The other student leaves

12   . . . . I . . . . like playing the piano except for practic-

13   ing. But to play . . . ., you have to practice . . . .

Kinds of Modifiers

You can turn almost any adjective into an adverb by adding -ly.

ADJECTIVE complete   perfect   hopeful   violent   smooth   nice
ADVERB   complete**ly** perfect**ly** hopeful**ly** violent**ly** smooth**ly** nice**ly**

Some adjectives, however, already end in -ly.

ADJECTIVES   lovely, leisurely, friendly

It would be awkward to add another -ly to adjectives like these in order to make them into adverbs. Therefore you do not make adverbs of them. Instead you usually use a group of words that give the same meaning as an adverb (in a *lovely* way, in a *leisurely* manner).

Some words may be used either as adjectives or as adverbs without any change. To be sure about how a particular word is being used, ask yourself what it modifies. If the word modifies a noun or a pronoun, it is an *adjective*. If it modifies a verb, an adjective, or another adverb, it is an *adverb*.

EXAMPLES The early bus leaves at six. (*Early* is an adjective modifying *bus*.)

We left early for school. (*Early* is an adverb modifying *left*.)

She jumped and landed hard. (*Hard* is an adverb modifying *landed*.)

Hard work gets results. (*Hard* is an adjective modifying *work*.)

Ellen is a fast runner. (*Fast* is an adjective modifying *runner*.)

She runs fast. (*Fast* is an adverb modifying *runs*.)

EXERCISE A. If the italicized word is an adjective, write *adj.* above it. If it is an adverb, write *adv*. When in doubt, find the word the adjective or adverb modifies. Remember that a word that modifies a noun or a pronoun is an adjective. A word that modifies a verb, an adjective, or an adverb is an adverb. (Add 5 points for each correct answer.)

1. The plane circled the field and *slowly* came in for a landing. adv

2. You should not drive too *fast,* but a *slow* driver can also be dangerous. adv

3. I arrived *late* for the meeting yesterday. adv

4. A *late* arrival is better than none. adj

5. Marjorie has been taking lessons on the cello *lately.* adj

6. The bell interrupted Arny's *leisurely* account of his trip. adj

7. Miss Remington certainly does work *hard.* adv

8. Pandas have *hardly* ever been born in captivity. *adv* ✓

9. That was a *hard* test, but you should have passed it *somehow.* *adv*

10. I watched the *early* show, but I did not go to bed *early.* *a*

11. The bus *nearly* had an accident yesterday. *adv* ✓

12. Tom walked towards the squirrel *quickly,* and the squirrel ran *away.* *adv* ✓

13. Mr. Acoli *first* said that I could make up the test, but on *second* thought he *adj* changed his mind.

14. "You will go *far,* young man," Dr. Young *often* assured me.

EXERCISE B. Underline the adjectives in the following paragraph, and circle the adverbs. (Do not underline *a, the,* or *an.*) If you are not sure about a word, find the word it modifies. Treat words like *my* and *his* as pronouns, not adjectives, unless your teacher directs you otherwise. (Add 2 points for each correct answer.)

A MODERN PLAYWRIGHT

1   Lorraine Hansberry is an especially interesting modern playwright.

2   Several years ago, New York drama critics proudly gave her their highly

3   respected award for the best American play of the new theater season. She

4   was then the youngest American playwright, the fifth woman, and the first

5   black to achieve this honor. Her much-celebrated play was *A Raisin in the*

6   *Sun.*

7   Miss Hansberry deeply believed that all people have within them the

8   ability somehow to change the universe dramatically. She vividly

9   recognized the vast power of human potential once it has been forced into

10   action. Because she clearly saw the incredible beauty of every person, she

11   knew it is an enormous error to waste lives. She knew that each person

12   has some dream. If this dream dies, then a very important part of a

13   person's life surely dies. No dream can be allowed to shrivel up slowly

14   like "a raisin in the sun."

15   Recently *A Raisin in the Sun* was produced on Broadway as a musical.

16   Now called *Raisin,* the musical version of the popular play incorporates

17   the tribal music and dances of the African people.

Prepositions

When you write a sentence about two different things, you often want to show how one thing is related to the other. Take a cat and a tree, for instance. You could say that the cat was *in* the tree, *under* the tree, *near* the tree, *behind* the tree, *above* the tree, or use yet another word. *In, under, near, behind,* and *above* are all prepositions.

A preposition is a word that shows the relationship between a noun or pronoun and some other word in the sentence.

EXAMPLES   I will gladly lend that book to you.
The red house on the corner is ours.
The dog hid underneath the porch.
The flood damaged several buildings near the harbor.
He ran after the bus.

Here are some of the most commonly used prepositions:

COMMON PREPOSITIONS

about	before	during	of	to
above	behind	except	off	toward
across	below	for	on	under
after	beneath	from	outside	until
against	beside	in	over	up
along	between	inside	past	upon
among	beyond	into	since	with
around	by	like	through	within
at	down	near	throughout	without

EXERCISE A. In each blank insert a suitable preposition from the list above. Try to use as many different prepositions as possible. (Add 10 points for each correct answer.)

1. We rode our bicycles . . . . the bridge and . . . . the trail.

2. . . . . an hour, we had traveled ten miles.

3. . . . . this rate, we would reach town . . . . suppertime.

4. There was a good wind . . . . us.

5. Sharon rode . . . . some broken glass.

6. . . . . fifteen minutes, her front tire went flat.

7. Sharon repaired the tire . . . . a short time.

8. . . . . this time we rested.

Generally, a preposition does not stand alone in a sentence. Usually, it begins a group of words that ends with a noun or a pronoun.

A group of words that begins with a preposition and ends with a noun or a pronoun is called a prepositional phrase.

EXAMPLES along the road   for you and them
near me   throughout lunch
below the bridge   between us and the airport

The noun or pronoun that follows a preposition is the *object* of the preposition. It may have one or more modifiers.

EXAMPLES A man on a horse rode across the field.

A man on a **yellow** horse rode across the **wet rocky** field.

EXERCISE B. Underline the prepositional phrases, including any modifiers, in the paragraph below. Circle each object of a preposition. (Add 5 points for each correct answer.)

TURTLES AND TRIBAL LAW

1   The turtle was an important animal for many Native Americans The
2   Iroquois believed that the world rested on a turtle's back. The turtle is
3   regarded by some tribes as very clever. In one story, through deceit, the
4   turtle beats the deer in a race. Some Pueblos perform a turtle dance. They
5   carry turtle-shell rattles at their knees, wear belts of bells, and carry a
6   gourd rattle in the right hand. During the turtle dance of the Iowa tribe, the
7   dancers imitate the turtle's movements.

Conjunctions and Interjections

A <u>conjunction</u> is a word that joins words or groups of words.

By means of conjunctions we bring together words and groups of words to form one complete expression.

EXAMPLES   <u>John</u> **and** <u>his sister</u> are studying.
            <u>Pat must stay</u>, **but** <u>Chris can leave</u>.

Conjunctions may also be used in pairs.

EXAMPLES   **Neither** <u>Ken</u> **nor** <u>Sally</u> is here.
            Both <u>Cathy</u> **and** <u>Marsha</u> have left.

Here are some frequently used conjunctions.

and	or	either—or	both—and
but	for	neither—nor	

An <u>interjection</u> is a word that expresses strong emotion and is not related grammatically to other words in a sentence.

It is easy to spot an interjection because it is usually separated from the rest of the sentence by punctuation.

EXAMPLES   **Whew!** You caught the ball.
            Well, you have my book.
            Hey, that is my pen.

EXERCISE. The following sentences contain conjunctions and interjections. Underline each conjunction, and circle each interjection. (Add 10 points for each correct answer.)

EX. (Wow!) The dress <u>and</u> scarf look beautiful together.

1. Phew! This is such a cold and rainy day.

2. I am wearing warm clothes, but I am still so cold.

3. Neither Marsha nor Pete can come to the show or the party.

4. The boys and girls in the show are waiting patiently.

5. Gee, this is a difficult assignment.

6. Jay or Mike might win the contest, but Pete won't.

Which Part of Speech?

Nouns, pronouns, verbs, adjectives, adverbs, prepositions, conjunctions, and interjections are the eight parts of speech. Every word in the English language can be classified as one or another part of speech. This idea is important and useful. When you analyze how a sentence is put together, you must usually decide what part of speech each word is.

A word's use determines its part of speech.

EXAMPLES   The **air** is fresh. I **air** the blankets. (noun and verb)

Todd is coming **down** tomorrow. The monkey ran **down** the ladder. (adverb and preposition)

I bought a new **radio**. I like **radio** programs. (noun and adjective)

She went **outdoors**. I like the great **outdoors**. (adverb and noun)

He performs **daily**. It is a **daily** paper. (adverb and adjective)

EXERCISE. Write in the blank provided the part of speech of each italicized word. Be sure you know how the word is used before you decide. (Add 10 points for each correct answer.)

EX. The rain may *last* all afternoon.   EX. ..... *verb* ...

EX. She was the *last* person in line.   EX. .. *adjective*

1. The children will *play* in the playground.   1. ....

2. John and I will be in the school *play*.   2. ....

3. The strong *current* here is dangerous.   3. ....

4. He disliked the *current* fashion.   4. ....

5. The bird flew *over* the mountain.   5. ....

6. Are you coming *over* tonight?   6. ....

7. Can you *reverse* the order of the players?   7. ....

8. She put the car in *reverse*.   8. ....

9. We looked *for* Sally.   9. ....

10. We waited patiently, *for* we knew she was busy.   10. ....

Chapter Review

EXERCISE A. In the blanks in the following sentences, write in the word that best completes each statement. (Add 10 points for each correct answer.)

1. A noun names a person, place, thing, or . . . .

2. A word used in place of a noun is called a(n) . . . .

3. We can think of these words as noun . . . .

4. A word that modifies a noun or pronoun is called a(n) . . . .

5. A word that modifies a verb is called a(n) . . . .

6. Adjectives answer the questions *what kind? which?* and *how* . . . .?

7. A(n) . . . . verb may be used with an action verb or a linking verb to make the meaning of the verb clear.

8. A linking verb is so called because it links the subject of a sentence to a word in the . . . .

9. A group of words that begins with a preposition and ends with a noun or pronoun is called a(n) . . . .

10. The noun or pronoun that follows a preposition is called the . . . . of the preposition.

EXERCISE B. Over each word in italics write one of the following abbreviations to identify its part of speech: *n.* for a noun; *pron.* for a pronoun; *adj.* for an adjective; *v.* for a verb; *adv.* for an adverb; *prep.* for a preposition; and *conj.* for a conjunction. (Add 2 points for each correct answer.)

NEW YORK CITY AND BACK

1 My *family* *went* to New York City *during* my parents' vacation. *We* had

2 *only* two days for sightseeing, so we *crowded* as much *into* the *available*

3 time as possible. *First,* all of us *took* a special *sightseeing* bus *for* the high

4 *points. This* bus *took* us to Wall Street, Radio City, and Chinatown. *It* also

5 went *through* Greenwich Village. The *next* day was *clear, and* we

6 *immediately* decided to go to the *top* of the Empire State Building. The

7   *view* was *excellent*. We *could* see as far as *Connecticut*. The *official* guide

8   told *us* the day was *unusually* clear. *That* evening, we ate *at a French*

9   restaurant. There *are* restaurants *of almost* every *nationality* in New York

10   City. *Afterward,* we went to Radio City Music Hall, where there was a

11   *huge stage* show. On our way home, we went *through* the Lincoln Tunnel.

12   *Despite* our *hurry,* we took *enough* time to see the *university in* Princeton,

13   New Jersey. It *has* a *particularly beautiful campus.* The *next* day we

14   arrived *home safely.*

EXERCISE C. Show the part of speech of the italicized words by writing the correct abbreviation above each word. Be sure you understand how the word is used in the sentence before making up your mind. (Add 5 points for each correct answer.)

1. This book is for you *and* Pete. con

2. The horse stumbled on the first *step* and refused to budge. noun

3. Willis ate a *leisurely* breakfast and sauntered off to school. ADV

4. Do you *like* milk or lemon in your tea? verb

5. Silence fell in the room *like* a weight.

6. She has the *will* to succeed, but she *will* need more than that. noun

7. Work *fast* or you will never finish in time. ADV

8. Geraldo ran a *fast* first kilometer in the race. ADV

9. The child gave the conductor a *friendly* smile. ADJ

10. We all had a good *swim* at the lake. NOUN

11. Do you ever *swim* after Labor Day? Verb

12. The street was *nearly* deserted. ADV

13. *Beside* the desk was a tall brass lamp. preposition

14. He ate an apple *besides.* ADV

15. I often *down* a quart of milk when I am really thirsty. Verb

16. Look *down* the mountain and tell me what you see. preposition

17. The runner fell *down* at the finish of the race. prep

18. They get their water from a *well.* noun

19. *Well,* it's nice to see you. interj

Cumulative Review

A. Draw a vertical line between the complete subject and the predicate in each sentence. Underline the verb, including helping verbs. (Add 5 points for each correctly marked sentence.)

1. The world of dance attracts people from many backgrounds.
2. Maria Tallchief was born on the Osage reservation in Oklahoma.
3. She was the prima ballerina with the New York City Ballet Company for eighteen years.
4. Doris Humphrey spent her youth in Illinois.
5. She joined the Ted Shawn and Ruth St. Denis dance company.
6. This dancer also created dances of her own.
7. One of the lead dancers with the American Ballet Theatre is Fernando Bujones, a native of Cuba.
8. The critics have praised him highly.
9. Any list of outstanding dancers must include Judith Jamison.
10. Her skillful jazz movements thrill audiences.

In each of the following sentences, underline the complete subject and circle the simple subject.

11. Mikhail Baryshnikov is a classical ballet dancer.
12. He has danced in a work called *Pas de "Duke"* with Jamison.
13. The lovely ballet is set to the music of Duke Ellington, the jazz musician.
14. Another famous pair of dancers is Margot Fonteyn and Rudolf Nureyev.
15. Their fame is worldwide.
16. Their devoted audiences often bought tickets for their performances well in advance.
17. The number of admirers of ballet seems to be increasing greatly.
18. People are interested in both dances that tell stories and dances that have no plot.
19. The great classical ballets such as *Swan Lake* and *Romeo and Juliet* are always popular.

20. A night at the ballet can be a memorable experience.

B. Underline the simple subject once and the verb twice in each of the following sentences. Some sentences contain compound subjects, compound verbs, or both. Be sure to underline all parts of a compound subject or a compound verb. (Add 5 points for each correct answer.)

THE GREAT WALL OF CHINA

1   The Great Wall of China is one of the most famous attractions in the Far
2   East. During the third century B.C. the Chinese people built the wall along
3   a northern border and stopped the invasions of enemy tribes. The wall
4   with its many watchtowers is thousands of kilometers long. Stone and
5   brick make the wall very sturdy. It varies in height from six to ten meters.
6   A walkway between three and four meters wide runs along the top of the
7   wall. In ancient times guards patrolled this long and narrow walkway.
8   Today, of course, China does not depend on the wall for its defense. The
9   wall, however, is a symbol of China's glorious past.

C. In the space to the left of each sentence, write one of the following code letters to show what kind of sentence it is. (Add 20 points for each correct answer.)

a—simple sentence with one subject and one verb
b—simple sentence with compound subject
c—simple sentence with compound verb
d—compound sentence

.... 1. The Chicago fire of 1871 was a terrible disaster, but some good results came from it.

.... 2. The rebuilders of the city had an enormous task but soon devised faster and better methods of building houses.

.... 3. Chicago's new ''balloon'' houses have been a common type of home construction ever since.

.... 4. The modern fireproof building and the first skyscrapers also began in Chicago.

.... 5. Some of the tallest and most original apartment buildings in the world have been built there.

Building Vocabulary: More About Context

In reading, the meaning of unfamiliar words can be determined by clues given by other words. This is known as determining the meaning of words by *context*. Context may mean the entire subject of a book or article, or only the surrounding words—the sentence or paragraph in which a word is used. The surrounding words are called the *verbal context*.

The verbal context determines in which of its possible meanings a word is used.

Most words in English have more than one standard meaning. The context shows which meaning a word *must* have for a sentence to make good sense.

EXAMPLES   She played the beam of her flashlight on the roof of the attic.
I could see that one of the beams was rotten.

In the first example you know that the *beam* is a *beam of light*. The second example makes good sense only if you take *beam* in a different sense—as the *beam of wood* that supports the roof of a house.

The verbal context may show a new or more precise meaning for a familiar word.

We build up our vocabularies from familiar words. When you read that "rust had *eaten* away the iron hinges of the door," you build on the general meaning of *eat (to consume)* for the more precise meaning of what rust does to iron.

Study the two meanings given for each word below. Be ready to decide which meaning fits each context in the exercise that follows.

adhere /ad hír/, *v.*   1. To stick to, as glue does. 2. To agree with a person, a group, or an idea.

agitate /áj ə tāt/, *v.*   1. To make something move in an irregular way; to shake. 2. To stir up the mind or emotions.

concession /kən sésh ən/, *n.*   1. The act of giving in to someone, or the thing given. 2. A business operated on the premises of another business, by a lease.

exquisite /éks kwi zit/, *adj.*   1. Very beautiful, delicate, or refined. 2. Strong, intense, extreme.

frivolous /frív ə ləs/, *adj.*   1. Trivial, petty, unimportant. 2. Light-minded, gay, silly.

humane /hyū mán/, *adj.*   1. Kind, warm, sympathetic. 2. Of things or activities tending to make human life better.

satire /sát īr/, *n.*   1. A kind of writing in which evil or foolishness is held up to scorn. 2. The use of wit and sarcasm to attack a person or action.

speculate /spék yə lāt/, *v.*   1. To think deeply about something, forming theories about it. 2. To invest money at considerable risk but with the hope of a good profit.

tolerate /tól ə rāt/, *v.*   1. To let something happen without trying to interfere. 2. To stand or put up with; to suffer or endure.

turbulent /tɚ byə lənt/, *adj.*   1. Very excited or confused. 2. Marked by irregular motion.

EXERCISE. The ten words defined in this lesson are used below in context. Only one of the two meanings given on page 39 applies in each context. Decide which meaning is appropriate, and write the number of this meaning in the space to the left of each context. (Add 10 points for each correct answer.)

.... 1. Adhesive tape is so named because it *adheres* to things.

.... 2. The mechanism of a washing machine *agitates* the clothes in order to make them clean. A wind *agitates* the surface of a lake.

.... 3. My sister runs the magazine *concession* at the train station.

.... 4. The design of the ancient tapestry, which was worked out in delicate colors and in great detail, was *exquisite*.

.... 5. We all enjoyed the *frivolous* comedy we saw on television.

.... 6. The *humane* hunter freed the trapped animal and watched it scurry away.

.... 7. The speaker spoke sarcastically of her opponents' program and made them uncomfortable with her biting *satire*.

.... 8. Until we have more facts, there in little point in *speculating* about life on other planets.

.... 9. After being indoors all morning, my eyes could not *tolerate* the bright afternoon light.

.... 10. The canoe swung wildly this way and that and nearly sank in the *turbulent* waters below the rapids.

REVIEW EXERCISE. In the space to the left of each word, write the letter of the best meaning listed at the right. (Add 10 points for each correct answer.)

.... 1. blemish   a. a member of a privileged class

.... 2. mimic   b. to go under water

.... 3. gaudy   c. to stick out

.... 4. replica   d. to imitate

.... 5. balmy   e. a surface flaw

.... 6. protrude   f. frantically hungry

.... 7. submerge   g. showy

.... 8. ravenous   h. an exact copy

.... 9. aristocrat   i. mild

.... 10. farce   j. something absurd

Spelling: Choosing Between _ie_ and _ei_

As you remember from your reading of "A Note on Spelling" (page 281), the English language has more sounds than it has letters in the alphabet to represent them. Furthermore, you saw in your examination of the consonant and vowel charts that the same sound can often be spelled in *more* than one way. These two facts about our language account for the difficulty almost all of us have in spelling words containing the vowel combinations of *ie* and *ei*.

The following words all have *ie* or *ei* in them: *fiend, friend, mischief, height, foreign,* and *rein.* They look and sound so different that you may think them impossible to group or spell correctly. Fortunately, there is a simple rhyme which can help you with the *ie–ei* problem:

RHYME			EXAMPLES
Use *i* before *e*,	brie f	belie ve	frie nd
Except after *c*,	recei ve	cei ling	percei ve
Or when sounded like /ā/,	frei ght	wei ght	vei l
As in *neighbor* or *weigh.*			

EXERCISE A. Using the information you have learned, write *ei* or *ie* in the blanks in each word in the sentences below. Say the rhyme to yourself to help you decide which order of letters is correct. (Add 10 points for each correct answer.)

1. There are . . . . .ght (one more than seven) club members present.

2. He is so conc. . . . .ted about his part in the play that he won't talk to anyone.

3. Laura is Uncle Ted's favorite n. . . . .ce.

4. In a monarchy, the king or queen r. . . . .gns supreme.

5. Jeffrey heaved a sigh of rel. . . . .f at his lucky escape.

6. When did you rec. . . . .ve that strange message?

7. How much w. . . . .ght did you gain?

8. We will try to keep the meeting br. . . . .f.

9. Lynn conc. . . . .ved of the perfect football tactic.

10. Karen and Marcia promised that they would always tell each other the truth and never practice dec. . . . .t.

Certain words do not fit into the groups that you have been studying. Here are five of these exceptions:

neither   either   seize   weird   leisure

In each word above *ei* is used despite the fact that it is neither "after *c*" nor "sounded like /ā/." Therefore, you must simply memorize the spelling of these five words.

Other exceptions are:

height   foreign

Can you explain why these two words are also exceptions?

EXERCISE B. Correctly fill in the blank in each of the following words with *ei* or *ie*. (Add 5 points for each correct answer.)

1. n. . . . . .ghborly	11. l. . . . . .surely
2. rec. . . . . .pt	12. gr. . . . . .ve
3. f. . . . . .ld	13. sh. . . . . .ld
4. h. . . . . .ghten	14. p. . . . . .ce
5. v. . . . . .n	15. sl. . . . . .gh
6. w. . . . . .rdly	16. th. . . . . .f
7. for. . . . . .gner	17. pr. . . . . .st
8. shr. . . . . .k	18. fr. . . . . .ndly
9. misch. . . . . .f	19. s. . . . . .zure
10. . . . . . .ghteen	20. rel. . . . . .ved

EXERCISE C. Use any ten words from Exercise B above in sentences of your own. Write your answers on a separate piece of paper. Underscore the *ei* and *ie* words. (Add 10 points for each correctly spelled *ei* or *ie* word.)

REVIEW EXERCISE. Pronounce each word below. Decide whether you must add *s* or *es* to each to form the plural of the noun or to change the verb. Then write the *s* or *es* form of the word in the blank. (Add 10 points for each correct answer.)

1. glass	6. relax . . . .
2. witch.	7. church. . . . .
3. tax.	8. approach. . . . .
4. buzz	9. waltz. . . . .
5. gas.	10. furnish . . . .

The Sentence Base

The flexibility of the English language makes it possible to write sentences of great length. But even the longest and most complicated sentence is built up on a straightforward and easily grasped framework called the *sentence base*. There are fundamentally only a few ways in which sentences can be put together. Once you recognize the basic kinds of English sentences, you can fit any sentence into one of these patterns, and you can build up sentences of your own on one of them. A firm grasp of the sentence base is one of the basic tools for saying *exactly what you mean* in writing.

LESSON **23**

The Sentence: A Framework for Ideas

A sentence may have a two-part base consisting of the simple subject and the verb.

EXAMPLES   The parachute jumper | sank gently down.

My father and Uncle Jim | went to Duluth and stayed for a week.

Both of the sentences above are built up on a two-part base consisting of the subject and the verb. The parts of the sentence base may be compound, as in the second example, which has a compound subject and a compound verb. All of a sentence except the sentence base may be omitted, and the sentence will still be complete—it will make complete sense.

EXAMPLES   The jumper | sank.

Father and Uncle Jim | went and stayed.

The following subject-verb groups are *not* complete by themselves. In both of these examples something is missing.

EXAMPLES   The batter hit (*What did the batter hit?*)
That man is (*Who* or *what* is that man?)

The missing part in both of these examples is called the *complement* because it is necessary to *complete* the meaning of the verb.

Many sentences have a three-part base consisting of the simple subject, the verb, and the complement.

EXAMPLES
¹ The <u>batter</u> | <u>hit</u> | a **single**. That <u>man</u> | <u>is</u> | a **liar**.

(numbers above: 1 2 3   1 2 3)

Like the subject and the verb of a sentence, the complement may be compound—made up of two or more parts.

EXAMPLE
Mary Ellen | <u>wore</u> | her new **pantsuit** and turtleneck **sweater**

(numbers above: 1 2 3 3)

Subjects and complements are never found in a prepositional phrase.

EXAMPLE   The stories in this book held my interest.

The subject is *stories,* not book, which is in the prepositional phrase *in this book.*

EXAMPLE   I bought one of her tennis rackets.

The complement is *one,* not rackets, which is in the prepositional phrase *of her tennis rackets.*

EXERCISE. In the following paragraph, underline the simple subject of each sentence once and the verb twice. Circle the complement whenever there is one. Then, in the space at the end of the sentence, write *2* if the sentence has a two-part base and *3* if the sentence has a three-part base. The first sentence has been done for you as an example. (Add 5 points for each correctly marked sentence.)

1   The <u>newspaper</u> in our town <u>held</u> a frisbee (contest). ( ) The judges
2   established a set of rules. ( ) The grand prize was a trip to San
3   Francisco. ( ) The judges created three contest divisions. ( ) One
4   division involved competition between two players. ( ) The second
5   division tested distance. ( ) The winner threw the frisbee farther than
6   any other contestant. ( ) The last division involved a test of accuracy.
7   ( ) Frisbees were hurled through a hoop. ( ) Salvatore and Annette
8   both entered. ( ) Annette practiced steadily for a week. ( ) This was
9   her first contest. ( ) Sometimes she and Salvatore practiced together.
10 ( ) Salvatore had competed for the last two years. ( ) The day of the
11 contest arrived. ( ) Both Salvatore and Annette were nervous. ( )
12 Salvatore entered the third division. ( ) He did not win. ( ) Annette
13 joined the first division competition. ( ) She was defeated by a more
14 experienced contestant. ( ) Annette and Salvatore will compete again
15 next year. ( )

Action Verbs and Linking Verbs

A verb is a word that (1) *expresses action* or otherwise (2) *helps to make a statement*. These two different jobs are done by two different kinds of verbs. These two different kinds of verbs are called *action verbs* and *linking verbs*.

1. An action verb may occur in a two-part sentence base or in a three-part sentence base.

		1	2
TWO-PART BASE	The big tiger <u>cat</u>	suddenly <u>leaped</u>.	

<u>Marion</u> | <u>stood</u> absolutely still.

		1	2	3
THREE-PART BASE	The ferocious <u>bulldog</u>	<u>chased</u>	the tiger **cat**.	

<u>Ben</u> | <u>remembered</u> | his last **birthday**.

<u>Caroline</u> | always <u>loved</u> | horseback **riding**.

Notice that the action expressed by an action verb may be either physical (*leaped, stood, chased*) or mental (*remembered, loved*).

2. A linking verb usually occurs in a three-part sentence base.

The most common of all linking verbs is the verb *to be*. You should know and recognize its basic forms: *am, is, are, was, were, been*. Other common linking verbs are *appear, become, feel, grow, look, remain, seem, smell, sound*, and *taste*. Linking verbs are usually found in sentences with three-part bases because their job is to link the subject with a word in the predicate that describes or explains it (the complement).

	1	2	3
THREE-PART BASE	That <u>cat</u>	<u>is</u>	a fast **runner**.

The car's two front <u>tires</u> | <u>were</u> | **flat**.

<u>Rhoda</u> | <u>seems</u> | quite **happy**.

EXERCISE A. The verbs in the sentences below are italicized. Circle the *A* to the left of the sentence if the verb is an *action verb;* circle the *L* if it is a *linking verb*. (Add 10 points for each correct answer.)

A L   1. Our school *produced* a play last year.

A L   2. Students *wrote* the entire play.

A L   3. All the actors *were* students also.

A L   4. One teacher *became* the director of the play.

A L   5. The play *portrayed* the history of our state.

A L   6. All the students in the play *were* outstanding in English.

A L   7. The play *went* smoothly, in spite of a few setbacks.

A L   8. The audience *enjoyed* it immensely.

A L   9. They *applauded* with enthusiasm at the end.

A L   10. Our teacher *seemed* satisfied with all of us.

Helping verbs are used both with action verbs and with linking verbs. The verb *to be* may be a helping verb or a linking verb, depending on how it is used.

EXAMPLES   He **was** hit on the head by an apple. (The helping verb *was,* a form of *to be,* is used with the action verb *hit.*)

By tomorrow, she **will have** been absent for three days. (The helping verbs *will* and *have* are used with the linking verb *been,* a form of *to be.*)

An adverb may come between a verb and its helping verb.

EXAMPLES   Janice will **surely** be on time today.
The chain could **too easily** be broken like that.
We have **not** been to the park.

EXERCISE B. Underline the verbs, including any helping verbs, in the following sentences. Be careful not to make any adverbs or complements part of the verbs. Circle A or L as before. (Add 5 points for each correct answer.)

A L   1. Lydia has eaten a dozen pancakes for breakfast.

A L   2. Seven jack-o-lanterns are too many for one Halloween.

A L   3. Fortunately, the ocean liner had not yet sailed.

A L   4. The key will be left in the glove compartment.

A L   5. Please do not give any more ties for the clothing drive.

A L   6. Our best friends may sometimes be our severest critics.

A L   7. She would probably have walked home along the river.

A L   8. The quarterback was taken out of the game because of a back injury.

A L   9. The new school could not possibly be ready by then.

A L   10. Her track career will soon be over.

Finding the Direct Object

When the verb in a three-part sentence is an action verb, the third part of the sentence (the complement) is the part that receives the action of the verb. This receiver of the action is called a *direct object*.

A <u>direct object</u> is a complement, or completer, that receives the action of the verb or shows the result of the action. It answers the question *What?* or *Whom?* after an action verb.

In the following examples the words printed in red are all direct objects.

EXAMPLES   Her <u>roses</u> <u>won</u> an honorable **mention.**

The <u>boys</u> <u>dug</u> a long, narrow **ditch.**

The <u>earthquake</u> <u>broke</u> **windows** and <u>toppled</u> **trees.**

Notice that a direct object occurs only after an action verb. To find the direct object in a sentence, ask *whom?* or *what?* after the verb. If you cannot find an answer to these test questions, the sentence does not have a direct object.

EXAMPLES   The <u>ferryboat</u> <u>hit</u> a rock. (*Whom* or *what* did the ferryboat hit? *Rock* is the direct object.)

<u>It</u> <u>sank</u> near the shore. (*It sank,* the subject and verb, are complete by themselves. They do not have or need a complement.)

The direct object is never found in a prepositional phrase. If you apply the test questions with care, you will not be misled by sentences like these.

EXAMPLES   <u>Wilbur</u> <u>brought</u> the **box** of cookies. (*Whom* or *what* did Wilbur bring? He brought the *box.*)

<u>Evelyn</u> <u>met</u> her **friend** at the store. (*Whom* or *what* did Evelyn meet? She met her *friend.*)

In question sentences, the direct object may come ahead of the verb.

EXAMPLES   **What** <u>did</u> <u>Wilbur</u> <u>bring</u>?   **Whom** <u>did</u> <u>Evelyn</u> <u>meet</u>?

EXERCISE A. In each sentence, underline the subject once and the verb twice. Draw a line through each prepositional phrase. Then draw an arrow from the verb to the direct object. (Add 10 points for each correctly marked sentence.)

EX.   <u>Mr. Wilcox</u> <u>had read</u> some ~~of the books~~.

1. They planted six beds of tulips in the garden.

2. A bright bolt of lightning split the tree down the middle.

3. The rain washed the topsoil away.

4. Geraldo recited the first paragraph of the Gettysburg Address.

5. The bus tires often scrape the curb.

6. The city put a fence of redwood planks along the road.

7. Naomi eagerly ate her oysters.

8. Our team successfully blocked the kick.

9. Karen and Lois both play the violin in the school orchestra.

10. The spy delivered the package of microfilm to the contact.

EXERCISE B. Circle all the direct objects in the sentences below. *Caution:* Not all of the sentences have direct objects. (Add 5 points for each correct answer.)

THE SECRET OF MIDAS

1   The ancient Greeks told a story about a musical contest between the
2 god Pan and the god Apollo. Pan played pipes of reed, and Apollo played
3 a silver lyre. Pan and Apollo sang songs, and then they asked the listeners
4 for a decision. The mountain god Tmolus gave the award to Apollo, but
5 Midas, the king of Lydia, preferred Pan. Apollo was very angry. He
6 changed Midas' ears into donkey's ears. One should favor the strongest in
7 contests between the gods. Midas hid his ugly ears under his cap. His
8 barber discovered the dreadful secret. Midas threatened the barber with
9 punishment if he told. The barber could not resist the urge to tell. He dug
10 a hole at the river and then whispered the secret into the hole. He covered
11 the hole, with the secret in it, with earth. But reeds grew up there. Every
12 time the wind blew, the reeds whispered the secret of Midas. "Midas has
13 donkey's ears,'' said the reeds in a whisper. The whole country
14 eventually heard the secret, and Midas was covered with shame. What did
15 Midas do then? The story does not say. Perhaps Apollo relented.

A Linking Verb Needs a Subject Complement

A group of words consisting of nothing but a subject and a linking verb does not ordinarily make much sense. Usually, a linking verb needs a third part to complete its meaning. This third part is what the linking verb links to the subject. Logically enough, it is called a *subject complement.*

A subject complement is a complement that describes, explains, or identifies the subject.

The subject complement may be a noun, a pronoun, or an adjective.

NOUN   Judy's mother is a **lawyer**. (*Lawyer* identifies the subject.)

PRONOUN   The winner of the election might well be **you**. (*You* identifies the subject.)

ADJECTIVE   I remain **friendly** with our former neighbors. (*Friendly* describes or explains the subject.)

The subject complement may be compound—made up of two or more words, usually connected by *and* or *or.*

EXAMPLE   Alice is both an **actress** and a **photographer**.

The following are often used as linking verbs.

COMMON LINKING VERBS

appear	become	grow	remain	smell	taste
be	feel	look	seem	sound	

Some verbs may be either action verbs or linking verbs, depending on how they are used.

LINKING VERBS   Lemonade **tastes** good.
Marcy **looked** sleepy.

ACTION VERBS   We all **tasted** the lemonade.
Marcy **looked** for the answer.

EXERCISE A. Underline the subject complements in the sentences on page 50. In the space to the left of each sentence write *n.* if the complement is a noun; *pron.* if it is a pronoun; or *adj.* if it is an adjective. If a sentence does not contain a subject complement, write *O* in the blank. (Add 10 points for each correctly marked sentence.)

adj. EX. Yesterday morning was disastrous right from the beginning.

.... 1. In the first place, the toast was soggy.

49

.... 2. The cream tasted slightly sour.

.... 3. The breakfast was not a good one in any way.

.... 4. The bus driver deliberately ignored me.

.... 5. The next bus was an express and did not stop.

.... 6. It had become a real crisis.

.... 7. An unexpected rainstorm appeared from nowhere.

.... 8. I had forgotten my umbrella.

.... 9. I felt more and more unhappy.

.... 10. It was a discouraging morning.

EXERCISE B. Write the abbreviation *LV* or *AV* in the space to the left of each sentence, to show whether the italicized word is a *linking verb* or an *action verb*. (Add 10 points for each correct answer.)

.... 1. Ferdinand *smelled* the flowers.

.... 2. The eggs and fresh toast *smelled* delicious.

.... 3. Imogene *appears* unusually cheerful this morning.

.... 4. An empty bus *appeared* suddenly at the end of the block.

.... 5. Because of her exercising, Anita is *becoming* stronger.

.... 6. At a hint of fire, the principal *will sound* the alarm.

Complete the following sentences by writing an appropriate linking verb in the blank. Do not use the same verb twice.

EX. Johnny Maxwell *must be* a very happy person.

7. Tomorrow . . . . a better day.

8. The moon . . . . bigger through a telescope.

9. On rainy days I usually . . . . sad.

10. The cat . . . . friendlier as we brushed its fur.

Adverb or Adjective?

You may not always be sure whether to use the adjective form or the adverb form of a word. Two easy rules cover most such situations.

After a linking verb, use an adjective to modify the subject of the sentence.

After an action verb, use an adverb to modify the verb of the sentence.

EXAMPLES   That girl certainly looks **hungry**. (*Looks* is a linking verb and therefore is followed by the adjective *hungry*.)

That girl certainly eats **hungrily**. (*Eats* is an action verb and therefore is followed by the adverb *hungrily*.)

Their manners are **bad**. (linking verb)

They chew their food **badly**. (action verb)

The most puzzling situations are likely to occur after words that can be either linking verbs or action verbs, depending on how they are used. In such cases you must be guided by the *meaning* of the verb. Does it indicate an action—something really happening—or does it simply connect the subject with its complement?

LINKING VERBS   She sounded very **cautious** to me. (*Cautious* modifies *she*.)

The water tasted **suspicious**. (*Suspicious* modifies *water*.)

ACTION VERBS   He sounded his horn **cautiously**. (*Cautiously* modifies *sounded*.)

The detective tasted the water **suspiciously**. (*Suspiciously* modifies *tasted*.)

EXERCISE A. In each of the following sentences, underline the correct word of the two words in parentheses. (Add 10 points for each correct answer.)

1. He plays the piano very (beautiful, beautifully).

2. Maria, to our surprise, suddenly appeared (happy, happily).

3. Mrs. Kennedy got up and talked (brilliant, brilliantly).

4. That roast beef smells absolutely (delicious, deliciously).

5. Paying close attention, Maxine did the work (skillful, skillfully).

6. The problem seems (clear, clearly) enough to me.

7. On her first try, she painted rather (crude, crudely).

8. The parachutist floated (gentle, gently) down to earth.

9. He reads (quick, quickly).

10. Our neighbor appeared (sudden, suddenly) at the door with a message.

GOOD AND WELL

Distinguish between *good* and *well* as modifiers.

Use good to modify nouns and pronouns. Use well to modify verbs.

NONSTANDARD	The pianist played very *good*. She is working out *good*.
STANDARD	The pianist played very **well**. She is working out **well**.

Well is used as an adjective only when it means *in good health*.

STANDARD	She feels **well** now. (She no longer feels sick.)
ALSO STANDARD	She felt **good** after her exhilarating swim.

EXERCISE B.   For each of the following sentences underline the correct word of the two words in parentheses. (Add 10 points for each correct answer.)

1. The sailor certainly whittles (good, well).

2. After so many lessons, he finally drives (good, well).

3. From your description, that movie certainly sounds (good, well).

4. Everybody should eat (good, well) on their vacation.

5. No airplane could serve its passengers so (good, well).

6. The stream looks (good, well), but it may still be polluted.

7. In the darkness of the cave, they couldn't see very (good, well).

8. Everything you do must be done (good, well).

9. Aunt Martha was seriously ill, but she is now quite (good, well).

10. A cold shower seems especially (good, well) at the end of a hot day.

Chapter Review

EXERCISE A. Underline the verb, including any helping verbs, in each sentence. Then, if the verb is an action verb, write *AV* in the space provided at the left; if the verb is a linking verb, write *LV* in the space. (Add 10 points for each correctly marked sentence.)

.... 1. A man gathered mussels from a brook near Paterson, New Jersey, in 1857.

.... 2. Many hard objects were found in the cooked mussels.

.... 3. These objects certainly appeared worthless.

.... 4. The man threw some of them away.

.... 5. Then he grew thoughtful.

.... 6. He appeared at a jeweler's house with the remaining uncooked mussels.

.... 7. The jeweler gave him about thirty dollars for all the remaining mussels.

.... 8. The man felt excited by his unexpected good fortune.

.... 9. Eventually a pearl in one of the mussels was sold to a large jewelry firm for nine hundred dollars.

.... 10. Later this same pearl was purchased by an empress.

EXERCISE B. In each of the following sentences, underline the correct word of the two words in parentheses. (Add 10 points for each correct answer.)

1. The opera singer's voice sounded (good, well) last night.

2. My cousin still types (bad, badly) despite six weeks of practice.

3. He reacted (sudden, suddenly) to my suggestion.

4. After two weeks of the flu, Sara finally feels (good, well) again.

5. These roses smell (sweet, sweetly).

6. Sandra does everything (well, good).

7. Come (quick, quickly)! I smell smoke.

8. I felt (good, well) after our swim.

9. I can finish this homework (easy, easily) by nine o'clock.

10. My beagle does not see (well, good).

EXERCISE C. In the following paragraph, underline the subject of each sentence once and the verb twice. Circle each complement. In the space after each sentence, write a *2* if the sentence has a two-part base and a *3* if it has a three-part base. (Add 2 points for each correct answer.)

1 The Pawnee tribe tells a pretty story about the origin of the wild flower
2 larkspur. (   ) Dream Woman is a Pawnee goddess. (   ) She lives on
3 the other side of the sky. (   ) One day, the earth people attracted her
4 attention. (   ) She became curious about their activities. (   ) She cut a
5 hole in the sky and made a stalk for use as a ladder. (   ) The stalk was
6 fashioned out of the green material lining the sky. (   ) A few flecks of
7 the outside blue stuck to it also. (   ) Dream Woman descended the stalk.
8 (   ) But it was brittle from exposure to the sun. (   ) It broke into
9 thousands of pieces under her weight. (   ) The scattered pieces became
10 larkspur. (   ) You can find larkspur in many parts of the United States.
11 (   )

EXERCISE D. In the following paragraph, underline the direct objects once, and circle the subject complements. Some sentences have more than one complement. (Add 5 points for each correct answer.)

1 Merlin, the magician, once lent his magic wand to young Prince Arthur
2 for a while. The wand was very powerful. Arthur used it for his own
3 private purposes. Arthur's nurse called him for dinner. He was not
4 hungry in the least. He promptly transformed her into a crow. She felt
5 ridiculous in a tree and scolded him loudly from her perch. Arthur
6 mocked her and offered some kernels of corn to her. He did not fear a
7 crow. Eventually, Merlin came in search of the nurse. Arthur denied any
8 knowledge of her whereabouts. Merlin was wise and knew Arthur's
9 tricks. "You," said Merlin immediately, "are a liar!" Arthur could not
10 fool Merlin. Merlin promptly took back his magic wand. He changed the
11 crow back into the nurse. The nurse remained indignant and quite rightly
12 sent Arthur to bed without any supper.

Cumulative Review

A. Underline the subject of each sentence once and the verb twice. Include all parts of compound subjects and verbs. (Add 5 points for each correct answer.)

MIGHTY RIVERS OF AFRICA

1   The Nile and the Congo are the longest rivers in Africa. The Nile flows
2   through the desert and empties into the Mediterranean. The Congo makes a
3   great loop through the jungle and flows into the Atlantic. Most of Egypt's
4   water for irrigation and for sanitation comes from the Nile. Egypt has a dry
5   climate and depends on the Nile for a livelihood. The Congo and its
6   neighbors have a very wet climate. Some of the world's heaviest rainfalls
7   and some of the thickest jungles can be observed on the west coast of
8   Africa.

B. Write the letter *a, b, c,* or *d* in front of each sentence to explain what kind of sentence it is according to the following code. (Add 10 points for each correct answer.)

a—simple sentence with compound subject
b—simple sentence with compound verb
c—simple sentence with compound subject and compound verb
d—compound sentence

.... 1. My sister and I go hiking in the woods or try water-skiing at the beach.

.... 2. Unfortunately, we cannot do both at the same time, and no one else can, either.

.... 3. Sometimes I want to go hiking and she wants to water-ski.

.... 4. Then we argue and squabble about it.

.... 5. She prefers water-skiing, but I like hiking.

.... 6. We can always flip a coin and make up our minds that way.

.... 7. Dad and Mom both enjoy water-skiing but have little interest in hiking.

.... 8. Hiking near an isolated lake with a powerful motorboat available would be an ideal vacation for us, but such a vacation does not seem possible.

.... 9. Secluded hiking trails and gasoline-powered sports usually do not go together.

.... 10. For my part, I enjoy the silence of the deep woods and regret the shortness of our hiking trips in them.

C. Over each word in italics, write one of the following abbreviations to identify its part of speech: *n.* for noun; *pron.* for pronoun; *adj.* for adjective; *v.* for verb; *adv.* for adverb; *prep.* for preposition; and *conj.* for conjunction. (Add 2 points for each correct answer.)

INDUSTRIAL HISTORY

1   Railroads were *invented* in England over a century ago. *They* were

2   *originally* used to move coal *from* the *mine* to the factory. George

3   Stephenson's *powerful* locomotive *was* the *first* locomotive ever made.

4   *His* invention put *stagecoaches and* canals out of business. *Within twenty*

5   years, England was *covered* by a network *of* railroads. *Railway* construc-

6   tion brought sudden *wealth* to the country. People *bought* and sold

7   railroad stocks. *Some people* became rich *very* quickly. At *almost* the

8   *same* time the telegraph was invented by an American. *Telegraph* systems

9   made long-distance railroads and *fast* trains possible by providing a *means*

10   of quick and reliable *signal* control. The *steamship* was a *later* develop-

11   ment. *Wood* passed out of *favor* for boat-building and was replaced by

12   iron. The *demand* for iron rails *and* iron ships caused a great *expansion* in

13   England's *iron* and *steel* industry. *For* many years, *England* was by far

14   the world's *leading* producer of iron. Not *until* the *twentieth* century did

15   the United States *pass* England *in* steel production. As the automobile

16   *developed,* steel *manufacture* increased even *more,* and *today* the *car*

17   makers are large buyers of *steel,* both *here* and in England.

Building Vocabulary: Getting Meaning from Context

You generally meet an unfamiliar word in a context of some kind, surrounded by other words (the *verbal context*) whose meaning you already know. The words you know give clues to the meaning of the new word. If you can interpret these clues, you can often guess the meaning of the unfamiliar word.

The verbal context provides clues to the meanings of unfamiliar words.

Suppose that at first glance you are not sure what the word *chastised* means in the following sentence.

EXAMPLE   The chastised student was not allowed to go on the trip.

The rest of the sentence suggests that *chastised* must have something to do with being punished since the student was not allowed to go on the trip. *Punished* would be a good guess at the meaning of *chastised*.

Caution: Check your context guesses by looking up the words in a dictionary, both to make sure you are right about the meanings and to find other, related meanings.

EXERCISE. Each of the words printed in red is followed by a passage in which it is used. Determine the meaning of each word from its context. Then, in the space to the left of each word write the number of the meaning that fits this context, from the list of meanings given on page 58. (Add 10 points for each correct answer.)

WORDS IN CONTEXT

.... **inflammable** /in flám ə bəl/, *adj.*   At one time, most gasoline trucks dragged a short length of chain behind them to ground sparks that might endanger their *inflammable* contents.

.... **extinct** /ik stíngkt/, *adj.*   The passenger pigeon is one of the best examples of a species that has become *extinct* because of hunters. In recent years, the whooping crane has become nearly *extinct,* but may yet survive.

.... **refute** /ri fyút/, *v.*   Janine claimed that the pioneering spirit was dead in America. We easily *refuted* her with examples of people in modern life who had shown the independent spirit of the pioneers.

.... **concise** /kən sís/, *adj.*   Mr. Watson asked me to make my themes more *concise*. He pointed out that there is no virtue in using two words where only one is needed.

.... **coincide** /kṓ in síd/, *v.*   My spring vacation did not *coincide* with Bernice's this year. Her vacation began a week earlier than mine.

.... **eject** /i jékt/, *v.*   The umpire can *eject* a player from the game, and that player is not allowed to return.

.... **asset** /ás et/, *n.*   Marjorie may not be the smartest person in the class, but she gets the best grades. A willingness to work hard is her best *asset*.

.... **distort** /dis tórt/, *v.*   A newspaper may *distort* the truth by printing a candidate's remarks out of context.

.... **catastrophe** /kə tás trə fē/, *n.*   The San Francisco earthquake, which was followed by a fire, was a terrible *catastrophe*.

.... **compensate** /kóm pən sāt/, *v.*   The waiter felt that the customer's tip did not *compensate* him for the efforts he had made.

WORD MEANINGS

1. *Singular:* Anything of value belonging to a person or business. *Plural:* Everything belonging to a person or business that might be turned into money with which to pay debts.
2. A sudden and complete disaster; a great misfortune.
3. To happen at the same time.
4. To pay someone for something, especially a service.
5. Brief; saying much in a few words.
6. Of ideas, to make false in some way, to give a wrong impression of.
7. To throw or drive out.
8. No longer living or active; of species of animals without living descendants.
9. Easily set on fire.
10. To disprove a person or a person's views by giving arguments or evidence against them.

REVIEW EXERCISE. In the space to the left of each question, write the lettered word that best explains the word in italics. (Add 25 points for each correct answer.)

.... 1. If you *adhere* to an idea, do you (a) favor or (b) oppose it?

.... 2. If you are *agitated* in your mind, are you (a) peaceful or (b) upset?

.... 3. Would an *exquisite* work of art be (a) beautiful or (b) ugly?

.... 4. Would a *humane* action be (a) kind or (b) cruel?

Spelling: Three Sounds of ea

A letter combination that causes many spelling problems is *ea*. This pair of vowels is troublesome because it is used to represent several vowel sounds. Pronounce the words in the three word groups below:

1	*2*	*3*
pl**ea**sure	t**ea**ch	st**ea**k
h**ea**ven	app**ea**l	gr**ea**t

Try to identify the three different sounds of *ea* illustrated by the three word groups. In group *1*, *ea* sounds like /e/; in group *2*, like /ē/; in group *3*, like /ā/. This confusion exists because spelling has not changed to keep pace with changes in pronunciation. About a thousand years ago, during the period when Old English was spoken, both the *e* and the *a* in *ea* were sounded. The word *heaven*, for example, probably sounded something like this: /hā́ ə fen/. (The /f/ sound was often changed to a /v/ sound through the centuries.) Another example of the lag between spelling and pronunciation can be seen in the words in group *3*. In Shakespeare's time, /ā/ was commonly spelled *ea*, and a word like *deal* was pronounced /dāl/.

Thus, the English language retains many old spellings even though they no longer represent the way the words are pronounced now. You must therefore memorize the spellings of such words as *pleasure, teach,* and *steak*. You will notice that very few common *ea* words retain the /ā/ sound.

EXERCISE A. The *ea* in each word below has one of the three sounds you have been studying. Between the slanted lines next to each word, indicate the sound of the *ea* in that word by writing e, ē, or ā. (Add 10 points for each correct answer.)

1. ready ...../...../.....
2. treaty ...../...../.....
3. weather ...../...../.....
4. seal ...../...../.....
5. yea ...../...../.....

6. leather ...../...../.....
7. reason ...../...../.....
8. ahead ...../...../.....
9. break ...../...../.....
10. disease ...../...../.....

EXERCISE B. Write five words (other than those given in this lesson) in which *ea* is pronounced /e/, and five words in which it is pronounced /ē/. (Add 10 points for each correct answer.)

/e/   /ē/

·   ·
·   ·
·   ·
·   ·
·   ·

EXERCISE C. Write a short sentence for each word you wrote down in
Exercise B. Underline all *ea* words. (Add 10 points for each correct sentence.)

· ·
· ·
· ·
· ·
· ·
· ·
· ·
· ·
· ·

REVIEW EXERCISE. Write *ie* or *ei,* whichever is correct, in the blank space
in each word below. (Add 5 points for each correct answer.)

1. n. . . . .ghborly   11. n. . . . .ther
2. pr. . . . .st   12. perc. . . . .ve
3. h. . . . .ght   13. c. . . . .ling
4. bel. . . . .ve   14. conc. . . . .ted
5. gr. . . . .ve   15. misch. . . . .f
6. w. . . . .rd   16. for. . . . .gner
7. shr. . . . .k   17. br. . . . .f
8. l. . . . .sure   18. sh. . . . .ld
9. w. . . . .ght   19. gr. . . . .f
10. s. . . . .zure   20. rec. . . . .ve

CHAPTER 4

Building with Prepositional Phrases

In the following sentence, the two word groups printed in italics are prepositional phrases:

After a long, hard search, Henry found his bike *in the ditch.*

It would be difficult to express these same ideas in any other way, without using the two prepositional phrases. Very often, by means of prepositional phrases, you can say things that you cannot say as well in any other way. The prepositional phrase is one of the most useful tools, both for saying what you mean and for making what you say clear and interesting. In this chapter, you will study the formation and uses of the prepositional phrase.

LESSON 32

What Is a Prepositional Phrase?

A *preposition* is a word that shows a relationship between a noun or pronoun and some other word in the sentence. A *prepositional phrase* is a phrase that begins with a preposition and ends with a noun or a pronoun. Words like *of, for, with, from, through, near, since,* and *under* can all be used as prepositions.

What makes a phrase so useful is that it is a group of words that can be used like a single part of speech in a sentence. Notice the groups of words printed in red in these sentences.

EXAMPLES   Has anyone seen the girl **with red hair**? (used as an adjective to modify the noun *girl)*
The cat raced **down the stairs**. (used as an adverb to modify the verb *raced,* telling where the cat raced)

A prepositional phrase may consist of just two words—a preposition and a noun or pronoun.

EXAMPLES **near** home   **of** cookies   **without** you   **beside** her

The noun or pronoun may also have modifiers, in which case the prepositional phrase may contain several words.

EXAMPLES **after** a long, heavy   **beyond** the rugged, snow-covered
         rain   mountains

A single sentence may contain several prepositional phrases strung together, one after the other.

EXAMPLE   Judith Jamison performed **with** lovely grace **in** a short concert **of** modern dance.

EXERCISE A. Underline the prepositional phrases in the following sentences. (Add 10 points for each correctly marked sentence.)

EX. Under ideal conditions scientists can read some of our thoughts.

1. In the laboratory, volunteers have electrodes attached to their heads.

2. Electrodes transmit signals from the brain.

3. These signals, called brain waves, are recorded on a graph.

4. After many experiments, scientists can now identify the shape of certain brain waves.

5. A brain wave with a narrow peak indicates surprise.

6. When an ordinary sentence is flashed on a screen, the volunteer shows no sign of surprise.

7. The volunteer might read "For breakfast, Lois has a bowl of cereal with milk and fruit."

8. The brain-wave pattern of surprise does not appear on the graph.

9. The volunteer might then read "For dinner, Ed likes steak covered with onions and thumbtacks."

10. The word *thumbtacks* triggers a reaction of surprise.

EXERCISE B. Put parentheses around the twenty prepositional phrases in the following paragraph. Some phrases are quite long. Be sure to include all parts. (Add 5 points for each correct answer.)

1   Across the bay, cottages of whitewashed stone lined the road toward the
2   pier. Children played under the trees and bought cold drinks from local
3   stands. Dogs rested in the shade by the children. Every day on the stroke of
4   ten, the boat from the mainland docked there with passengers and
5   long-awaited mail and was greeted by a crowd of local citizens and visitors.
6   The wave-tossed boat crashed against the pilings of the pier, and the crowd
7   cheered the bravery of the captain. Once again she had brought her vessel
8   safely to port with a load of free-spending but seasick tourists.

The Adjective Phrase

An <u>adjective phrase</u> is a prepositional phrase that is used as an adjective to modify a noun or a pronoun.

ADJECTIVES	ADJECTIVE PHRASES
a very **strong** person	a person **of great strength**
a **rudderless** ship	a ship **without a rudder**

Like an adjective, an adjective phrase modifies a noun or pronoun by making its meaning more definite. Usually the adjective phrase answers one of these questions: *What kind? Which one? How many?* (or *How much?*).

WHAT KIND?　Edith Hamilton has written <u>books</u> **about folklore and mythology**. (what kind of books? books *about folklore and mythology)*

WHICH ONE?　The <u>building</u> **behind the library** is new. (which building? the building *behind the library)*

Notice that if the underlined nouns in the sentences above are replaced by pronouns, the phrases then modify the pronouns.

EXAMPLES　Edith Hamilton has written <u>some</u> **about folklore and mythology**.

The <u>one</u> **behind the library** is new.

EXERCISE A. Put parentheses around each adjective phrase in the following sentences, and draw an arrow to the noun or pronoun it modifies. (Add 5 points for each correctly marked sentence.)

EX. The sound (of falling rain) can be very soothing.

1. The woman in the blue coat walked away.

2. The family across the street just bought two cats.

3. Marjorie composes music for her favorite poems.

4. They liked the old-fashioned house with the wide porch.

5. The Perezes proudly served tomatoes from their own garden.

6. Books from the public library covered her desk.

7. That huge mahogany table in the hall is much too large.

8. A smaller one with a convenient drawer would be more suitable.

9. They brought home a few of every shape and size.

10. Patricia wanted a ticket for the football game.

11. Someone from Porlock rang the doorbell and interrupted him.

12. The waiter brought them a check for someone else's meal.

13. This hotel has a swimming pool, but the one down the street has a swimming pool and tennis courts.

14. Nothing under the sun could make me do it.

15. The fence along the edge stood very high.

16. A cave below the cliff sheltered them.

17. He brought home a mixed basket of apples and pears.

18. They dug a large trench for drainage.

19. The museum has a very old Navajo rug with a colorful design.

20. She ate her three thin slices of whole-wheat bread very quickly.

EXERCISE B. Write an appropriate adjective phrase in the blank in each sentence. The phrase should modify the noun or pronoun that comes immediately before it. (Add 10 points for each correct phrase.)

EX. An old house ......*near the glen*...... caught fire last night.

1. In the safe was a black box ....

2. The announcer .....*at the park*............. mispronounced the sponsor's name.

3. Last week we attended the game *in Indiana*.................

4. The one ....*at the bottom*....... belongs to me.

5. Some ....*or my nebors*..... are members of that club.

6. That new car ....*out back*....... belongs to Aunt Cathy.

7. Mr. Poiter has just returned from a trip ..*down south*..... *in VA* ....

8. Everyone .....*with mad cow disese* has been vaccinated.

9. An apartment ...*in NYC*.......... is no place to keep a large dog.

10. Finally, the child selected three *or his teammates*....

The Adverb Phrase

An <u>adverb phrase</u> is a prepositional phrase that is used as an adverb to modify a verb.*

Like adverbs, prepositional phrases may answer the question *when? where? how? why?* or *to what extent?* (*how long? how often?*).

EXAMPLES   He <u>hid</u> the money **in a tin can**.   (*Where* did he hide the money?
He hid it *in a tin can*.)
I <u>did</u> my shopping **after school**.   (*When?*)
I <u>painted</u> the chair **in a hurry**.   (*How?*)
They <u>were dancing</u> **for fun**.   (*Why?*)
That milk bottle <u>has been</u> there **for two days**.   (*How long?*)

Adverb phrases also answer many other questions.

EXAMPLES   I <u>thought</u> **of you** today.
The house <u>was built</u> **of brick**.
He <u>wrote</u> a very nice thank-you note **to the minister**.
He <u>had replaced</u> the old machine **with a newer model**.

Almost any adverb can be replaced with an adverb phrase.

ADVERB	ADVERB PHRASE
She campaigned **actively**.	She campaigned **in an active way**.
They left **hastily**.	They left **in haste**.
They got along **well**.	They got along **in a satisfactory way**.

Straightforward adverbs are often preferable to adverb phrases, but the phrase has one great advantage over the ordinary adverb: because the object of the preposition is a noun or a pronoun, adjectives (and adverbs modifying these adjectives) can be put into the phrase. With these extra modifiers, the phrase can have a much more precise meaning than a single adverb by itself.

EXAMPLES   She campaigned in a **dignified** and **active** way.

They left in **great** but rather **dangerous** haste.

*Adverb phrases are also occasionally used to modify adjectives or adverbs.

EXERCISE A. Put parentheses around each adverb phrase in the sentences below, and draw an arrow to the word it modifies. (Add 10 points for each correctly marked sentence.)

EX. The congresswoman unexpectedly called (at our house.)

1. She was campaigning for a third term.

2. She was accompanied by a television crew and radio announcers.

3. My father and mother have known the congresswoman for many years.

4. The camera operators shined bright lights on our faces.

5. Meanwhile, the congresswoman was discussing some issues with my parents.

6. The congresswoman left after fifteen minutes.

7. We were all dazed by this sudden visit.

8. The interview was shown on the evening news.

9. Several friends telephoned my parents after the newscast.

10. During dinner my parents and I discussed some issues.

EXERCISE B. Put parentheses around each prepositional phrase in the sentences below. Then, in the blank at the left, write *adj.* if the phrase is an adjective phrase and *adv.* if it is an adverb phrase. (Add 10 points for each correctly marked sentence.)

ADV. 1. Kitty watched the parade from an upstairs window.

ADJ 2. Ms. Etler wrote a book about two teen-age brothers.

ADJ 3. The chef made a large salad with crisp lettuce.

ADV 4. I delivered the sealed envelope in a hurry.

ADV 5. Mr. Sanford directed the play during Mrs. Knight's absence.

ADV 6. The whole family went to the homecoming game.

ADV 7. They didn't leave until one o'clock.

ADJ 8. The pictures in the locked file are missing.

ADV 9. The mayor always greets us with a big smile.

ADV 10. The National Air and Space Museum has become very popular with tourists, students, and scientists.

Placing Modifying Phrases Correctly

A misplaced phrase can spoil the effectiveness of a sentence and even change its meaning. To use prepositional phrases correctly, you must develop a feeling for their placement in sentences.

The usual position for a prepositional phrase is after the word it modifies.

ADJECTIVE PHRASE   Arnold told a <u>story</u> about fishing.

ADVERB PHRASE   Arnold <u>told</u> a story in the elevator.

The two sentences above make sense as they stand. If you try to combine them, however, you can create a sentence that is confusing.

UNCLEAR   Arnold told a story about fishing *in the elevator*.

Where did Arnold's fishing take place? In speaking, you use your voice to set off the phrase *in the elevator* from the rest of the sentence. In writing, however, the placement of this phrase makes it seem, at first glance, to modify *fishing*. But it is the telling of the story, not the fishing, that took place in the elevator. You can make the meaning of the sentence clear by placing the phrase *in the elevator* at the beginning of the sentence.

CLEAR **In the elevator** Arnold told a story about fishing.

An adjective phrase must nearly always come right after the word it modifies. An adverb phrase, however, may be moved about quite freely, often to the beginning of the sentence. If a sentence with two or more phrases sounds wrong to you, follow these steps to make the meaning clear: (1) Notice which words the phrases modify. Does the placement of an adverb phrase make it seem to modify the wrong word? (2) Try the adverb phrase in a different place in the sentence, especially at the beginning.

Even if both phrases are adjective phrases, you must make sure they are really saying what you want them to say. For example, how would you put these sentence parts together?

Caroline read a book   about a murder   on the Boston train

The phrase *on the Boston train* could be an adjective phrase modifying *murder*. If so, it should follow the word *murder* (as above), meaning that the book Caroline read told about a murder that took place on the Boston train. If you take *on the Boston train* to be an adverb phrase modifying *read,* you would mean something quite different (Caroline read her book while riding on the Boston train). You can show this different meaning by putting the phrase at the beginning of a sentence. There, since it has no earlier noun to modify, the phrase must be an adverb phrase.

67

EXAMPLE   **On the Boston train** Caroline <u>read</u> a book about a murder.

EXERCISE. Each of the following sentences does not make sense because the modifying phrase is in the wrong place. Underline each misplaced phrase, and show by a caret mark (∧) where the phrase belongs. (Add 10 points for (∧) where the phrase belongs. (Add 10 points for each correctly marked sentence.)

EX. Sherry served cold milk ∧ to the guests <u>in mugs</u>.

1. The truckers drove all day without rest in the pouring rain.

2. Jim told Mrs. Warren about the icebox in the rowboat.

3. Mr. Jefferson lectured about bridge construction in the auditorium.

4. Edythe could smell dinner in the oven on the porch.

5. Joan told Annie about the aircraft carrier in the library.

6. They built a house for the family with three chimneys.

Rewrite the following groups of words as sentences, placing the modifying phrases where they belong.

7. the guard at the main switch   7. . . . .
   turned the power off   . . . .
   on duty   . . . .

8. Harriet for new experiences   8. . . . .
   by her enthusiasm   . . . .
   is often carried away   . . . .

9. they took the puppy   9. . . . .
   with air vents   . . . .
   in a portable kennel   . . . .

10. Maria watches the sailboats   10. . . . .
    from the shady porch   . . . .
    in the glittering sunlight   . . . .
    of the Riverview Sailing   . . . .
    Club   . . . .

Chapter Review

EXERCISE A. Underline all the prepositional phrases in the following paragraph. (Add 4 points for each correct answer.)

GRACE WILEY'S SNAKES

1 Most people picture themselves with interesting careers. Some want
2 jobs that take them outside the realm of ordinary experience. Grace Wiley
3 had such a career. She was a handler of snakes. She had one of the
4 world's largest collections. She kept her snakes in the barn behind her
5 house and would show them to tourists. Inside the barn were cages with
6 vipers, rattlesnakes, fer-de-lances, kraits, and cobras. Throughout the
7 world people have at the same time feared and revered cobras. Cobras are
8 very large snakes that come from Asia or Africa. They have around their
9 neck a loose fold of skin that expands into a hood when they become
10 excited. Grace Wiley studied the cobras in her collection and learned
11 about their habits. During the attack the cobra rears straight upward. A
12 hand held above the standing cobra's head is outside its range. The cobra
13 must bite through its victim's skin and chew rather than simply strike it.
14 Grace Wiley often let a cobra hit against her flattened palm. As long as the
15 cobra couldn't grab and chew, it couldn't insert its venom into the blood.

EXERCISE B. Put parentheses around the prepositional phrases in the following sentences, and draw an arrow from the phrase to the word it modifies. (Add 4 points for each correct answer.)

1. Many ancient peoples had similar stories about the sky.

2. In one African folk tale, the sky is supported by two gods.

3. Libanja supports the eastern part with a pole, and Songo supports the western part.

4. Without their aid, the sky would fall, and people would become lizards.

5. Early Scandinavians also looked with concern at the sky.

6. One ancient tale tells of a mighty ash tree.

7. All of the universe is supported by this tree.

8. Its three great roots reach into the regions of the gods, of the giants, and of darkness and cold.

9. A serpent with a great hunger gnaws continuously at its root.

10. One day the tree may fall, and the universe may come crashing onto the heads of people.

11. The Greek god Zeus fought with skill and daring for control of the universe.

12. He punished his enemy Atlas in a severe manner.

13. Atlas bears the weight of the world on his back and separates the heavens from the earth.

EXERCISE C. Put parentheses around the prepositional phrases in the sentences below. Above each phrase write *adj.* for an adjective phrase (modifying a noun or pronoun) and *adv.* for an adverb phrase (modifying a verb). (Add 5 points for each correct answer.)

1. The trail to camp follows the river.

2. Veronica ran swiftly to camp and told her news.

3. The commander sent messengers to all the neighboring garrisons.

4. The enemy proceeded cautiously through the mountain passes and approached the settlements on the plains.

5. A stitch in time is not worth nine.

6. The line of least resistance may not be the shortest distance between two points.

7. The night attack took the enemy by surprise.

8. The new facts about the housing project presented a different viewpoint.

Cumulative Review

A. In the following paragraph, underline each subject once and each verb twice. Watch out for compound subjects and verbs. (Add 4 points for each correct answer.)

SURPRISE

1 Mary Kilpatrick and her mother made plans for a surprise party for
2 Mary's father. This year, Mr. Kilpatrick's birthday fell on a Sunday, and
3 Mary and Mrs. Kilpatrick were making an occasion of it. Several of
4 Mary's aunts and uncles live not far away. All of them were invited to the
5 party. They would bring their families. The whole party was planned well
6 in advance, and Mr. Kilpatrick knew nothing about it. At three in the
7 afternoon of Mr. Kilpatrick's birthday, all of the guests drove their cars to
8 a place just around the corner, out of sight. Then all of the cars drove up at
9 once, and the relatives piled out and surprised Mr. Kilpatrick.

B. Above each of the italicized words in the following paragraph, write one of these abbreviations to show its part of speech: *n.* for noun; *v.* for verb; *pron.* for pronoun; *prep.* for preposition; *adv.* for adverb; *adj.* for adjective; and *conj.* for conjunction. (Add 2 points for each correct answer.)

NAPOLEON'S DOWNFALL

1 *In* the year 1812 Napoleon *invaded Russia with* an army of *over*
2 530,000 men. *He entered* Russia in June *and* began the *long* march
3 *toward* Moscow. He *would* cover *every* mile of the *way laboriously on*
4 foot. The *Russian* army retreated slowly *before* Napoleon, *but finally*
5 *made a stand* at the city of *Borodino*. The battle of Borodino, in
6 September, 1812, *was* the *bloodiest battle* Napoleon had *fought* up to *that*
7 time. The *Russians* were defeated, and one week *later* Napoleon *occupied*
8 Moscow. The *next* day, Moscow *mysteriously* began to burn. Napoleon
9 had *only* 100,000 men in Moscow. *His* army was *dangerously* scattered
10 *along* the line of *communication with* France. The Russian *tsar* refused to
11 surrender. *Winter* came *quickly*. Napoleon was *forced* to retreat. *Under*

12 *attack by* the Russians and the *terrible* winter, Napoleon's army *gradual-*
13 *ly dissolved.* Over 500,000 of France's *finest* soldiers were *permanently*
14 lost. The backbone of Napoleon's power was broken.

C. For each of the following paragraphs, underline every direct object once, and circle every subject complement. If in doubt, find the verb in the sentence, and notice whether it is an *action verb* or a *linking verb*. Remember that an action verb takes a direct object, while a linking verb is followed by a subject complement. (Add 5 points for each correct answer.)

JAZZ

1 In the 1920's jazz was the most popular music in the United States. The
2 jazz sound filled theaters, cafés, and living rooms.
3 Many jazz musicians wrote their own words and music. Scott Joplin
4 and Jelly Roll Morton were two of the most famous jazz composers. They
5 and other song writers introduced jazz to New York City. In New York's
6 Harlem neighborhood, people heard the music of the young musicians
7 Duke Ellington and Louis Armstrong. These two jazz artists became
8 national celebrities.
9 One of the great jazz composers and singers was Bessie Smith. She
10 recorded many famous songs and formed her own traveling show.
11 The Jazz Age became a golden era in popular music for several reasons.
12 One reason for jazz's fame was its quick, rhythmic beat. It expressed the
13 fast pace of American life in the 1920's. Another reason was the
14 availability of new inventions. For the first time, people could buy radios
15 and phonographs. They could hear jazz tunes in their own homes.

Building Vocabulary: Using the Dictionary

When you meet a new word in reading or conversation, the context alone may not show the word's precise meaning, or it may show only one of several meanings which the word may have. In such a case you naturally check your context guess against a good dictionary.

Use a dictionary as a tool for building your vocabulary.

Merely looking up a new word in a dictionary is usually not enough to build the word into your vocabulary. To make the most of the help which a dictionary can give, you need to use it systematically.

1. Note the word's spelling, pronunciation, and part of speech. Check the *pronunciation key* if you are not sure how the word is pronounced.

2. Copy the word into the vocabulary section of your notebook. (Dividing the word into syllables, as in the dictionary, will help you master its spelling.)

3. In your notebook, give the context in which you first read or heard the word.

4. Copy the meaning that applies to the sentence you have in mind.

5. Write a sentence of your own to illustrate this meaning.

Step 5 is especially important. Until you know a word well enough to recognize it in a new context and use it in your own writing and speaking, you have not really made the word a part of your vocabulary.

WORD MEANING	**commodity:** (1) anything useful; (2) anything bought and sold.
ILLUSTRATION FOR MEANING (2)	Fresh vegetables are one of the few **commodities** that drugstores do not sell.

EXERCISE. Look up the words below in a dictionary, and supply the following information about each word: (1) Pronunciation: divide the word into syllables. (2) Illustration: study the definition, and then write a short sentence illustrating the chief meaning of the word. Notice the example below. Be sure that your sentence illustrates the meaning of the word in the part of speech indicated, since some words on the list may be used as two different parts of speech. (Add 5 points for each correct item.)

adept, *n.*   (1) .... *a - dept* ....   (2) *John needs to become more adept at revising his own writing.*

audible, *adj.*   (1) ....   (2) ....

....

eloquent, *adj.*   (1) ....   (2) ....

....

fantastic, *adj.*   (1) ....   (2) ....

....

hamper, *v.*   (1) ....   (2) ....

....

haughty, *adj.*   (1) ....   (2) ....

....

monopoly, *n.*   (1) ....   (2) ....

....

rebuke, *v.*   (1) ....   (2) ....

....

repel, *v.*   (1) ....   (2) ....

....

salient, *adj.*   (1) ....   (2) ....

....

vivid, *adj.*   (1) ....   (2) ....

....

REVIEW EXERCISE. In the space to the left of each word in the left-hand column, write the letter of the best meaning for that word. (Add 10 points for each correct answer.)

..... 1. coincide

..... 2. refute

..... 3. distort

..... 4. eject

..... 5. inflammable

..... 6. compensate

..... 7. extinct

..... 8. asset

..... 9. concise

..... 10. catastrophe

a. to reimburse

b. capable of being set afire

c. having no living successors

d. compact, terse

e. to be in the same place

f. a useful or valuable thing

g. to make crooked

h. a sudden disaster

i. to throw out

j. to disprove

Spelling: A Trio of Confusing Prefixes: <u>pre-</u>, <u>pro-</u>, <u>per-</u>

Words that begin with *pre-*, *pro-*, and *per-* are confusing because these three prefixes from the Latin both look and sound so much alike. There are two things you can do to avoid misspellings when writing a word that contains one of these troublesome prefixes. First, you can *pronounce* the word very carefully. Try to say the word, especially the prefix, with preciseness. Say *pre*caution, *pro*motion, *per*suade.

A second way to avoid confusion is by learning the *meaning* of each prefix, along with a simple, clearly understood word containing that prefix. Try to memorize the meaning (or meanings) of each prefix below and the example word that illustrates it.

PREFIX	MEANING	EXAMPLE
pre-	*before*	**pre**arrange (arrange before)
pro-	*forward*	**pro**mote (move forward)
per-	{ *through,*	**per**colate (seep through)
	thorough	**per**fect (thoroughly done)

EXERCISE A. In the blank in each sentence below, write the word whose meaning is given in parentheses. Each word you write should begin with *pre-*, *pro-*, or *per-*. (Add 20 points for each correct answer.)

1. The letter *g* . . . . the letter *h* in the alphabet.   (comes before)

2. A jet plane does not have a . . . .   (rotating blade device)

3. What does the weather forecaster . . . . for tomorrow? (foretell)

4. Don't try to . . . . this meeting, please.   (lengthen in time)

5. Lynn is the . . . . leader of this committee.   (continuing)

EXERCISE B. In the blank, add *pre-*, *pro-*, or *per-* to each word or word part below. Be sure that the new word you make has the meaning given in parentheses. (Add 20 points for each correct answer.)

EX. . . . . *pre* war (before the war)

1. . . . . .suppose (to suppose before)

2. . . . . .fessor (one who puts knowledge forward)

3. . . . . .sist (to remain throughout)

4. . . . . .nounce (to announce forward or to say)

5. . . . . .pare (to make ready before)

EXERCISE C. Use each of the words you made in Exercise B in a short sentence. Underline each word you select from Exercise B. (Add 20 points for each correct sentence.)

1. ....

2. ....

3. ....

4. ....

5. ....

REVIEW EXERCISE. Study the words below, and be prepared to write them from dictation. Pay special attention to the sound of the *ea* combination in each word. (Add 10 points for each correct answer.)

1. seal

2. great

3. scream

4. ahead

5. break

6. appeal

7. treaty

8. pleasure

9. disease

10. teach

CHAPTER 5

Commas Are for Clarity

Nobody ever talks in a perfectly flat, even voice. Your voice rises and falls in pitch, pauses or stops, and the words come quickly or slowly. All of these changes help you to convey meaning. In written English, punctuation marks take the place of these voice changes. They make sentences easier to understand and easier to read.

The comma is the most common of all punctuation marks. Like the changes in your voice in speaking, the comma separates groups of words, telling the readers where to pause. Above all, it helps the readers grasp the meaning of what they have read.

There are a few clear and easy-to-learn rules for deciding when a comma is or is not needed, and all of them have to do with making your meaning clear to your readers. In this chapter, you will study the rules for using commas correctly and the purposes behind these rules.

LESSON 40

How to Punctuate a Series

A *series* is three or more items (words or word groups) written one after the other.

Use commas to separate items in a series.

Commas are necessary to show what the items in the series—the words or word groups—really are. Without commas, the series may be as confusing to the readers as this example.

CONFUSING   The newspaper has three sections: world news, local news, sports and entertainment.

Does the newspaper have three or four sections? Is the sports and entertainment one section, or is there a separate section for sports and another one for entertainment?

CLEAR   The newspaper has these sections: world news, local news, sports, and entertainment.

A series may consist of verbs, adjectives, adverbs, or phrases as well as nouns.

VERBS IN SERIES   Ellen dawdled, hurried, and finally ran to the park.
PHRASES IN SERIES   We hunted in the woods, on the hill, and near the brook.

Notice that the conjunction *and* (or *or*) comes between the last two items in a series, usually with a comma before it. If all the items in a series are connected by *and* or *or,* no commas are needed.

EXAMPLE   Apply the paint <u>smoothly</u> **and** <u>evenly</u> **and** <u>steadily</u>.

You also place a comma between two adjectives that precede a noun, unless the adjectives are joined by a conjunction.

CORRECT   a <u>healthy</u>, <u>intelligent</u> boy   a <u>healthy</u> **and** <u>intelligent</u> boy

Never place a comma between an adjective and the word it modifies.

INCORRECT   At the party they served orange, grape, and lemon, drinks.

CORRECT   At the party they served orange, grape, and lemon drinks.

EXERCISE. Insert commas wherever they are missing. Some of the sentences are correct as written. (Add 5 points for each correctly marked sentence.)

1. Fishing hunting and skin diving are my favorite sports.

2. They saw three deer a rabbit and two opossums.

3. The water covered our towels lunch and magazines.

4. Luisa walked ran and even rode a bike to get here.

5. Photographers reporters and tourists got off the plane.

6. An infestation of insects damaged crops lawns and fruit trees.

7. Something flashed and sparkled and darted across the sky.

8. The grass trees and flowers glowed in the evening light.

9. We had a telephone electricity and even hot water in our cabin.

10. This restaurant serves breakfast lunch and dinner.

11. The garden had roses tulips and irises.

12. The man had a long narrow and sad face.

13. Red blue and silver fish flashed in the lagoon.

14. I need pineapple and carrots and bananas for the gelatin salad.

15. Mom eats lunch in a restaurant at a diner or sometimes at her desk.

16. She gave him a warm good-looking jacket for his birthday.

17. Iris wanted to be a lawyer an employment counselor or a teacher.

18. We had to pay for our own gas electricity and hot water for the apartment.

19. Marita took lessons in ballet modern dance and yoga.

20. Ossie had a tie with a blue green and yellow paisley pattern.

A Compound Sentence Needs a Comma

For the sake of variety, you can often combine two or more simple sentences into a compound sentence. A compound sentence is made up of two or more simple sentences joined by <u>and</u>, <u>but</u>, <u>or</u>, <u>nor</u>, <u>for</u>, or <u>yet</u>.

Use a comma before <u>and</u>, <u>but</u>, <u>or</u>, <u>nor</u>, <u>for</u>, or <u>yet</u> when it joins the parts of a compound sentence.

Always keep in mind that a compound sentence contains two (or more) subjects and that each subject has its own verb.

EXAMPLES   I bought a pair of earrings for Mother**, and** Dad bought her a necklace for her birthday.
Ms. Salkeld decided before lunch to buy a new car**, but** the whole afternoon was taken up by details of the purchase.

Long sentences, like these examples, are hard for the eye to grasp without some kind of help, and you provide that help in the form of commas. When a compound sentence is short, a comma is not necessary.

EXAMPLES   Fish <u>swim</u> **and** <u>birds</u> fly.
He <u>liked it</u> **but** <u>I didn't</u>.

EXERCISE A. Supply the necessary commas. Remember that if the two parts of a compound sentence are short, a comma is not needed. (Add 10 points for each correct answer.)

1. Snakes are both legless and armless but plates attached to moveable ribs allow them to swim and crawl.

2. Contrary to legend, a snake's tongue is not forked but a snake does feel and smell with the aid of its tongue.

3. A snake, in danger, covers a hole with its head and its young slip down the hole to safety.

4. Rattlesnakes do not always rattle before striking nor should you expect this warning sign when in the woods.

5. You can determine the age of a tree by the number of rings it has but the number of rattles on a rattlesnake does not tell how old it is.

6. A rattlesnake gains a new rattle each time it sheds its skin and this may occur more than once a year.

7. Sometimes the rattlesnake does not replace the rattles that break off or sometimes two or more rattles grow within a year.

8. Some cobras are capable of forming a hood by expanding the moveable ribs behind the head and this feature makes them easy to identify.

9. The cobra is more aggressive than the rattlesnake and its venom is more powerful.

10. Some countries are free of snakes but the United States is not one of them.

Do not confuse a compound sentence with a simple sentence that has a compound predicate. A compound sentence usually requires a comma before the conjunction. A compound predicate does not.

INCORRECT The storm caused great damage, and washed away several bridges. (This is a simple sentence with a compound predicate. Both verbs have the same subject and should *not* be separated by a comma.)

CORRECT The storm caused great damage **and** washed away several bridges.

If a compound predicate contains more than two verbs, the rule for commas in series applies.

CORRECT The storm damaged houses, blew down trees, **and** washed away bridges.

EXERCISE B. Insert the missing commas in the following paragraph. (Some commas are needed to separate items in a series.) Watch out for compound predicates. (Add 10 points for each correct answer.)

1   The giant statues of Easter Island in the Pacific Ocean were first
2   investigated in 1722 and they still hold a mystery for historians scientists
3   and other visitors to the island. The figures were carved one thousand
4   years ago from volcanic rock on one side of the island and then were
5   moved to the other side. Observers wonder how the people of Easter
6   Island could have carried pushed or pulled these huge statues. Some of the
7   statues weigh twenty-five metric tons and stand three meters tall.
8   According to one story the statues walked across the island themselves but
9   this story is clearly fanciful. People may have used large sledges strong
10   ropes and many workers to move the statues. No one knows all the facts
11   about the statues and the mystery surrounding them continues.

Commas for Interrupters

Both in writing and in speaking you often use expressions like *however* and *on the other hand* that are not strictly necessary. Because such expressions break up, or interrupt, a sentence that would be complete without them, they are called *interrupters*. You separate an interrupter from the rest of the sentence with commas. The commas make the sentence easier to read.

Use commas to set off expressions that interrupt the sentence.

EXAMPLE   He went, of course, because he was afraid.

Only one comma is necessary when the interrupter comes at the beginning or at the end of the sentence.

EXAMPLES   On the other hand, I can hardly blame her.

She might have taken the train, for example.

Here are some of the most common interrupters:

on the contrary	to tell the truth	however	I suppose
generally	in my opinion	naturally	in fact
on the other hand	for example	of course	I think

Some of these expressions are not always used as interrupters.

INTERRUPTER   She will, I suppose, get angry and go home.
NOT AN INTERRUPTER   I suppose she will get angry and go home.

A few words like *why, well,* and *yes* are often used to begin a sentence. When they are used in this way, they are introductory words.

Use a comma to set off introductory words.

EXAMPLES   Why, who would have believed it?
Well, I'm not convinced.

An *appositive* is a word that identifies or explains the word that follows it. It is usually set off with commas. An *appositive phrase* is an appositive with its modifiers.

Appositives and appositive phrases are usually set off with commas.

EXAMPLES   Venus, the evening star, is actually a planet.
Enrico Romaro, the tallest boy in the class, led the singing.

Helen Freeman, <u>the valedictorian and without question the most remarkable person to graduate from this school in years,</u> went to Stanford.

If the appositive is a single word (especially someone's name) closely related to the preceding word, the comma is not necessary.

EXAMPLES   My brother <u>David</u> caused much damage.
We gave a birthday party for my sister <u>Joyce</u>.

EXERCISE A. Underline the various kinds of interrupters. Insert commas where needed. (Add 10 points for each correctly marked sentence.)

1. Why I don't know what the world's coming to!

2. In my opinion that person is up to no good.

3. Well don't expect Angie to arrive here early.

4. Ireland the Emerald Isle lies off the coast of Europe.

5. In fact you'll enjoy the book.

6. Just at twilight the finest hour of the day the moon rose.

7. The auditorium was a gift of Henry Allerdyce the financier.

8. He speaks I believe the truth.

9. Constance Whitman the helicopter pilot promised to be there.

10. I told them on the contrary that my brother Eric is a salesman.

EXERCISE B. Insert commas wherever necessary. (Add 10 points for each correctly marked sentence.)

1   Edythe White my neighbor wants to act. In my opinion she would make
2   a fine performer. She studies acting with Reynold Williams the famous
3   director at a theater workshop. A theater workshop is of course an acting
4   school connected to a theater. Naturally students can try out for roles in
5   theater performances. Edythe will no doubt audition for one of the roles in
6   a summer production of *The Glass Menagerie*. In fact the director told her
7   that she had a good chance of getting a part. Indeed Edythe can sing and
8   dance as well as act. To tell the truth you would say that she comes alive
9   when on stage. Eventually Edythe would like to appear in musical
10   comedies as well as in dramas.

Commas in Dates and Addresses

In a date or an address consisting of two or more parts, put a comma after each part.

DATE   On <u>December 19, 1981,</u> we moved to our present address.
ADDRESS   My cousins live at <u>175 Wood Street, Akron, Ohio 44303</u>.

The parts of a date may include the time of day, the day of the week, the month (with the day of the month), and the year. Except at the end of a sentence, a comma must follow each item in a date made up of any two or more of these parts.

EXAMPLE   At 6:00 P.M., Monday, November 9, 1981, they returned.

The parts of an address should include the street number and the street, the city, the state and ZIP code, and the country, if the letter is mailed from outside it.

EXAMPLE   1260 Bowman Street, Brooklyn, New York 11220, U.S.A.

Note the ZIP code follows the state with no punctuation between it and the state.

EXERCISE A. Insert the necessary commas in the following sentences. (Add 20 points for each correctly punctuated sentence.)

EX. My friend from Greenwich, Rhode Island, is visiting me.

1. On Saturday July 28 1982 my sister got married.

2. The return address is 631 Chatham Lane Houston Texas 77027.

3. He lives at 287 Austin Street Duluth Minnesota 55803.

4. Since Friday August 13 1982, I have been taking piano lessons.

5. Mail the letter to 25 Foster Lane Billings Montana 59102.

EXERCISE B. Insert the necessary commas in the following sentences. Three sentences are correct as they stand. (Add 4 points for each correctly marked sentence.)

1. This letter was sent from 18 Grassmere Avenue Flint Michigan 48504.

2. She also visited friends in Dallas and Midland.

3. On October 1 1847 Maria Mitchell discovered a new comet.

4. World War II ended on September 2 1945.

5. Stacy Kempner moved from East Brunswick New Jersey to Boulder Colorado.

6. On June 1 1937 Amelia Earhart started out from Miami Florida on her final flight.

7. My cousin, Mary Lee, lives in Atlanta New Mexico not in Georgia.

8. Abigail Adams died on October 18 1818.

9. Tony's address is 194 Foothill Drive Ogden Utah 84403.

10. The Leonards sailed on Friday November 7 1980 for a trip to Europe.

11. Darlene used to live at 1002 Carson Avenue Baltimore Maryland 21224.

12. Martin Luther King, Jr., was born on January 15 1929 in Atlanta Georgia.

13. Relatives from Charleston West Virginia are visiting us.

14. We stopped at Houston Texas on our way to Mexico.

15. Room 2930 52 Whitney Way Erie Pennsylvania 16511 is the address given in the letter.

16. Next week we hope to drive to Stockbridge Massachusetts.

17. The wedding took place on Monday December 28 1981 at 2:00 P.M.

18. Melba has just returned from a trip to Paris France.

19. My home until 1980 was on Michigan Boulevard in Chicago.

20. These pictures were taken last month at Lake George New York.

21. *Old Ironsides* was launched on October 21 1815.

22. Elizabeth Barrett lived at 50 Wimpole Street London England.

23. On September 12 1846 she married Robert Browning.

24. It took Narcissa Whitman four months to travel from Missouri to the Columbia River in 1836.

25. Gwendolyn Brooks was born in 1917 and has lived for most of her life in Chicago Illinois.

Chapter Review

EXERCISE A. Insert commas where needed to separate words or phrases in a series. (Add 10 points for each correctly marked sentence.)

1. You will have to take shirts pants socks and shoes.

2. Small yellow shrill birds flew across the field.

3. We bought bread and cheese and milk.

4. The reporter interviewed the mayor wrote the article and then typed it.

In the following sentences, set off the interrupters by commas.

5. For example your voice was too soft at the beginning.

6. I still say however that she should have tried harder.

7. The nation's economy we think will improve.

In the following sentences, insert commas where necessary to separate the parts of addresses and dates.

8. During her senior year, her address was East Hall 203 Milnor Avenue Buffalo New York 14218.

9. All records for dates prior to January 23 1907 were destroyed in the fire of November 1919 that burned down City Hall.

10. The building at 17 Lamar Drive Kansas City Missouri is for rent.

EXERCISE B. Insert the missing commas in the following paragraph. (Add 2 points for each correctly placed comma.)

WOULD YOU BELIEVE?

1   You are no doubt used to hearing about basketball centers football ends
2   and baseball pitchers who are more than six feet six inches tall. Indeed the
3   greatest former star of basketball Wilt Chamberlain is more than seven
4   feet tall. Wilt however would look rather small beside either Robert
5   Pershing Wadlow or Albert Johann Kramer. Kramer a giant from the
6   Netherlands is officially listed as eight feet four inches tall but Wadlow
7   attained a height of eight feet eleven. His greatest recorded weight was
8   491 pounds but at the time of his death he weighed only 439 pounds.

85

9   Wadlow the tallest person of all time died on July 15 1940 in Manistee
10 Michigan. Jane Bunford the tallest woman in medical history measured
11 seven feet eleven inches. She was born on July 26 1895 and lived in
12 Birmingham England. Delores Pullard born in De Quincy Louisiana was
13 seven feet tall at the age of seven and at the age of fourteen she was
14 credited with a height of eight feet two inches but medical evidence shows
15 that her true height was seven feet five-and-one-half inches. The tallest
16 living woman Tiliya lives in a village in Bihar State northeastern India
17 and her height is said to be seven feet five inches. Circuses have often
18 claimed giants eight or nine feet tall but these claims do not stand up.
19 Circus giants in fact are usually under contract not to be measured. No
20 circus giant has ever been found to be taller than Wadlow Kramer or Jane
21 Bunford. One circus for example claimed the "World's Tallest Man" of
22 nine feet six inches but he was found to be under seven feet four. Why
23 even respectable scientists get carried away with this game of claims.
24 Until 1872 anthropologists biologists and doctors believed that Daniel
25 Cajanus a Finn was nine feet three-and-a-half inches tall and the greatest
26 giant who ever lived. His bones were dug up and measured in fact two feet
27 less. Ivan Stepanovich Lushkin a member of the Russian Imperial
28 Regiment of Guards lived from 1811 to 1844. He was reported to have
29 attained the height of almost eight feet four inches but modern investiga-
30 tion indicates that his maximum height was in fact only seven feet
31 ten-and-one-quarter inches. It was just a tall tale!

Cumulative Review

A. Underline the subject of each sentence once and the verb twice. Circle any complements. (Add 4 points for each correct answer.)

1. Two police cars and a fire engine arrived on the scene and blocked traffic in both directions.

2. Miss Diaz brought a macaw back with her from South America.

3. Myron looked for the cat, but he could not find it.

4. The bear turned from the trail and ran away through the woods.

5. The mayor spoke with a loud voice, but nobody in the audience paid much attention to his speech.

6. A few people visited the polls and voted.

B. In the following paragraph, identify the part of speech of each italicized word by writing the appropriate abbreviation above it: *n.* for noun; *pron.* for pronoun; *adj.* for adjective; *v.* for verb; *adv.* for adverb; and *prep.* for preposition. (Add 4 points for each correct answer.)

1   One *of* the worst fires in *human* history *occurred* in London, *England,* in
2   1666. The *fire* began *near* the London Bridge. *It* spread *slowly* at first, but
3   *soon* nearly the *entire* city went up in flames. The fire *raged* for *three* days
4   and *consumed* eighty-nine *churches,* 13,200 houses, and four hundred
5   streets. Londoners *in* the destroyed city *promptly* accused *their* enemies,
6   the French, *of* starting the *tragic* fire. *Nobody* could prove *this,* however.
7   *Probably* the fire *began by accident.*

C. The complements in the following paragraph are italicized. Indicate the kind of complement by writing above each the abbreviation *d.o.* (for direct object) or *s.c.* (for subject complement). (Add 10 points for each correct answer.)

1   Staten Island is *one* of the five boroughs of New York City. It received
2   its *name* in 1609 from Henry Hudson. He named *it* after the States
3   General of the Dutch Republic. There was once an old vaudeville *joke*
4   about how the island got its *name.* As the Half Moon sailed into The
5   Narrows, a sailor sighted *land* off the coast of New Jersey. He pointed to

6 it and asked, "Iss dat an *island?*" The Dutch bought the *region* from the
7 American Indians. Unfortunately, the English also purchased the *island*.
8 Actually, Staten Island was bought on six separate occasions. In 1898, it
9 officially became *part* of New York City.

D. Put parentheses around all the prepositional phrases in the following paragraphs. Above each phrase, write the abbreviation *adj.* if it is an adjective phrase or *adv.* if it is an adverb phrase. (Add 4 points for each correct answer.)

THE BEGINNINGS OF FRANCE

1   The great empire of the Romans was declining. The great roads built by
2   the Romans were destroyed, and the aqueducts no longer carried any
3   water. Gradually, uncivilized tribes from areas to the east of the Rhine
4   moved west and settled in large areas under Roman rule. The Franks, a
5   tribe from the Main Valley, moved into the lands between the Rhine and
6   the Somme and occupied Belgium and northern France. During the
7   decline of Roman strength, the Franks seized power, and by A.D. 500 they
8   ruled most of Gaul. *France,* the modern name for the region then called
9   Gaul, comes from the word *Frank.*

10   A century later, France had broken up into several small kingdoms, but
11   in 719 a Frankish king named Charles Martel seized power and reunited
12   France. Meanwhile, the Moors had conquered most of northern Africa
13   and Spain, and they were threatening other European countries. Then in
14   the year A.D. 732 the Moors actually invaded France. In a great battle near
15   Tours, France, the invading army was defeated by Charles Martel. By his
16   victory, he showed that he was well named indeed, for *Charles Martel*
17   means *Charles the Hammer.* He saved Europe from invaders.

Building Vocabulary: Dictionary Meanings

If you had to rely purely on your own experience with words in context, your knowledge of the meanings of many words would be limited indeed. That is why a dictionary is so useful. The meanings which a dictionary gives for a word are a kind of summary of all the different contexts in which the word is used—all the meanings it may have.

The dictionary meanings of a word are based on actual contexts in which the word has been used.

Dictionary makers do not make up word meanings out of their own heads. They collect dozens, sometimes hundreds, of contexts in which a word has been used. They find these examples everywhere—in literature, in newspapers, in speeches, and in government documents. For a word like *competitor,* for example, the contexts might include

CONTEXTS   The **competitors** in the track meet were matched.
A business must keep up with its **competitors.**

By studying and comparing the contexts in which the word is used, dictionary editors are able to write a concise summary of its meaning that will fit every context. This dictionary meaning of a word is its *definition.* For *competitor,* this might be

DEFINITION   **competitor:** One who strives for the same goal as another; a rival.

EXERCISE.   Study the contexts in which each word below is used. Then, to the left of the number, write the letter of the definition on the next page that fits the contexts in which each word is used. (Add 10 points for each correct answer.)

CONTEXTS

. . . .   1. **abhor** /ab háur/, *v.*   Truly to love justice, a person must also *abhor* injustice. The decent people of the earth *abhor* crimes.

. . . .   2. **discord** /dís kaurd/, *n*   The two speakers' dislike of one another was a source of *discord* during the discussion.

. . . .   3. **intricate** /ín tri kit/, *adj.*   The wiring of an electronic computer is extremely *intricate*. The procedure for launching a satellite is an *intricate* one.

. . . .   4. **banish** /bán ish/, *v.*   Hearing about other people's troubles will often *banish* our own worries.

.... 5. **consistent** /kən sís tənt/, *adj.* Clement had all B's on his last report card; he certainly was *consistent*.

.... 6. **hysterical** /his tér i kəl/, *adj.* A person who laughs or cries for no reason may be *hysterical*.

.... 7. **appalling** /ə páu ling/, *adj.* Cruelty to animals is *appalling* to most of us. The sinking of the *Titanic* was an *appalling* disaster.

.... 8. **eligible** /él ə jə bəl/, *adj.* The Constitution says that to be *eligible* for the Presidency a person must be at least thirty-five years old and ''a natural-born citizen.''

.... 9. **plausible** /pláu zə bəl/, *adj.* Beverly's explanation seemed *plausible* enough until we found out what really happened.

.... 10. **colossal** /kə lós əl/, *adj.* The building of the Panama Canal was a *colossal* undertaking. The *colossal* height of Mount Everest is awe-inspiring.

DEFINITIONS

a. To dislike intensely, with a feeling of disgust; to shrink from in fear and loathing.
b. Shocking; causing fear and horror with a feeling of helplessness.
c. To put out of a country; to drive from one's thoughts.
d. Huge; gigantic.
e. Keeping to the same principles or kind of behavior.
f. Harsh disagreement between persons; confused, ugly sound.
g. Suitable or qualified for something; fit to be chosen.
h. Emotionally out of control; wild, frantic.
i. Complicated; made up of many small details.
j. Seemingly true but without proof one way or the other.

REVIEW EXERCISE. In the space to the left of each sentence, write the letter of the best meaning for the italicized word. (Add 20 points for each correct answer.)

.... 1. ''I can't *tolerate* a player who breaks training,'' said the coach.
a. dislike   b. put up with   c. be friendly with

.... 2. The judge *speculated* that bad housing is a cause of crime.
a. guessed   b. insisted   c. thought

.... 3. This device automatically *ejects* the used blade from the razor.
a. sharpens   b. takes hold of   c. throws out

.... 4. The custom of dueling is now *extinct*.
A. well known   b. no longer in existence   c. illegal

.... 5. The large crowd did not *hamper* the efforts of the firefighters.
a. cheer   b. approve   c. interfere with

Spelling: Words Containing the Prefixes <u>mis-</u>, <u>dis-</u>, and <u>un-</u>

If you have to stop after writing the first *s* in the word *misspell* and wonder whether to use one *s* or two, or debate about whether to use one or two *n*'s in *unnatural,* take heart. You can spell these words and a great many other similar ones by learning to think of such words as being made up of two parts—a base word and a prefix added to the beginning of the base word to change its meaning. Look at the words below to see how this is done:

PREFIX		BASE WORD		NEW WORD
mis	+	understand	=	**mis**understand
mis	+	step	=	**mis**step
dis	+	appear	=	**dis**appear
dis	+	satisfied	=	**dis**satisfied
un	+	usual	=	**un**usual
un	+	numbered	=	**un**numbered

Can you think of a rule to help you spell words containing the prefixes *mis-, dis-,* and *un-?* Here it is:

When adding a prefix that ends with a single consonant to a base word, write the prefix first and then the base word. Do not change the spelling of either.

EXERCISE A. Join each prefix and base word below to make a new word. Write the new word, correctly spelled, in the blank. (Add 10 points for each correct answer.)

PREFIX		BASE WORD		NEW WORD
1. mis	+	behave	=	....
2. dis	+	obey	=	....
3. un	+	kind	=	....
4. mis	+	state	=	....
5. dis	+	similar	=	....
6. un	+	named	=	....
7. un	+	needed	=	....
8. mis	+	statement	=	....
9. un	+	noticed	=	....
10. dis	+	please	=	....

EXERCISE B. Make a new and appropriate word by adding the prefix given in parentheses to the italicized word in each sentence below. (Add 20 points for each correct answer.)

1. The third word on your paper is . . . . *spelled.* (mis)

2. They were so frightened they were . . . . *able* to say a word. (un)

3. The salt began to . . . . *solve* in the warm water. (dis)

4. That remark of yours was quite . . . . *necessary.* (un)

5. His last statement was intentionally . . . . *leading.* (mis)

EXERCISE C. Use five of the ten words from Exercise A in separate original sentences. (Add 20 points for each correct answer.)

1. . . . .

2. . . . .

3. . . . .,. . . . .

4. . . . .

5. . . . .

REVIEW EXERCISE. Study the words below, and be prepared to write them from dictation. Pronounce the prefix in each word carefully, and then listen carefully to the prefixes when your teacher dictates the words. (Add 5 points for each correct answer.)

1. precaution
2. perfect
3. prearrange
4. propeller
5. persist
6. precedes
7. prolong
8. permanent
9. predict
10. perforate

11. promotion
12. prepare
13. professor
14. persuade
15. percolate
16. pronounce
17. provide
18. precise
19. proposal
20. perfume

Review

SUBJECT AND VERB. In the following paragraph, underline the subject of each sentence once and the verb twice (including helping verbs). Then, in the space after each sentence, show what *kind* of sentence it is according to the following code. (Add 5 points for each correctly marked sentence.)

a—simple sentence with one subject and one verb
b—simple sentence with compound subject
c—simple sentence with compound verb
d—simple sentence with compound subject and compound verb
e—compound sentence

1. Virginia Hamilton has become a popular writer in America. (   ) 2. *M. C. Higgins the Great* and *The Planet of Junior Brown* are two of her best-known novels. (   ) 3. Both books have won the John Newbery Medal for outstanding children's literature. (   ) 4. She began her writing in high school but did not become a successful writer right away. (   ) 5. She worked very hard in college, and after college she sent many stories to magazines. (   ) 6. The magazines did not publish the stories, but Virginia never lost hope. (   ) 7. Her husband and her friends encouraged her and gave her advice. (   ) 8. Later, after many months of hope, Virginia's luck changed. (   ) 9. Her writing was published, and readers were enchanted with her storytelling. (   ) 10. Virginia relies on childhood memories in her writing. (   ) 11. She spent her childhood in Yellow Springs, Ohio, on her family's farm. (   ) 12. She and her four brothers and sisters heard stories about their ancestors. (   ) 13. Many stories were about the Civil War and the Underground Railroad. (   ) 14. Virginia's grandparents were fugitive slaves and traveled to Ohio along a network of secret hiding places. (   ) 15. Virginia never forgot these stories. (   ) 16. Today, Virginia and her husband still live in Ohio, and both work as writers. (   ) 17. Writing is difficult work, and Virginia must spend hours each day on it. (   ) 18. She creates characters and imagines their thoughts. (   ) 19. After months of work, a story is completed.

(   ) 20. Such writing is difficult, but Virginia encourages young writers by her success. (   )

PARTS OF SPEECH. Identify the part of speech of each italicized word. Above the word write one of the following abbreviations: *n.* for noun; *pron.* for pronoun; *adj.* for adjective; *v.* for verb; *adv.* for adverb; *prep.* for preposition; and *conj.* for conjunction. (Add 4 points for each correct answer.)

MOTHER GOOSE

1   The *nursery* stories and nursery *rhymes* called "Mother Goose stories"
2   *have* a *long history,* and *their* origins in many cases cannot *be* traced. Some
3   of *them first appeared* in *book* form in a *book* printed in *Venice* in 1550.
4   *During* the *seventeenth* century in *France* the stories were *already* known
5   as "Mother Goose stories," *and early* in the eighteenth century, one of the
6   *French* books was translated *into English. Later* an Englishman *published*
7   a collection of *rhymes* called "Mother Goose's Melody."

THE SENTENCE BASE. Indicate the sentence base in each of the following sentences. Underline the subject of each sentence once and the verb twice (including helping verbs). Circle the complement, and above it write *d.o.* for a direct object and *s.c.* for a subject complement. Some sentences are compound or have compound parts, but not every sentence has a complement. Remember that a subject complement follows a linking verb while a direct object comes only after an action verb. (Add 5 points for each correctly marked sentence.)

1. Rufino Tamayo from Mexico paints beautiful, large murals for public buildings.
2. His paintings and his sculptures are popular among Americans.
3. Critics praise his works for their unique colors and powerful themes.
4. People fill Tamayo's canvases.
5. They dance by the sea, reach for the moon, and live in harmony with nature.
6. Dr. Shannon Lucid is working in the astronauts' training program.
7. She parachutes into water.
8. Someday, Dr. Lucid may pilot the space shuttle.
9. Engineers and medical specialists help her in training.
10. Physical stamina is an important quality in an astronaut.

94

11. The ordinary household light bulb may be a thing of the past.

12. A recently invented bulb can burn for five years.

13. This new bulb will cost over $10, but it will save energy.

14. Pluto, a distant planet, is the coldest planet in our solar system.

15. Scientists and astronomers calculate its temperature at 400 degrees below zero F.

16. Days on Pluto are longer than days on Earth.

17. Pluto completes a single rotation in six days and nine hours.

18. From Pluto the sun would look like a distant speck of light.

19. The tallest building in the world rises majestically above Chicago.

20. It is the Sears Tower, and it is 110 stories tall.

THE PREPOSITIONAL PHRASE. Put parentheses around the prepositional phrases in the following paragraphs. Decide whether each phrase modifies a noun or pronoun (an *adjective* phrase) or a verb (an *adverb* phrase). Write the abbreviation *adj.* above each adjective phrase and *adv.* above each adverb phrase. (Add 2 points for each correct answer.)

1   Anne was traveling in Europe with her parents for the summer. They
2   stayed in France during the month of August. Anne had learned before
3   coming to Europe that in France everyone used metric weights and
4   measures. The metric system is based on powers of ten. Multiplication or
5   division by ten would give you a larger or smaller unit of measure. Length
6   is measured in meters. One thousand meters is called one kilometer. The
7   prefix *kilo* means one thousand (10^3). Anne's parents taught her a rule of
8   thumb about the metric system. One kilogram roughly equals two pounds,
9   one liter is slightly more than one quart, and one kilometer is somewhat
10   more than one half of a mile. This rule can be used for most situations
11   except those where precise measurement is required. Anne found it useful
12   throughout her stay in Europe. In all the stores, milk was sold by the liter
13   and potatoes by the kilogram.
14   On August 17, all of the family went to a bike race held outside town.
15   The course for the race was twenty kilometers. The course ran over a flat
16   paved track through the woods. Anne knew that a twenty kilometer course

17 roughly equaled ten miles but she wanted a more precise figure for the
18 length of the course in miles. In the dictionary, she found that one
19 kilometer equals .621 miles. By multiplying, she discovered that the race
20 course equaled 12.42 miles.

21 Anne waited with her parents at the starting line. They had brought
22 chairs and placed them beneath the trees. After the starting shot, they
23 drove in their car to the finish line. The winner of the race reached the
24 finish line before them. This cyclist had traveled the course in fourteen
25 minutes at a speed of approximately 86 kilometers per hour or about 53
26 miles per hour. This speed did not break the record for this event. The
27 crowd gathered around the winner and cheered. Anne decided that she
28 would train during the year and compete next summer.

PUNCTUATION. Add the commas that are missing from the following paragraph. (Add 5 points for each correct answer.)

1 In these days of jet planes space travel and satellites, we do not always
2 remember the recent development of flight. Yet the age of flight is in fact a
3 very new chapter in our history and we are still even today only at the
4 beginning of it. Actually some people can still remember the Wright
5 brothers' first flight at Kittyhawk North Carolina on December 17 1903.
6 Within a few years, flight across the Atlantic became possible and on May
7 20 1927 Colonel Charles A. Lindbergh one of the first American mail
8 pilots began his solo flight. He set out from Roosevelt Field and reached
9 Le Bourget Airport Paris France the following day May 21.

CHAPTER 6

Sentence Fragments and Run-on Sentences

A *run-on sentence* is a little *more* than a complete sentence while a *sentence fragment* is a little *less*. Both are serious errors which interfere with the writing of clear, effective sentences. Even though you may know perfectly well just what a sentence is, there are certain situations in which it is quite easy to fall into the trap of writing something that is *less* than a complete sentence (a sentence fragment) or *more* than a complete sentence (a run-on sentence). By learning to recognize these situations, as you will in this chapter, you can also learn to avoid both of these sentence errors.

LESSON 48

Spotting Sentence Fragments

A sentence fragment is a separated part of a sentence that does not express a complete thought.

A part of a sentence may become so important to the writer that it becomes separated from the sentence with which it belongs. The result is a sentence fragment. Suppose, for example, that you saw a famous tennis player who had her picture in all the papers. This would be exciting and important. It might therefore seem sensible to write:

EXAMPLE   Yesterday, I saw Tracy Austin. *A famous tennis player*.

But *what* about *a famous tennis player?* As this group of words is written, the reader cannot be sure whether it belongs with the preceding sentence or introduces a new idea. Notice that while *player* might be the subject of a new sentence, this group of words by itself does not tell us anything about the tennis player because it does not have a verb. The confusion can be cleared up very easily, however, simply by attaching the word group to the preceding sentence. Then it is seen at once that it serves to identify *Tracy Austin*—she is the famous tennis player.

EXAMPLE   Yesterday, I saw Tracy Austin, a famous tennis player.

Notice how the fragments on page 98 are corrected by the addition of the missing sentence parts.

FRAGMENT	The boat on the river.
SENTENCE	**The boat on the river** was heading for a collision.
FRAGMENT	Drinking a glass of juice.
SENTENCE	A <u>man</u> <u>was sitting</u> at the counter **drinking a glass of juice**

In each case, a verb or a subject, or both, must be added before the word group can be part of a complete sentence. A complete sentence needs both a subject and a verb.

EXERCISE A. All of the following word groups are *written* as sentences, but some are actually sentence fragments rather than sentences. In the space at the left, write *S* if the word group is a sentence, *F* if the word group is a fragment. Remember that a complete sentence must have both a subject and a verb. (Add 10 points for each correct answer.)

.... 1. At the foot of the tallest mountain.

.... 2. The lights were visible at the foot of the tallest mountain.

.... 3. There we saw three blackbirds sitting on a fence.

.... 4. Three blackbirds sitting on a fence.

.... 5. A quarterback famous for his ability on offense.

.... 6. The flag flapping gently in the morning breeze.

.... 7. Even for all the tea in China I wouldn't do it.

.... 8. Breakfast cereal without fruit.

.... 9. The author of at least three best-selling novels, all published in at least four languages on three continents.

.... 10. It was Margaret O'Reilly herself.

EXERCISE B. In the space provided, rewrite each of the following sentence fragments, adding whatever words are necessary in order to make a complete sentence. (Add 20 points for each correct sentence.)

1. Before the end of the program.

....

2. The chair next to the fireplace.

....

3. But never came back again.

....

4. Asked about her ambitions.

....

5. Not the patient in the bed by the window.

....

98

Phrase Fragments

Three kinds of phrases are often written as fragments: the prepositional phrase, the infinitive phrase, and the appositive phrase. The temptation to write these phrases as if they were complete sentences is especially great when they come near the end of a sentence and contain several modifiers. Remember, however, that sentence completeness has nothing to do with length. Even a very short group of words like *someone laughed* can be a complete sentence provided (1) it has a subject and a verb, and (2) it expresses a complete thought.

The Prepositional Phrase A prepositional phrase is a phrase that begins with a preposition and ends with a noun or pronoun. The noun or pronoun may have modifiers, and several prepositional phrases may be strung together, one after the other. When a prepositional phrase acts as an adjective or adverb (as it almost always does), it must be connected as closely as possible with the word it modifies. It should *not* be cut off as a sentence fragment.

FRAGMENT	We had excellent seats. *On the fifty-yard line. (On the fifty-yard line* is an adjective phrase modifying *seats*.)
ATTACHED	We had excellent seats on the fifty-yard line.
FRAGMENT	The Smyths finally sold their farm. *To an energetic Texan. (To an energetic Texan* is an adverb phrase modifying *sold*.)
ATTACHED	The Smyths finally sold their farm to an energetic Texan.

The Infinitive Phrase An infinitive is a verb form that can be used as a noun, an adjective, or an adverb. The word *to* usually comes before the infinitive. An infinitive may introduce a group of related words. Together, the infinitive and the related words make up an infinitive phrase. The infinitive phrase should *not* be written as a sentence fragment.

FRAGMENT	Ms. Peters told me. *To return the books this afternoon. (To return the books this afternoon* is an infinitive phrase modifying the verb *told*.)
ATTACHED	Ms. Peters told me to return the books this afternoon.

The Appositive Phrase An appositive is a word that means the same as the word it follows and explains it in some way. An appositive and its modifiers make up an *appositive phrase*. An appositive phrase should always be closely connected with the word it explains, not cut off as a sentence fragment.

FRAGMENT	We read a book about Marie Curie. *The scientist who discovered radium and polonium. (Scientist,* with the other italicized words, is an appositive phrase explaining who Marie Curie was.)
ATTACHED	We read a book about Marie Curie, the scientist who discovered radium and polonium.

EXERCISE. Each numbered item contains two word groups. If both word groups are complete sentences, write *S* for sentence in the blank at the left. If one of the word groups is a fragment, write *F* for fragment, and correct the fragment. (Cross out the period and the incorrect capital letter, and write a small letter above.) Put a comma before an appositive. (Add 10 points for each correctly marked sentence.)

.F.. EX. On my birthday, we went to the Riverview, a large amusement park.

.... 1. Every year, the United States imports millions of bananas from Latin America. The world's leading banana producer.

.... 2. For five years she was not heard from. She was lost in the jungle.

.... 3. In the middle of the night, Alfredo was suddenly awakened. By a curious humming noise outside his window.

.... 4. To some, he seemed merely mistaken. To others, he appeared actually dishonest.

.... 5. For her novel about life in New England, Joan Blos won the Newbery Medal. An award for children's literature.

.... 6. The salesman told me. To wait at the front desk.

.... 7. The next speaker was Dr. Widdicomb. A family doctor.

.... 8. The bill will probably be defeated. Even after all our efforts.

.... 9. My sister is learning lacrosse. A Native American game.

.... 10. My parents asked me. To be home by 8 P.M.

100

The Participial Phrase Fragment

A *participle* is a verb form that can be used as an adjective. A present participle, indicating present time, is formed by adding *-ing* to the verb. A past participle, indicating past time, is formed by adding *-ed, -d,* or *-t* to the verb.

EXAMPLES The student sitting by the door comes from Venezuela. (*Sitting* is the present participle form of the verb *sit*. It acts as an adjective to modify the noun *student*.)

Sent by my friend Betty, this box arrived yesterday. (*Sent* is the past participle form of the verb *send*. It acts as an adjective to modify the noun *box*.)

Be careful not to confuse participles used as adjectives with participles used in verb phrases.

PARTICIPLE The *laughing* clown rode his bicycle.
VERB PHRASE The clown was *laughing* as he rode his bicycle.

A participle may introduce a group of related words. Together, the participle and the related words form a *participial phrase*.

EXAMPLES Playing at the playground, the children seemed happy. (Together, the participle *playing* and the prepositional phrase *at the playground* make up a participial phrase that modifies the noun *children*.

The collage, mounted on the wall, appealed to me. (Together, the participle *mounted* and the prepositional phrase *on the wall* make up a participial phrase that modifies the noun *collage*.)

The participial phrase should never stand alone; it must never be separated from the sentence in which it belongs.

FRAGMENT I just saw Charles. Running around the track.
CORRECTED I just saw Charles running around the track.
FRAGMENT Mom saw Mark. Riding his bike.
CORRECTED Mom saw Mark riding his bike.

Note that a word that ends in *-ing* and looks like a verb (*laughing, sleeping, working*) cannot stand as the verb in the sentence unless it has a helping verb with it (*is laughing, has been sleeping, were working*).

EXERCISE. Underline the participial phrases in the following sentences. Then draw an arrow from the participle to the noun or pronoun it modifies. Do *not* underline an *-ing* word that is used with a helping verb as the verb of a sentence. (Add 10 points for each correct sentence.)

EX. Gunning his engine, the police officer pulled away from the light.

1. He buried himself in his newspaper, ignoring his problems.

2. Laying aside her notes, the speaker improvised her lecture.

3. Yesterday we were refinishing our picnic table.

4. She watched the windows of the bus anxiously, hoping to see her friend.

5. Teresa was hoping to visit us, but she could not get away.

6. Ossie came down the ladder, carrying his pail of paint.

7. Falling against the step, he cut his leg rather badly.

8. Telling everyone loudly about the injustice of it all, Jon delayed the meeting for an entire hour.

9. Belinda at last found the rake and was happily raking up leaves and burning them in bonfires for the rest of the afternoon.

10. All of the letters lying there in the basket are for the mail carrier.

What Makes a Sentence Complete?

In writing you begin a sentence with a capital letter and end with a period, a question mark, or an exclamation point. The capital letter and the end mark of punctuation are signals to the reader that what comes between them is a complete sentence. When you make the mistake of using these signals with a group of words that do not make a complete sentence, the result is a sentence fragment.

A complete sentence expresses a complete thought and makes sense by itself. The subject of a sentence is the part about which something is being said. The predicate is the part that says something about the subject. An incomplete sentence (sentence fragment), on the other hand, does not make sense by itself. It leaves the reader with an unanswered question. If a group of words leaves you hanging in some way, the chances are that it is a sentence fragment; it needs additional words to complete it.

EXAMPLES   *After* Haley threw the main switch. (What happened then? This is a sentence fragment.)

If you don't remember to buy the cheese. (What will happen if you don't remember? This group of words does not say what will happen. It is a sentence fragment.)

Words like *after, although, because, if, since, unless, when,* and *while* often lead writers into writing sentence fragments. Word groups that begin with these words do not express complete thoughts and do not make sense by themselves. They raise questions that can be answered only if they are part of complete sentences.

EXAMPLES   The lights went out after Haley threw the main switch. (This is now part of a complete sentence.)

If you don't remember to buy the cheese, you can't make any ham and cheese sandwiches.

EXERCISE. To the left of each numbered item, write *S* if it is a complete sentence and *F* if it is a sentence fragment. (Add 10 points for each correct answer.)

.... 1. Because Evelyn had been frightened by a bear near camp.

.... 2. Because she was not tall enough, Kelley dropped basketball.

.... 3. Candace found the trail when she got to the mouth of the canyon.

.... 4. Where neither of us had ever been before.

.... 5. While Cynthia was wandering around in the dark.

.... 6. While she was at camp last summer, Mari passed lifesaving.

.... 7. Although an old boot and a can of beans were found in the cave.

.... 8. Since no one had lived there for many years.

.... 9. Unless you can pass the swimming test before the end of the summer.

.... 10. Don't take a canoe out unless you can swim.

REVIEW EXERCISE. The following paragraph contains sentence fragments of many of the kinds you have studied so far in this chapter. Correct each fragment by crossing out the period and inserting a comma if it is needed. Cross out the incorrect capital letter, and write a small letter above it. (Add 10 points for each correct answer.)

1   Benjamin Franklin began his famous publishing career in Philadelphia.

2 The largest city in colonial America. Starting a printing shop. He soon

3 became the most successful printer in the colonies. Through hard work

4 and diligence. He bought the *Philadelphia Gazette*. A dull, poorly printed

5 sheet. Appearing weekly. Soon Franklin made it amusing, lively, and

6 informative. Writing many of the articles himself. In 1732 Franklin wrote

7 the first *Poor Richard's Almanac*. Under the pen name "Richard Seaver."

8 Almanacs were read carefully every year by colonial Americans. *Poor*

9 *Richard's* soon became the most popular almanac. Owing to its reputation

10 for wise and witty sayings. In 1730 Franklin became printer for

11 Pennsylvania. A position which made him even more successful. He

12 began small printing shops in New York and South Carolina. With hopes

13 of expanding his business throughout the colonies.

Avoiding Run-on Sentences

A complete sentence presents a single basic idea. The end mark and the capital letter that signal the end of one sentence and the beginning of a new sentence show the reader where one idea ends and a new one begins. A sentence fragment is confusing because it gives the reader only part of an idea. A run-on sentence is confusing in a different way. By running together two or more complete sentences, it gives the reader no help in deciding where one idea ends and a new one begins.

EXAMPLES   Claudine ate roast beef her dog ate hamburger.
What can the purpose of his visit have been, it puzzles me.

A <u>run-on sentence</u> consists of two or more sentences separated by a comma or by no mark of punctuation.

The simplest way to correct the run-on sentences in the examples above is to put in two end marks—a period in the first example, a question mark in the second. (The first word in each sentence is then capitalized, of course.)

EXAMPLES   Claudine ate roast beef. Her dog ate hamburger.
What can the purpose of his visit have been? It puzzles me.

There is another way of correcting a run-on sentence when the parts are statements (sentences that end with a period). The run-on sentence can be changed into a compound sentence.

EXAMPLE   Claudine ate roast beef, but her dog ate hamburger.

Remember, however, that two sentences should only be combined in a compound sentence when the ideas they present are closely related in some way.

EXERCISE A. Some of the following sentences are correct as they stand, but others are run-on sentences. In the space at the left, write *S* for each correct sentence and *R* for each run-on sentence. Correct the run-on sentences by crossing out the small letter and putting in a suitable end mark and a capital letter where they belong. (Add 20 points for each correctly marked item.)

..... 1. It worries me to see you go without a coat you could easily catch cold.

..... 2. Why do you suppose leaves change color in the fall it certainly does make the countryside pretty.

..... 3. How beautiful that hillside is when the aspens have all turned yellow, they look like gold in the sun.

.... 4. Just because the train was two hours late, you have no excuse for losing your temper that way.

.... 5. The Japanese lanterns swayed gently in the breeze, casting a delicate yellow light on the porch and on the buffet.

EXERCISE B. Correct the run-on sentences in this paragraph. Watch out for sentences that are compound or have compound parts. (Add 10 points for each correct answer.)

1   Juanita and Daisy wanted to use their spare time constructively Juanita
2 had a beautiful singing voice and Daisy played guitar well. They thought
3 they might entertain hospitalized children on weekends it would give
4 them experience and allow them to put their talents to use. They contacted
5 two local hospitals and found they could work as volunteers their help
6 would be appreciated. Several of their friends became interested in the
7 project it was decided they would form a small troupe. Juanita and Daisy
8 would perform folk songs, Catherine would do acrobatic stunts, and
9 Theresa and Judy would perform magic tricks surely the show would be a
10 success. The girls rehearsed for two weeks before the first show they were
11 all somewhat nervous. The hospital officials thought that after lunch on
12 Saturday would be a good time for the show the children's recreation
13 room was set aside for the occasion. Not too many props were needed
14 Juanita's parents loaded the props in the car on Saturday morning and took
15 them to the hospital. There were about seventy-five children in the
16 audience several doctors and nurses were also there. Everyone applauded
17 loudly at the end of the show and the hospital asked the troupe to come
18 back next week the show was a huge success.

Chapter Review

EXERCISE A. In the space to the left of each item, write *S* if it is a complete sentence or *F* if it is a fragment. (Add 10 points for each correct answer.)

.... 1. Collecting antiques can be both fun and profitable.

.... 2. For the sake of starting a collection.

.... 3. Merely because a piece appeals to you.

.... 4. Often antiques increase in value with age.

.... 5. A special piece of delicate design.

.... 6. Fun exploring the history of special items.

.... 7. A potbellied stove from the 1890's is still in good condition.

.... 8. Sitting around the stove on cold December evenings and imagining previous owners.

.... 9. Homemade toys from the turn of the century.

.... 10. We found that going to antique shows makes history more vivid.

EXERCISE B. In the space to the left of each item, write *S* if it is a single, complete sentence or *R* if it consists of two or more run-on sentences. Correct the run-on sentences by adding the proper end marks and the missing capital letters. (Add 10 points for each correct answer.)

.... 1. Did you ever read about bees how amazing they are!

.... 2. They are not merely interesting, they are also useful.

.... 3. Bees carry pollen from one flower to another.

.... 4. Some farmers rent hives from professional beekeepers during the blossoming season, their crops are larger as a result.

.... 5. How many different kinds of bees there are they must number in the thousands.

.... 6. We usually see only honeybees and bumblebees, occasionally we see a honeycomb also.

.... 7. Most bees can sting, it is the bee's method of protecting itself.

.... 8. Bumblebees are larger than most of the other bees they are hairy insects.

.... 9. Did you know that the bee is very systematic, it finds all of the
flowers of one kind and then flies to the flowers of another kind.

.... 10. Are there any books in our library about bees, I want to read more
about them bees are very interesting.

EXERCISE C. This paragraph contains both sentence fragments and run-on
sentences. Correct the errors by adding or crossing out periods and capital
letters as necessary. (Add 10 points for each correct sentence division.)

DOLLARS AND SCENTS

1   The skunk is a well-known member. Of the weasel family. It is found
2 throughout most of North America. Often living in a hollow tree or a
3 burrow. It is nocturnal, usually seeking its food at night. But also being
4 seen or smelled sometimes during the day. The skunk is famous. For a
5 certain peculiar habit, it can squirt a fluid with a very disagreeable odor.
6 A very effective means of defense. It sometimes sends the fluid a distance
7 of ten or twelve feet, but the strong odor travels for miles. As a result,
8 other animals usually stay away from skunks. Skunks eat frogs, gophers,
9 reptiles, and squirrels. They help the farmer. By eating insects and field
10 mice. Sometimes the skunk also raids the henhouses. An important source
11 of profit to the farmer. Because of the skunks' odor and their eating
12 habits, nobody really likes them. Except the farmers who raise skunks for
13 their fur. Skunk fur is widely used in fur coats. The body of the skunk also
14 yields an oil. Of use in the manufacture of ointment.

Cumulative Review

A. In the space to the left of each sentence, write *T* if the statement is true and *F* if it is false. (Add 10 points for each correct answer.)

.... 1. A noun is a word that expresses action.

.... 2. A pronoun is never the object of a preposition.

.... 3. Some adverbs answer the question *how often*.

.... 4. An adjective may modify an adverb.

.... 5. A verb is a word that names a person, place, thing, or idea.

.... 6. An adjective may be used as a subject complement.

.... 7. A prepositional phrase consists of a preposition and its object.

.... 8. The same word is sometimes used as an adjective and an adverb without any change in spelling.

.... 9. The modifier *good* should not be used as an adverb in writing.

.... 10. Prepositions sometimes modify verbs.

B. Underline the subject of each sentence once and the verb twice (including helping verbs). Identify each italicized word by writing above it one of these abbreviations: *d.o.* for direct object; *s.c.* for subject complement; or *o.p.* for object of a preposition. (Add 10 points for each correctly marked sentence.)

1. Spiders are perhaps the most *unpopular* of all insects.

2. Some of the most famous spiders are indeed very *poisonous*.

3. Everyone has heard far too *much* about the famous black widow.

4. On the other hand, very few have actually seen a *black widow*.

5. The black widow is *common* in the South and Southwest.

6. Most of the common spiders are *harmless*.

7. Even harmless spiders, however, can inflict a nasty *bite*.

8. One of the most frightening spiders is the *tarantula*.

9. A full-grown tarantula has a leg-spread of five *inches*.

10. Its bite is not nearly as *dangerous* as is generally believed.

C. The following sentences contain prepositional phrases and appositive phrases. Put parentheses around each phrase; insert commas where necessary. Draw an arrow from the phrase to the word it modifies, or identifies or

109

explains. Then, in the blank at the left, indicate whether the phrase is appositive (*app.*) or prepositional (*prep.*). (Add 10 points for each correctly marked sentence.)

.... 1. Some inventors make a great deal of money.

.... 2. The invention may be only a gadget for everyday use.

.... 3. The inventor then obtains a patent on the new invention.

.... 4. The patent a government document protects the inventor's rights.

.... 5. Margaret E. Knight one of the first women to receive an American patent invented various mechanical devices and cutting machines.

.... 6. Many a millionaire's wealth has come from oil.

.... 7. Some Texas farmers sell the mineral rights on their land.

.... 8. Drilling a costly process can ruin even a wealthy person.

.... 9. Some people make fortunes through wise speculations.

.... 10. Elizabeth Arden a financial genius ran a highly successful cosmetics company.

D. In the following paragraph, some commas are missing, and others should be removed. Correct the punctuation as necessary. (Add 5 points for each correct answer.)

1   Bernard Baruch financier industrialist economist and diplomat was
2   born in Camden South Carolina, on August 19 1870. Graduating from the
3   College of the City, of New York in 1889, Baruch became a member of
4   the Stock Exchange, and pursued a career in finance. He made a fortune at
5   an early age and then he turned his attention to the finances of the
6   government. He was an advisor to Presidents Wilson Roosevelt Truman
7   Eisenhower and Kennedy. Some historians hold that Baruch an advisor to
8   five presidents exerted a greater influence on American government than
9   any other person who did not hold a major political office. He gave a large
10 portion of his private fortune to educational institutions. In fact a school
11 now bears his name. The Bernard M. Baruch, College is located at 17
12 Lexington Avenue New York New York 10010.

Building Vocabulary: Explaining What Words Mean

There are a good many situations in which you must explain the meaning of words. Perhaps you use a term that your readers or listeners do not know, or you use a word that has more than one meaning (and many words do). If you are trying to be very clear, you must often explain which meaning you intend. Most important, perhaps, explaining a word's meaning helps you to understand the word and use it accurately.

When you explain what a word means, you are *defining* the word. The definition may be one word or it may be several. To be of any use, all the words in a definition must be understood by the readers or listeners. The definition must also explain the word as it is used *in context*.

An accurate definition of a word can usually be substituted for it in a sentence.

Suppose you read this sentence in a book:

EXAMPLE   Two violent hurricanes **annihilated** many towns on the island.

The context gives you some help with the meaning of *annihilate*. In a dictionary you may find a definition like this: "to reduce to nothing; to destroy completely." Does the definition fit the context? You try it out in the original sentence to see.

EXAMPLE   Two violent hurricanes **destroyed completely** many towns on the island.

Study the following definitions. Try to think of sentences in which each word could be used. Check your sentences by substituting the definition for the word defined.

altercation /ául tər ká shən/, *n.*   An angry, quarrelsome argument.

annihilate /ə nī́ ə lāt/, *v.*   To destroy completely.

anonymous /ə nón ə məs/, *adj.*   Written or done by a person whose name is unknown or concealed.

appropriate /ə prṓ prē it/, *adj.*   Suitable; fitting.

ascertain /ás ər tã́n/, *v.*   To find out with certainty; to make sure of.

aspiration /ás pə rã́ shən/, *n.*   Ambition; a strong desire for honor or advancement.

compute /kəm py-ū́t/, *v.*   To work out by arithmetic; to figure.

exclude /iks klū́d/, *v.*   To keep a person or thing out of something.

renounce /ri noúns/, *v.*   To give up or deny something, especially an idea, by a formal decision and statement.

superfluous /sū́ pər flū əs/, *adj.*   Over and above what is needed; unnecessary.

EXERCISE.   In each blank, write the word from this lesson that best fits the context. Check your answers by substituting for the word the definition given above. (Add 10 points for each correct answer.)

111

1. When Lucy Stone, the feminist, graduated from Oberlin College in 1847, she . . . . the opportunity to write the commencement address because she would have had to let a man deliver it.

2. Another book would be . . . ., Rosalie felt, since she had already borrowed more than she could read this month.

3. Blue jeans and a sweat shirt are . . . . clothes for a picnic but not for a formal party.

4. All knowledge of the . . . . author of the old ballad "Sir Patrick Spens" is lost in the mists of time.

5. It does not take a calculator to . . . . the difference between twenty-five and thirty-six dollars.

6. "I must . . . . the truth of your charge," said the judge, "before I can take any action."

7. A good newspaper tries to . . . . mere opinion from its news columns, which should be completely factual.

8. The . . . . between the two rivals became more and more noisy and finally ended in a fight.

9. Jane Goodall was filled with an . . . . to become a successful ethologist.

10. A conqueror may . . . . an entire nation, but its ideas, if they are true, will live on.

REVIEW EXERCISE. In the space to the left of each word, write the letter of the best meaning listed at the right. (Add 10 points for each correct answer.)

.... 1. satire	a. confused, ugly sound
.... 2. turbulent	b. easily set on fire
.... 3. inflammable	c. to twist out of shape
.... 4. eloquent	d. excited or confused
.... 5. monopoly	e. to dislike intensely
.... 6. abhor	f. to permit or put up with
.... 7. discord	g. complete control over a product
.... 8. distort	h. forceful and persuasive
.... 9. banish	i. to put out of a country
.... 10. tolerate	j. sarcastic wit

Spelling: Adding -ing to Words Ending in Silent e

When you want to write a verb such as *hope* or *blaze* after a helping verb (*am, is, are,* etc.), do you hesitate before writing the final *e,* and wonder whether to keep or drop the *e* before you add the *-ing?*

Look at the pairs of words below, and see if you can determine a pattern:

us**e**—us**ing**	writ**e**—writ**ing**
lin**e**—lin**ing**	car**e**—car**ing**

How do you think *hope* and *blaze* should be spelled when *-ing* is added to them? A very simple rule will help you remember what to do:

Drop the final silent e before adding -ing.

EXCEPTIONS die—dying }
lie—lying } Change the *ie* to *y* before adding *-ing*.
tie—tying }

dye—dyeing } Keep the silent *e* before adding *-ing*
(meaning *color* or } to distinguish this word from *dying*.
coloring) }

EXERCISE A. Add *-ing* to each of the following words. Write the new word in the blank. (Add 10 points for each correct answer.)

1. prove. . . . . 6. vie. . . . .

2. explore . . . . 7. approve. . . . .

3. complete. . . . . 8. scare . . . .

4. lie . . . . 9. dye . . . .

5. promise. . . . . 10. hesitate . . . .

EXERCISE B. Mentally add *-ing* to each word in parentheses below. Then write the new word in the blank. Each new word will modify the italicized word in that sentence. (Add 10 points for each correct answer.)

1. The doctor looked sadly at the . . . . *man.* (die)

2. We listened to the . . . . *announcement.* (excite)

3. We put too much . . . . *powder* in the bread. (bake)

4. The . . . . *bear* was the best act in the circus. (dance)

5. The *man* . . . . about the movie seemed intelligent. (inquire)

6. My aunt is now a . . . . *physician.* (practice)

7. Myra looked at the gift with .... *eyes*. (shine)

8. The fabric shrank during the .... *process*. (dye)

9. What a .... *face* you have this morning! (smile)

10. Laura received .... *news* from her teacher. (encourage)

EXERCISE C. Choose five verbs (other than those used in this lesson) that end in silent *e*. Write the verbs in the first column below, and then write them with *-ing* added. (Add 10 points for each correct answer.)

VERB	VERB WITH *-ing* ADDED
1.	....
2.	....
3.	....
4.	....
5.	....

REVIEW EXERCISE. Study the words below, paying special attention to the spelling of the prefix in each word. Be ready to write the words from dictation. (Add 4 points for each correct answer.)

1. misunderstand

2. unusual

3. misspell

4. disagree

5. unnamed

6. misbehave

7. dissimilar

8. unable

9. misstate

10. unnoticed

11. displease

12. unnecessary

13. dissatisfied

14. unkind

15. misstep

16. disappear

17. unnumbered

18. disobey

19. misleading

20. misstatement

21. unnatural

22. dissolve

23. misplace

24. disapproval

25. unnerve

CHAPTER 7

Understanding Capital Letters

In written English, capital letters are used to signal certain kinds of words and to begin sentences. Like punctuation, capitalization helps the reader to understand what the writer is saying. For clear and effective writing, it is just as important to know when to capitalize as it is to know when to use commas and periods.

Capitals for Proper Nouns

Names (like George or Chicago) are words that refer to particular persons, places, or things. Such words are called *proper nouns*. You capitalize them to show that they apply to one particular person, place, or thing. All the nouns that are not proper nouns are called *common nouns* and are *not* capitalized.

Capitalize the names of persons.

PROPER NOUNS	COMMON NOUNS
Emily Dickinson	poet (any poet)
Moses Malone	athlete (any athlete)
Mary, Henrietta, and Louise	girls (any girls)

People are not the only individuals that have names. The names of particular businesses, government bodies, and other organizations are also proper nouns and must be capitalized.

Capitalize the names of business firms and other organizations.

EXAMPLES   Adler Junior High School   Radio Corporation of America
University of Wisconsin   the Salvation Army

Words like *junior high school, corporation,* and *university* should never be capitalized unless they are used as part of a name, referring to a particular school, company, or university.

EXAMPLES   Chicago University   *but* my sister's university
the Biltmore Hotel   *but* at a nearby hotel

Do not capitalize the name of a company's product unless it is part of a proper name.

EXAMPLES   The Firestone Tire and Rubber Company
       but   Firestone tires, the tires on our car

EXERCISE A. In the space to the left of each pair, write the letter of the one that is correctly capitalized. (Add 10 points for each correct answer.)

.... 1. (a) Better Business Bureau   (b) Better Business bureau

.... 2. (a) Birdseye peas   (b) Birdseye Peas

.... 3. (a) a famous General   (b) a famous general

.... 4. (a) Harvard University   (b) Harvard university

.... 5. (a) a High-School student   (b) a high-school student

.... 6. (a) the Pennsylvania rail-   (b) the Pennsylvania Railroad
         road

.... 7. (a) Texaco gasoline   (b) Texaco Gasoline

.... 8. (a) the Ford motor Com-   (b) the Ford Motor Company
         pany

.... 9. (a) Schwinn bicycles   (b) Schwinn Bicycles

.... 10. (a) the Shubert Theatre   (b) the Shubert theatre

EXERCISE B. Insert the missing capital letters in the following sentences. Cross out any incorrect capital letter, and write the correct small letter above it. (Add 5 points for each correct answer.)

EX. A Salvation ~~A~~*a*rmy ~~T~~*t*ruck pulled up in front of our house.

1. There is a fine University in our town, but Wilbur's brother is set on going to Dartmouth college.

2. Mr. Benson, who is a salesperson for the Williams sporting goods company, likes the Starlight motel better than any Hotel in town.

3. The Lodge's full name is the Benevolent and protective order of Elks.

4. Crystal is a member of the National organization for Women.

5. The book was published by the firm of harcourt Brace Jovanovich, Inc., a Publishing Company.

6. Andrea Clement, a former investigator for the department of Justice, now teaches at Matthew Wood high school.

7. Langston has an account at the first national bank of Chicago.

116

More Capitals for Proper Nouns

The name of a city, lake, state, country, or any other geographical location is capitalized because it refers to a particular place.

Capitalize the names of particular places and regions.

EXAMPLES   Rochester, Minnesota, Lake Texoma, Long Island
Kruger National Park, Snake River, Welland Canal
Bay of Fundy, Asia

You do not capitalize compass directions (north, east, south, west), but when directions are used as names of particular regions, they become names and are therefore capitalized.

EXAMPLES   Portland and Seattle are cities in the Northwest.
The wind is from the west. The Franklins live east of town.

Months, days of the week, and holidays are capitalized, and so are the names of special or important events.

Capitalize the names of special events and calendar items.

EXAMPLES   The Super Bowl in January is pro football's annual championship game.
Histories of the Revolutionary War make fascinating reading.
Thanksgiving Day always falls on a Thursday.
We went to the Kentucky Derby.

Remember, however, that seasons are *not* capitalized (spring, summer, fall, winter).

EXAMPLE   We worked all winter to get the boat ready for the spring.

Capitalize the names of nations, races, and religions.

EXAMPLES   Sweden   Caucasian   Methodist

EXERCISE A. Add capitals where they are necessary in the sentences on page 118. When in doubt about whether to capitalize a word or not, decide if it is a proper noun (a proper noun refers to a specific person, place, or thing) or a common noun. Correct any incorrect capitals. (Add 4 points for each correct answer.)

EX. The largest Country in South america is brazil.

1. Fertilizing wisconsin's light soil improved the crops.

2. Their new office building is on third avenue in new york City.

3. We went to the Fox Theater to see the movie about india.

4. Our ranch is in brewster county, texas.

5. The soil in Oak creek canyon is exceptionally rich.

6. My great-grandparents came down the Ohio river on a barge.

7. During our trip to canada, we stopped on cape breton island.

8. When you were in australia, did you visit melbourne?

9. Our play is set in Sherwood forest near nottingham.

10. I like stories about the West in pioneer days.

11. We went through grant's pass, northwest of medford in oregon.

12. The bears in Yellowstone Park are also famous in the east.

EXERCISE B. Capitalize any proper nouns mentioned in the paragraph below. (Add 5 points for each correct answer.)

1   People who remember pearl harbor know that it took place on a sunday,
2 but not many know what day of the week iwo jima fell, or when the battle
3 of the bulge took place. Of course, most important battles in modern
4 history lasted for many days. Even naval engagements, such as the battle
5 of midway, took several days. In the middle ages, this was not so, and
6 such decisive struggles as the battle of agincourt lasted only a day. The
7 fate of nations was decided in a few hours of fighting between small
8 armies. But we must remember that all england in Elizabethan times had
9 only five million people. The boston tea party during our war of
10 independence involved only a dozen people or so, and the War of Jenkins'
11 ear was the result of an insult to a single person.

Capitals for Proper Adjectives

An adjective formed from a proper noun is called a *proper adjective*. Most proper adjectives are formed from the name of a nation, a race, or a religion, but some are also formed from the names of people.

Capitalize adjectives formed from the names of nations, races, religions, and other proper nouns.

	NATION	RACE	RELIGION	PERSON
PROPER NOUNS	America	Caucasus	Buddhism	Elizabeth
PROPER ADJECTIVES	American	Caucasian	Buddhist	Elizabethan

Notice that many proper adjectives are also used as nouns when they mean an individual, such as *an American, a Chinese,* or *a Catholic*.

A noun used with a proper adjective is not capitalized unless it is itself a proper noun.

NOT	English Silverware	an Irish Setter	a Protestant Church
BUT	English silverware	an Irish setter	a Protestant church

(but: the First Baptist Church, the name of a particular church)

Do not capitalize the names of school subjects, except languages and course names followed by a number.

EXAMPLES	mathematics	history	science
	Latin	English	French
	Geometry I	History II	Biology I

Capitalize words that refer to God.

EXAMPLES　　God　　　the Lord

The word *god* is not capitalized when it refers to gods of ancient mythology. The names of particular gods within mythology are, however, capitalized, just as other proper nouns are.

EXAMPLES　　Thor, the thunder god
　　　　　　the god of war
　　　　　　Athena, the goddess of wisdom

EXERCISE. Correct the capitalization in the following paragraphs, adding capital letters where needed and taking out unnecessary capitals. (Add 4 points for each correct answer.)

1   I visited my sister at college last week. She is taking several courses,
2 including English, french, american history, and Economics. My sister
3 wants to become a doctor when she graduates and is applying to schools
4 in california and new York. She is also applying to northwestern
5 university in the Midwest.

6   My brother has already graduated from College, where he majored in
7 Education. Today he is teaching mathematics classes in Japan, a country
8 in the far east. My father wants to cross the pacific ocean to see him, but
9 my mother would rather wait another year.

10   My brother writes long letters about life in Japan. He lives close to a
11 buddhist temple and has many friends among the monks there. Buddhism
12 is only one of Japan's many religions. Other faiths include christianity
13 and judaism.

14   I would like to visit my brother in Japan because I love to travel. If I had
15 the money, I would cross the sahara, climb the mountains in tibet, and sail
16 the sea of japan to reach him.

17   In order to travel, however, one must be familiar with the world's
18 Geography. Until recently, I thought the country micronesia was in the
19 caribbean sea. It is actually in the Pacific ocean.

REVIEW EXERCISE. Correct the capitalization in these sentences, which review all the capitalization rules up to this point. (Add 5 points for each correct answer.)

1. The package of French Novels came in the mail on monday.

2. Mrs. waybridge is with Moore's transportation company.

3. The battle of vincennes took place farther West than any other engagement of the revolutionary war.

4. The priest at the catholic Church was born right here in lyme.

5. Anita Welles is famous for her russian Salad Dressing.

6. Aunt Bea's Company is named for neptune, the Roman God of the Sea.

120

Capitals for Titles

A title shows a person's job, rank, or position. It is often capitalized.

Capitalize a title when it comes before a person's name.

EXAMPLES   Ms. Louisa Abbott   Mayor Leone   Captain Meggs

You do not usually capitalize a title when it follows a person's name or when it is used without the name. However, a title may be capitalized when it is used in direct address or if it refers to a high official or to someone for whom you wish to show special respect. The word *president* is usually capitalized when it refers to the President of the United States.

EXAMPLES   "What is your opinion, Senator?" inquired the interviewer.
Mario Cuomo, Governor of New York, addressed the group.
The Chief Justice of the United States rose to speak.
The President will address the nation tomorrow.

When they are used as titles, words that show family relationships are capitalized like other titles.

EXAMPLES   We took Aunt Helena with us. (*Aunt* comes before the name.)
I asked Father to take us for a sail. (*Father* takes the place of the name.)
My mother is in Mexico just now. (The pronoun *my* shows that *mother* merely states a relationship and is not used as a name or a title.)

Capitalize the first and last words and all important words in the titles of books, magazines, and newspapers.

Words like *the, a, an, and,* and *of* in a title are not capitalized unless they are the first word in the title. (You may recall that names of companies and historical events are treated in the same way.)

EXAMPLES   *The Incredible Journey*
The Adventures of Tom Sawyer
Gone with the Wind

The article *the* used before the name of a magazine or newspaper is not considered part of the title and is therefore not capitalized unless it begins a sentence.

EXAMPLES   the *Atlantic* (magazine)
the *Springfield Union* (newspaper)

In printing, the title of a book, magazine, or newspaper is italicized. In handwriting and in typing, underlining takes the place of italics.

EXERCISE A. Capitalize the following book, magazine, and newspaper titles as you would if they were used *within* sentences. (Add 10 points for each correct item.)

1. *daughter of the mountains*
2. the *chicago tribune*
3. the *musical quarterly*
4. *the decline and fall of the roman empire*
5. the *san francisco chronicle*
6. *field and stream*
7. *the texas monthly*
8. *to kill a mockingbird*
9. *a tale of two cities*
10. *pride and prejudice*

EXERCISE B. Correct the capitalization in the following sentences, adding capital letters where needed and taking out any unnecessary capitals. (Add 4 points for each correct answer.)

1. My mother has just been made President of her company.
2. Indeed, aunt mabel told me she subscribed to *time*.
3. We were all addressed by the president of the Parent-Teachers' association.
4. We were interviewed by a Reporter from the *hillside news*.
5. The president likes to get away from Washington on hot days.
6. The singing was led by colonel Graves of the marine corps.
7. When grandmother Newman comes to visit, she always brings presents.
8. I called judge MacIntyre to ask about the potatoes.
9. Nora Ephron has written books called *crazy salad* and *scribble scribble*.
10. The Captain of the ship, Lieutenant Homer Creech, received a personal letter from secretary of the navy Smith.
11. Do you mean, Uncle, that you never read the *Kansas City star?*
12. After dinner, Mother read aloud from Wanda Gág's translation of *Snow White and the seven dwarfs*.
13. Several of my relatives voted for governor Martha Layne Collins.

Chapter Review

EXERCISE A. Supply needed capitals for the names of persons and organizations in these sentences. (Add 4 points for each correct answer.)

1. Has Audrey joined the tuesday literary club?

2. It was Ms. Samuels who was made a vice-president of the Chase manhattan bank.

3. The whole faculty of the Clara Barton high school was there.

4. The employees of the whizzy breakfast cereal company met at the metropolitan theater.

5. Truck drivers often stop at the tip top diner.

6. There is a big sale at murphy, carlson and company.

7. A speaker from faust & company lectured at the optimists club.

8. The Nelsons have joined the first Methodist church.

EXERCISE B. Correct the capitalization in the following sentences, adding capital letters where needed and taking out any unnecessary capitals. (Add 2 points for each correct answer.)

1. The battle of gettysburg continued through the fourth of July, 1863, and vicksburg fell on the same day.

2. Both uncle roy and my Father were members of the nineteenth infantry division during the korean war.

3. My aunt was a nurse in north africa.

4. Bella's favorite foods are French Toast and New England clam chowder.

5. I love the Spring because we always visit washington during cherry blossom time to see my aunt and uncle.

6. A french family on our block celebrates Bastille day every july.

7. Gloria Kliger's older sister moved to greenwich village in new york City.

8. Among the religions practiced in india are buddhism, hinduism, and christianity.

9. Last monday the spanish consul gave a talk to the romance language club at our High School.

10. The canadians have a national holiday called dominion day which they celebrate every year on the first day of july.

11. St. Paul's church is the oldest church in our town.

12. The movie *Casablanca* was set in the Northwest section of africa.

13. Marcia Smith works in washington, and her friend Jessie Robinson works in new york.

14. The latin name for the greek Goddess Aphrodite is venus.

EXERCISE C. Correct the capitalization in the following sentences. (Add 5 points for each correct answer.)

1. My uncle has written a book called *Everyday weather for you.*

2. Becky has a summer job working for the *norwich bugle*.

3. I saw the story about commander kay in the *wisconsin alumni Bulletin*.

4. We subscribe to the sunday edition of the New york times, and it always arrives early Sunday morning.

5. Jacqueline says her favorite animal story is *ring of bright water,* but I like *the call of the wild* much better.

6. One of the high holy days in judaism is rosh hashanah.

EXERCISE D. Supply capitals where needed. (Add 4 points for each correct answer.)

1   Herring fishing in norway lasts from january through march. The best
2 norwegian codfish come from the lofoten islands. The Norwegians ship
3 dried cod to mediterranean countries such as italy, and also to South
4 america. Several countries, including norway, fish in the atlantic ocean off
5 the coast of massachusetts. In central sweden, the people still wear their
6 native costumes to church on sunday. The lapps live in the far north of
7 scandinavia. Their clothes date back to the middle ages in style and look a
8 little like santa claus suits. Some lapps live in finland, a country which
9 gained its independence after world war I.

Cumulative Review

A. Write the part of speech above each italicized word, using these abbreviations: *n.* for noun; *pron.* for pronoun; *adj.* for adjective; *v.* for verb; *adv.* for adverb; *prep.* for preposition; and *conj.* for conjunction. (Add 5 points for each correct answer.)

COAL

1 One *solution* to America's *energy* problems *rests* in coal. The United

2 States *fortunately* has enough *coal* to last four hundred years. Much of *it,*

3 however, is *high-sulfur* coal. *This causes* air *pollution* when it burns.

4 Scientists *are inventing* ways of turning coal *into* gas. This gas *can replace*

5 *petroleum* as a valuable source of heat *in* homes, factories, *and stores*. *It*

6 does not *dangerously* pollute the *atmosphere* when it burns.

B. Put parentheses around each of the prepositional phrases in the sentences that follow. Then underline the word the phrase modifies, and write *adj.* or *adv.* in the space to the left of each sentence to show whether the phrase is used as an adjective or as an adverb. (Add 10 points for each correctly marked sentence.)

.... 1. Indira opened the door with her sore right arm.

.... 2. Corinne opened the door with the little window.

.... 3. The price for such inferior merchandise is far too high.

.... 4. The sound of a hundred singing birds awakened him.

.... 5. The horse reared and bolted across the wheat field.

.... 6. None of this petty squabbling is worth the time it takes.

.... 7. The moth flew toward the nearest light.

.... 8. They took her to a fancy restaurant.

.... 9. They saw the movie on television.

.... 10. The tightrope artist walked with grace and agility.

C. Underline the subject of each sentence once and the verb twice. Circle each complement and above it write *s.c.* for a subject complement and *d.o.* for a direct object. Some sentences are compound or have compound parts. Watch out for prepositional phrases. (Add 10 points for each correctly marked sentence.)

1. The idea of living forever has captured people's imaginations.

2. Explorers have searched without success for the fountain of youth.

3. Ponce de León sailed north from Puerto Rico and explored Florida for the Spanish government.

4. He had heard reports about a fountain of youth in Florida and unsuccessfully sought it.

5. Water from this legendary fountain appears in Nathaniel Hawthorne's story "Dr. Heidegger's Experiment."

6. The water restores the bloom of youth to four old people.

7. Immortality is not always a blessing.

8. Zeus gave immortality to Tithonus, the mortal husband of Aurora, the goddess of dawn.

9. Unfortunately, the gift did not include eternal youth.

10. Death finally appeared the real blessing to Tithonus.

D. In the following paragraph, attach any sentence fragment to the sentence with which it belongs, and supply the period and the capital letter to correct any run-on sentence. Insert missing commas. (Add 5 points for each correct answer.)

1   Soon after the Murphy family had moved into their new home in
2 Webster Minnesota they were invited to dinner. By the Swensons their
3 next-door neighbors. With grateful feelings for the Swensons the Mur-
4 phys arrived for dinner with their three children but a large yellow dog
5 followed them. Into the house. The dog as it turned out was extremely
6 friendly, it put its paws upon the shoulders of each child in turn and licked
7 the child's face. The dog was hungry as well as friendly, in due course it
8 went to the dining room. And began licking the clean plates set out on the
9 table it entered the kitchen, and Mr. Murphy remarked, "That's a
10 remarkable dog you've got there, Mr. Swenson." The Swensons were
11 astounded, they had thought the dog belonged to their new neighbors. The
12 two families decided to find the dog's owners then they set to work
13 washing the dishes for dinner.

Building Vocabulary: Synonyms

A synonym is a word that means nearly the same thing as another word.

A synonym is really a kind of one-word definition. You use synonyms all the time, to explain the meaning of an unfamiliar word and to give your writing variety and interest. You do not need to say merely that a thing is *big,* a word for which there are many synonyms. You can say that it is *huge, gigantic, enormous, monstrous,* and so on.

Notice that synonyms have *nearly,* not exactly, the same meaning. There are no exact synonyms. Words that are synonyms for one another are simply more or less close in meaning. To find out whether two words are close enough, you test them much as you test a full definition—by trying the words out in a context.

Close synonyms can be substituted for each other in sentences.

EXAMPLE   Losing his wallet caused Whitney considerable ~~anguish~~ pain.

In this example, the word *pain* can be substituted for *anguish* without changing the meaning. *Pain* and *anguish* are synonyms. In the following example, however, *anguish* cannot take the place of *pain:*

EXAMPLE   The pain caused by a sprained ankle can be almost unbearable.

Anguish cannot replace pain in this sentence because *anguish* means only one kind of pain—the mental kind. The sentence is about physical pain, the kind that an aspirin may relieve.

Study the definitions of the following words. Think of contexts in which each word might be used. Try to find at least one synonym, or one-word definition, for each word on the list.

aversion /ə vɜ́r zhən/, *n.*   A feeling of keen awareness of something with, at the same time, a strong desire to be rid of it.

commend /kə ménd/, *v.*   To mention a person or thing with approval.

congenial /kən jḗn yəl/, *adj.*   Easy to get along with because of similar tastes or interests; of a group of persons, getting along well together.

congregate /kóng grə gāt/, *v.*   To come together in a crowd.

futile /fy-ū́ təl/, *adj.*   Not producing any result whatever.

inevitable /in év ə tə bəl/, *adj.*   Impossible to prevent; sure to happen.

potent /pṓt nt/, *adj.*   Of persons, having great power and authority; of ideas or other impersonal things, very strong, influential, or effective.

restrict /ri stríkt/, *v.*   To keep within narrow bounds.

ruthless /rū́th lis/, *adj.*   Showing no pity; without mercy.

thwart /thwaurt/, *v.*   To oppose someone's purpose and keep it from being carried out.

EXERCISE. Each word in italics is a synonym for one of the words presented in this lesson. In the space to the left, write the word from this lesson that has nearly the same meaning as the italicized word. (Add 10 points for each correct answer.)

.... 1. Dorothea Dix campaigned against the *unmerciful* treatment of patients in mental institutions.

.... 2. Universal human misery is one of the *unavoidable* results of modern warfare.

.... 3. Cats usually regard baths with *strong dislike*.

.... 4. The speaker's most *powerful* argument for democracy was that it is more efficient than totalitarianism.

.... 5. I found the club members a *friendly* group and decided that I would like to join them.

.... 6. Because our dog is inclined to frighten mail carriers and small children, we have had to *limit* it to the backyard.

.... 7. It is *useless* to think that you can master any skill without hard work and plenty of practice.

.... 8. After school, we often *gather* at the park across the street.

.... 9. Ann Story believed that she could help *prevent* a British takeover of Vermont.

.... 10. I am sure that Mrs. Hutchinson will *praise* my performance in the play.

REVIEW EXERCISE. Some of the italicized words in the following sentences are used incorrectly. In the space to the left of each sentence, write an *I* if the word is incorrectly used and a *C* if it is used correctly. (Add 20 points for each correct answer.)

.... 1. We *refuted* Victor's arguments so effectively that he had to agree with us.

.... 2. The actors were so *audible* that even in the front row we could not hear them.

.... 3. People who become *hysterical* are usually so quiet that no one notices them.

.... 4. In most states, you must be sixteen to be *eligible* for a driver's license.

.... 5. Mrs. Markham wrote, "You've discussed your topic well in the first four paragraphs; the last paragraph, however, is *superfluous*."

Spelling: Words Containing the Suffixes -ly and -ness

Suffixes enable you to get multiple use from English words. If you know the base word *polite,* for example, you can make the words *politely* and *politeness* simply by adding the suffixes *-ly* and *-ness.* Fortunately, these two useful endings cause few spelling problems. Examine the two lists of words below.

-ly	*-ness*
mad + ly = madly	deaf + ness = deafness
brief + ly = briefly	pleasant + ness = pleasantness
cool + ly = coolly	thin + ness = thinness
final + ly = finally	plain + ness = plainness
wide + ly = widely	strange + ness = strangeness
complete + ly = completely	hoarse + ness = hoarseness
heavy + ly = heavily	kindly + ness = kindliness
stingy + ly = stingily	drowsy + ness = drowsiness

From your examination of the two lists above, can you make up two rules about adding *-ly* and *-ness?*

Here are the two easy rules:

When adding the suffixes -ly and -ness to a base word (except if the word ends in y) do *not* change the spelling of the base word.

If the base word ends in y, change the y to i before adding -ly or -ness.

EXCEPTIONS   truly   duly

In what way are these two words exceptions? (The spelling of the base words *true* and *due* is changed when *-ly* is added.)

EXERCISE A. Join each base word and its suffix to form a new word. Write the new word in the blank. Apply the two rules you have learned. (Add 10 points for each correct answer.)

1. dark + ness = ...

2. natural + ly = ...

3. brave + ly = ...

4. messy + ness = ...

5. beautiful + ly = ...

6. weary + ness = ...

7. due + ly = ...

8. trustful + ness = ...

9. incomplete + ness = ...

10. day + ly = ...

EXERCISE B. Mentally add either *-ly* or *-ness* to the base word in parentheses that comes after each of the following sentences. Then write the new word in the blank space in the sentence. (Add 10 points for each correct answer.)

1. Angela was sorry that she had spoken .... to her friend. (angry)

2. My brother's .... is one of his worst traits. (stubborn)

3. Their homework is .... quite neat. (general)

4. The dog's .... was frightening. (fierce)

5. Spiders treat their insect victims ....(cruel)

6. Your .... this morning was understandable. (tardy)

7. Did you close the letter with " .... yours"? (Sincere)

8. No, I used "Yours .... " instead. (true)

9. Patty broke the new vase.. . (accidental)

10. The storm came on with great .... (sudden)

EXERCISE C. Use any five of the new words you made for Exercise A in separate, short, original sentences. (Add 20 points for each correct answer.)

1. ....

2. ....

3. ....

4. ....

5. ....

REVIEW EXERCISE. Mentally add -ing to each word below. Then write the -ing word, correctly spelled, in the blank. (Add 10 points for each correct answer.)

1. smile........................   6. dye........................

2. die........................   7. promise ....

3. explore ....   8. vie ....

4. complete......................   9. shine......................

5. hesitate ....   10. dance ....

CHAPTER 8

A Verb Agrees with Its Subject

People who say *we does* or *the car run* make a very obvious mistake in *subject-verb agreement*. In writing and speaking, you must be careful to make the subject and verb of a sentence (or clause) agree in number.

LESSON 65

Singular and Plural

A noun or pronoun may refer to one thing or to more than one thing. The difference is called a difference in the *number* of the noun or pronoun. Most nouns and personal pronouns show a change in number by a change in the form of the word.

When a word refers to one person, place, thing, or idea, it is singular in number. When a word refers to more than one, it is plural in number.

Most nouns change from singular to plural by adding *s* or *es* to the singular form of the word, but some change in other ways. A few nouns do not change at all—the plural form is exactly the same as the singular form. In the following examples, the changes from singular to plural are printed in red.

SINGULAR	PLURAL	SINGULAR	PLURAL
athlete	athletes	knife	knives
house	houses	ox	oxen
box	boxes	goose	geese
address	addresses	sheep	sheep

Other words like *goose* that form the plural by a vowel change are *man (men), woman (women), mouse (mice),* and *foot (feet).*

The personal pronouns are entirely different in the singular and plural, except for *you,* which never changes.

SINGULAR	I, me	you	he, she, it; him, her, it
PLURAL	we, us	you	they, them

EXERCISE A. In front of each of the words listed on page 132, write *S* or *P* to show whether the word is singular or plural. (Add 5 points for each correct answer.)

..... 1. birds   ..... 8. cloud   ..... 15. laundries

..... 2. clock   ..... 9. scarves   ..... 16. ribbon

..... 3. loudspeakers   ..... 10. radios   ..... 17. lice

..... 4. bicycle   ..... 11. women   ..... 18. waltzes

..... 5. they   ..... 12. sink   ..... 19. mouse

..... 6. losses   ..... 13. he   ..... 20. leaves

..... 7. teeth   ..... 14. children

EXERCISE B. In the following passage, circle all of the singular nouns and pronouns. There are twenty-seven of them altogether. Underline all of the plural nouns and pronouns. There are twenty-three of them altogether. When in doubt about a word, ask whether it means just one thing or more than one. (Add 2 points for each correct answer.)

1   Before people understood the laws of the universe, they thought the

2   world was inhabited by spirits. Some of these spirits were good and some

3   were evil. Spirits were thought to inhabit natural objects. Belief in some

4   of these good and bad spirits has, to an extent, been carried over to the

5   present day, forming the basis of superstitions. Today, bad omens such as

6   black cats, cuckoos, and snakes are considered objects of fear by many

7   people. A common English superstition is that it is unlucky to sweep dirt

8   out the front door. To do this is to sweep away good fortune. Some French

9   people believe that it is unlucky to touch iron. A common German

10   superstition is that no fire may come where a stork has a nest. An Italian

11   superstition maintains that snakes are guardians of buried treasure. A

12   common American belief is that to break a mirror means seven years of

13   bad luck. Many folks believe that a four-leaf clover and a rabbit's foot

14   bring good luck.

Matching the Verb to Its Subject

There is a very good reason for paying attention to the *number* of a noun or pronoun. Often, the form of a verb depends on the number of its subject, which may be a noun or pronoun.

A verb agrees with its subject in number.

SINGULAR   Martha walks to school every day. She likes the fresh air.
The new road bypasses the town. Vanessa skates at the rink.

PLURAL   The girls walk to school every day. They like the fresh air.
The new roads bypass the town. The boys skate at the rink.

In the examples above, notice that when the subject is singular (*Martha, She, road, Vanessa*), the verb, too, is singular in number. (The *s* or *es* ending often occurs in verbs that are singular in number.) When the subject is plural (*girls, they, roads, boys*), the verb is plural.

The important helping verbs *to have* and *to do* agree with their subjects just as other verbs do.

SINGULAR   Frances has always liked swimming.
He certainly does eat a hearty breakfast.

PLURAL   They have always liked swimming.
His brothers certainly do eat a hearty breakfast.

That troublesome verb *to be* has more forms than any other verb and therefore more chances for errors in subject-verb agreement. Study the forms of *to be* below and memorize them.

SINGULAR	PLURAL	SINGULAR	PLURAL
(I) am	(we) are	(I) was	(we) were
(you) are	(you) are	(you) were	(you) were
(he, she, it) is	(they) are	(he, she, it) was	(they) were

The most common error that occurs with *to be* is the use of the singular forms *is* and *was* with the plural pronoun *they* or with a plural noun.

NONSTANDARD   They *was* almost sure to win.
Hurry! The geese *is* getting out.

STANDARD   They **were** almost sure to win.
Hurry! The geese **are** getting out.

EXERCISE A. Determine the number of the subject in each sentence. Then find the correct one of the two verbs given in parentheses that agrees in number with the subject. Underline the correct verb. (Add 10 points for each correct answer.)

1. Railroads (is, are) becoming more popular among travelers.
2. The *Metroliner* (connect, connects) Boston and Washington, D.C.
3. We (pays, pay) for our ticket at Union Station.
4. Before the train (leaves, leave), the conductor shouts, "All aboard!"
5. Other trains (is passing, are passing) our train at high speeds.
6. I stay awake, but my sister (falls, fall) asleep.
7. The conductors on board (is asking, are asking) for tickets.
8. I (shake, shakes) my sleeping sister to wake her.
9. "We (has passed, have passed) Baltimore," I tell her.
10. "Wake me when the train (reach, reaches) New York," she replies.

EXERCISE B. Change each subject from singular to plural or from plural to singular. Also change the verb so that it agrees with the subject in number. (Add 20 points for each correct sentence.)

EX. Clouds cover the sky along the horizon.
A cloud covers the sky along the horizon.

1. A man was running frantically away from the fire.

. . . .

2. The city closes the beaches in September.

. . . .

3. They like to daydream about faraway places.

. . . .

4. Last summer I was at the beach almost every day.

. . . .

5. The elm trees have been growing here for a century.

. . . .

Watch Out for Phrases!

When the verb comes right after the subject, there is usually no problem in deciding what form the verb should have. But in many sentences, the subject and the verb are separated by various modifiers, and these modifiers can be confusing. Prepositional phrases, in particular, cause problems. A phrase containing a *plural* noun may follow a *singular* subject; or a phrase containing a *singular* noun may follow a *plural* subject. In such cases, the verb agrees with the subject, as in any other sentence.

The number of a subject is not changed by a prepositional phrase following the subject.

> EXAMPLES   Shadow<u>s</u> (from the castle wall) <u><u>fall</u></u> across the lawn.
> (plural subject, plural verb).
> One <u>girl</u> (from that whole group of schoolgirls) <u><u>insists</u></u> on walking.
> (singular subject, singular verb)
> One bad <u>apple</u> (in a basket of good ones) often <u><u>spoils</u></u> the rest.
> (singular subject, singular verb)

The parentheses around the phrases in the examples should remind you of an important point: the subject of a sentence is never found in a prepositional phrase. The noun or pronoun in a phrase modifying this subject has no effect on the verb, which must still agree in number with its subject.

Most people have a natural impulse to make the verb agree with the noun that comes closest in front of it, but this impulse can cause errors when that noun happens to be part of a prepositional phrase. To avoid such errors, mentally drop out the prepositional phrase. Then find the verb and its subject, and *make them agree*.

EXERCISE A. Each of the following sentences contains one or more phrases modifying the subject. Cross out these adjective phrases, and underline the subject once and the verb twice. (Add 10 points for each correctly marked sentence.)

EX.   <u>Dozens</u> ~~of pigeons from the pen on the roof~~ <u><u>fly</u></u> in circles.

1. One person among the new members objects to the proposal.

2. All of the cows in the herd turn their backs to the storm.

3. The date of the play has not yet been set.

4. Some of the change rightfully belongs to Laura.

5. The book with the pictures contains material on Africa.

6. The height of the two brothers surprises people.

7. The committee of property owners meets here tomorrow.

8. Several people with folding chairs and camp beds were waiting patiently at the head of the ticket line.

9. Tourists in Mexico often find Aztec relics.

10. Students at our junior high school start school at 8:30 A.M.

EXERCISE B. In the following paragraph, there are two forms for most verbs. Cross out the one that does not agree with the subject. If in doubt, cross out the prepositional phrases, and find the subject of the verb. (Add 10 points for each correct answer.)

MARTIANS, ANYONE?

1   Scientists at a leading American university (has, have) been collecting
2   jokes. In their opinion, jokes about outer space (reveal, reveals) our
3   hidden fears of the unknown. Perhaps a civilization on one of the distant
4   planets (has, have) grown more powerful than ours. If invaders from one
5   of these older and wiser civilizations (come, comes) to earth, will we
6   know how to stand up to them? Questions of this kind apparently (worry,
7   worries) us. According to the scientists, jokes about space invaders (calm,
8   calms) our inner fears. Often, the invader in these jokes (turn, turns) out
9   not to be so smart after all. A short story about two Martians especially
10   (amuse, amuses) me. The creatures from Mars walk up to a parked car
11   and (order, orders) it to take them to its leader. The parked car says
12   nothing. Finally, one Martian, after repeated threats, (kick, kicks) the car
13   and breaks its headlights. ''Shame on you!'' says the other Martian. ''You
14   should never hit a person with glasses!''

Problems with Pronouns

Any word that takes the place of a noun is called a *pronoun*. Certain kinds of pronouns, called *indefinite pronouns,* cause problems in subject-verb agreement. Some of these pronouns are always plural in meaning, while others are always singular in meaning, but their number is not always clear when they are modified by prepositional phrases. To avoid mistakes, you must know which pronouns are plural and which are singular.

The following pronouns are singular and take a singular verb: anybody, anyone, each, either, everybody, everyone, neither, nobody, no one, one, somebody, someone.

When they are used as subjects, these singular pronouns are often followed by prepositional phrases that contain plural nouns. In such cases, there is a tendency to make the verb agree with the plural noun rather than with the singular pronoun. This is because the object of the preposition comes after the pronoun subject and is therefore closer to the verb.

NONSTANDARD   Each of the hamsters *have* been fed. (*Hamsters* is in a prepositional phrase and cannot be the subject of the verb.)

STANDARD   Each of the hamsters **has** been fed.

NONSTANDARD   Everyone on both teams *are* out to win.

STANDARD   Everyone on both teams **is** out to win.

Notice that most of these singular pronouns contain the idea of "one" —any*one,* any*body,* and so on. These pronouns are used to mean just one out of a group or the members of a group thought of individually, one at a time. As subjects, therefore, these singular pronouns require singular verbs (anyone *is,* anybody *was*).

To avoid mistakes in using a singular pronoun, mentally drop out any prepositional phrase that follows it. This will show at once the correct form of the verb to use.

NONSTANDARD   Each one of these color slides *belong* to my mother.

STANDARD   Each **one** (of these color slides) **belongs** to my mother.

The following pronouns are plural and take a plural verb: both, few, many, several.

EXAMPLES   **Both** of the boys **have lost** their bicycles.

               Several of us **want** to go on a class picnic.

EXERCISE A. Put parentheses around any prepositional phrase that follows an indefinite pronoun. Then find and underline the subject of the sentence once, and draw two lines under the correct one of the two verb forms given in parentheses. (Add 10 points for each correct sentence.)

EX. One (of my brothers) (work, works) in Alaska.

1. Both of these games (bore, bores) my father.

2. Neither of the cows (was, were) a prize winner at the state fair.

3. Either of your suggestions for the meeting (suit, suits) me.

4. Everyone from nine to ninety (is, are) going to the parade.

5. Few, however, ever (stay, stays) to the end of the program.

6. Surely someone in one of these classes (do, does) know the answer.

7. No one from outer space (has, have) landed in our back yard.

8. Each of these fortunate young people (has, have) won a trip to Death Valley with all expenses paid.

9. Several of the English poets (is, are) buried in Westminster Abbey.

10. Anyone with a love of mystery stories (enjoy, enjoys) Agatha Christie's books.

EXERCISE B. Some of the verbs in the following sentences do not agree with their subjects. Cross out any incorrect verb, and write the correct form above it. (Add 10 points for each correct answer.)

1. Neither of the two researchers were aware of the problem.

2. Everyone in the room were talking at once.

3. Every spring the apples from this one tree fills several baskets.

4. A story in the newspapers recently tells of a prize cabbage weighing nineteen kilograms.

5. Several members of my class has been absent this week.

6. Two bales of wastepaper was lying in the middle of the road.

7. A pound of feathers weigh as much as a pound of gold.

8. The clothes for our family all come from the same store.

9. One of these stories was very funny.

10. A box of old coins were buried at the foot of a large oak tree.

Reversed Word Order in Sentences

The most common way of putting a sentence together is with the subject first, followed by its verb. In certain kinds of sentences, however, this order is reversed—the verb, or part of it, comes first and then the subject. Sentences of this kind may cause you to make errors in agreement. To avoid such errors, you must be careful to determine the subject and make the verb agree with it.

HERE AND THERE

When the subject follows the verb, as in sentences beginning with here and there, be especially careful to determine the subject and make sure that the verb agrees with it.

EXAMPLES Here is something to remember me by. (*Something* is the subject.)

There are eleven bananas in that bunch. (*Bananas* is the subject.)

You can make sure that the subject and verb agree by mentally putting the subject first and the verb next.

NONSTANDARD There *was* two men under the bridge. (plural subject, singular verb)

STANDARD There were two men under the bridge. (= *Two men were under the bridge*—plural subject, plural verb)

The contractions *here's* and *there's* are short for *here is* and *there is*. Use them only with singular subjects.

NONSTANDARD *There's* (= There is) those girls from Elmwood School.

STANDARD There are those girls from Elmwood School. (plural subject, plural verb)

An adverb phrase is often placed first in a sentence for emphasis. When the phrase begins the sentence, it has the same effect as *here* and *there*.

EXAMPLES Under the bridge stand two men.

At the bottom of the hole was a tiny newborn rabbit.

QUESTION SENTENCES

In sentences that ask a question, the subject may come after the verb or between two parts of a divided verb. To check for subject-verb agreement, turn the sentence around in your mind, putting the subject first.

EXAMPLES   <u>Has</u> <u>Maxwell</u> <u>lost</u> his gloves again? (= *Maxwell has lost?*)

Where <u>are</u> Paula's glasses? (= *Glasses are where?*)

EXERCISE A. In each of the following sentences, underline the subject once, and then underline twice the correct form of the verb in parentheses. (Add 10 points for each correct sentence.)

1. There (go, goes) the ships with all their flags flying.

2. At the top of the hill (stand, stands) a beautiful old church.

3. Down the runway and out over the bay (roar, roars) the two jets.

4. (There's, There are) not many cookies left in the jar.

5. (Do, Does) the children never get tired of running around?

6. At the bottom of the rubbish heap there (was, were) a box of valuable gems.

7. On the lawn (lie, lies) the shells of three broken birds' eggs.

8. There (is, are) only three clarinet players in the entire band.

9. (Has, Have) the preference of the members been expressed?

10. There (was, were) several moths hiding in the clothes closet.

EXERCISE B. Correct any error in subject-verb agreement by crossing out the incorrect verb and writing the correct form above it. (Add 10 points for each correctly marked sentence.)

EX. ~~Where's~~ *Where are* the eggs for Uncle Findley's breakfast?

1. In an album on the top shelf there is some pictures of my mother.

2. Where is that book about the space program?

3. There's several boys waiting for you on the front steps, Emilio.

4. Here at last was an opportunity for Lee to express herself.

5. Have one of the girls brought in the mail yet?

6. Here's the oranges you wanted.

7. There was too many raisins in that pudding for Maxine's taste.

8. Does either of your parents play tennis?

9. On the beach beside the dock there was three or four canoes.

10. There has been various explanations for the mayor's change of plans.

DON'T and DOESN'T

Many people mix up the contractions *don't* and *doesn't,* particularly in everyday speech. Remember that *don't* is short for *do not* and that *doesn't* is short for *does not. Don't* should be used with all plural subjects and the pronouns *I* and *you. Doesn't* should be used with all singular subjects except *I* and *you.*

SINGULAR	PLURAL
(I) don't	(we) don't
(you) don't	(you) don't
(he, she, it) doesn't	(they) don't
(Gabriella) doesn't	(the girls) don't

NONSTANDARD   Willis *don't* like maple syrup.

STANDARD   Willis <u>does</u>n't <u>like</u> maple syrup. (*doesn't = does not,* the correct form for a singular subject)

NONSTANDARD   The people in the lifeboat *doesn't* need our help.

STANDARD   The <u>people</u> in the lifeboat <u>do</u>n't <u>need</u> our help. (*don't = do not,* the correct form for a plural subject)

EXERCISE A. Change each singular subject to a plural subject and each plural subject to a singular subject. Make the verb agree with the new subject, as in the example. (Add 10 points for each correct sentence.)

EX. The cats don't like fish. *The cat doesn't like fish.* . . . . . .

1. Your books don't interest me. . . . .

2. This child doesn't tell lies. . . . .

3. The elephant doesn't forget. . . . .

4. The boxes don't weigh much. . . . .

5. He just doesn't like me. . . . .

6. The oxen don't eat enough. . . . .

7. Travelers don't usually ask directions. . . . .

8. The geese don't remember. . . . .

9. She doesn't give much help. . . . .

10. The mouse doesn't like the cheese. . . . .

EXERCISE B. Underline the subject of each sentence, and then fill in the blank with the correct contracted form of *to do*—*don't* or *doesn't*. Check the answers by trying out the uncontracted forms (*do not, does not*) before filling in the blank. Watch out for prepositional phrases. (Add 4 points for each correct sentence.)

EX. A can of peanuts .. *doesn't* .. last long at our house.

EX. Three quarts of milk ... *don't* ... just vanish into thin air!

1. A whole box of crackers . . . . last more than a few days.

2. Rita Mazour . . . . want to go to the circus.

3. . . . . anyone like chicken with rice?

4. Julie's parents . . . . let her watch television very much.

5. This book about Sojourner Truth . . . . belong to me.

6. . . . . the Beck family live here any more?

7. Those bikes across the street . . . . belong to any of us.

8. The hairdresser . . . . always do such a good job.

9. The rings of Saturn . . . . look so clear in a photograph.

10. Everyone . . . . enjoy skating as much as we do.

11. The conductor of the orchestra . . . . want to change.

12. Viola . . . . want to play the flute any more.

13. Any friend of yours . . . . need to apologize.

14. People . . . . often refuse thanks for good deeds.

15. The actors in the play . . . . all have big parts.

16. . . . . a person with responsibilities ever take chances?

17. It simply . . . . matter to me which movie we go to.

18. The moon . . . . look so large when it's low in the sky.

19. The people from the moving company . . . . want to wait.

20. This ball-point pen . . . . look much like mine.

21. The students in my class . . . . all think as you do.

22. I . . . . understand the problem, and Loomis . . . . either.

23. A person with red hair . . . . always have a fiery temper.

24. . . . . some solution to your problems seem likely?

25. Good grades . . . . just happen by themselves.

What About Compound Subjects?

A compound subject consists of two or more connected subjects that have the same verb. Usually, the parts of a compound subject are connected by the conjunction *and, or,* or *nor.* The number of the subject depends on which of these conjunctions is used.

Compound subjects joined by <u>and</u> take a plural verb.

This rule contains no surprises. The *and* joins two things together, making two—which is what we mean by plural.

EXAMPLES   The westbound <u>express</u> **and** the freight <u>train</u> <u>**were** derailed</u>.

An old <u>oak</u> **and** an American <u>elm</u> **<u>stand</u>** beside the front door.

When we use *and* to join the parts of a compound subject, we mean both together. When we use *or* (or *nor*), on the other hand, we mean one or the other but *not both.*

Singular subjects joined by <u>or</u> or <u>nor</u> take a singular verb.

EXAMPLES   The <u>lilac</u> **or** the <u>honeysuckle</u> **<u>has</u>** been moved.

The <u>road</u> to the right **or** the <u>one</u> straight ahead **<u>leads</u>** home.

Sentences of this kind often begin with *either* (or *neither*).

EXAMPLES   **Either** the <u>tug</u> **or** the <u>ferry</u> **<u>was</u>** off course.

Neither the <u>geranium</u> **nor** the <u>fern</u> **<u>gets</u>** enough water.

If both parts of a compound subject joined by *or* or *nor* are plural, the verb must, of course, be plural also.

EXAMPLE   <u>Soldiers</u> **or** police <u>officers</u> <u>**were** blocking</u> all the exits.

EXERCISE A. Underline the correct one of the two verb forms in parentheses. (Add 10 points for each correct answer.)

TWO ANGLERS

1   Betty Salvio and Pat Huggins, the girl who lives next door to Betty,

2   (like, likes) to go fishing at Lake Pewauskee. Either Betty or Pat generally

3   (get, gets) someone to take them out to the lake, and then they and all the

4   other people who are fishing there (spend, spends) hours at a time just

143

5   catching a couple of catfish. Once in a while some old-timer or some

6   really devoted angler (claim, claims) that there are bass in that lake, but

7   neither Betty nor Pat (has, have) ever caught one, nor (has, have) anyone

8   else ever caught any. Neither their lack of success nor the thought of how

9   much time they have wasted there, however, (keep, keeps) them from

10 going back to try again. Some people from the city and even a few local

11 business people (think, thinks) nothing of spending their whole vacation

12 there. Either the hook or the bait they use (is, are) no good, apparently. At

13 any rate, Betty and Pat freely (admit, admits) their failure at Lake

14 Pewauskee.

EXERCISE B. Some of the verb forms in the following sentences are incorrect. Cross out each incorrect verb, and write the correct form above it. Remember that *or* and *nor* mean *either one but not both*. Singular subjects joined by *or* or *nor* require the singular form of the verb. (Add 10 points for each correctly marked sentence.)

1. The toy soldier and the stuffed dog was thrown away in the trash.

2. Either the car or the boat are going to be sold.

3. The throw rug and the slipcover were both made by hand.

4. The house next door and one around the corner is painted pink.

5. Either the dog or the cat have to stay outside.

6. The sounds of helicopters and horns from trucks in the street wakes me up too early some mornings.

7. Either a cold or some kind of virus infection have kept him in bed since Monday.

8. Neither the battery nor the generator are out of order.

9. The leaves and the grass trimmings has to be raked today.

10. The performers and the fans were dancing.

Chapter Review

EXERCISE A. In each of the following sentences, put parentheses around the prepositional phrases, underline the subject, and circle the correct one of the two verb forms given in parentheses. (Add 4 points for each correct sentence.)

1. One of the Christmas tree ornaments (is, are) hand painted.

2. His passion for Bartlett pears (grow, grows) with each bite.

3. (Was, Were) neither of the two orchestral pieces played well?

4. Everyone from the New England states (is, are) to leave at once.

5. Three of the rarest coins in the collection (was, were) missing.

6. Several of the students in my class (do, does) play soccer well.

7. The light from the neon signs in the store windows (is, are) bright enough.

8. Everyone in our choral group obviously (love, loves) to sing.

9. The prices of the various items on sale at the department store luggage counter (was, were) clearly marked.

10. Anyone with a desire to play and patience enough for practicing during long stretches of time (make, makes) a good piano student.

11. In the center of each table (sit, sits) a bowl of fresh flowers.

12. Where (was, were) the other members of the committee during the meeting?

13. After the meeting, only two cups of juice (was, were) left.

14. (Has, Have) Lisa or Margrit told you about the news broadcast yet?

15. No one from our school ever (go, goes) there.

16. Alfie and Louise sometimes (do, does) their homework together.

17. (Don't, Doesn't) several of you leave for camp tomorrow?

18. The pens and the books (was, were) on the table a minute ago.

19. Neither Ethel nor that friend of hers (want, wants) to leave yet.

20. Behind the band (come, comes) a few of the most elaborate floats.

21. Each of the five contestants (wants, want) the prize.

22. Neither of the pets (was, were) housebroken.

23. Both of the girls from that club (has, have) won trophies.

24. The beneficiaries from the insurance policy (has, have) not received as much money as expected.

25. The solution to the mysteries surrounding the crimes (was, were) given by the detective.

EXERCISE B. The following paragraphs contain errors in subject-verb agreement. Cross out each incorrect verb, and write the correct form above it. (Add 10 points for each correct answer.)

MORNINGS

1   A dairy farmer's mornings is full of chores. The workday usually begin
2   before dawn. In the barn there is many cows waiting to be milked. The
3   farmer turn on the milking machines, which make this job easier. Each of
4   the cows are hooked to a hose that pumps the milk into a nearby tank. The
5   milk don't stay in the tank very long. A truck come to empty the farmer's
6   tank every other day. This truck take the milk to a nearby dairy plant.
7   From the dairy plant, the milk is delivered to stores.

8   A dairy farmer's morning are also the time for tending the calves,
9   cleaning the barn, and repairing the machinery. Few of us is ever as busy
10   as a dairy farmer during the morning.

Cumulative Review

A. In the following sentences, find the simple subject, verb, and direct object or subject complement. (Not every sentence contains a direct object or a subject complement.) Above the appropriate word, write *s.* for subject; *v.* for verb; *d.o.* for direct object; *s.c.* for subject complement. (Add 10 points for each correctly marked sentence.)

1. John Smith became the leader of the colony at Jamestown, Virginia.

2. Pocahontas helped the settlers in Jamestown.

3. Most farms in the colonies were very small in the early days.

4. The only roads were narrow trails among the trees.

5. River transport became particularly important.

6. Many towns used boats for contact with other places.

7. Almost everything was made by hand.

8. Even nails were produced by blacksmiths.

9. Most settlers grew their own food.

10. In time, trade with other colonies grew more important.

B. Put parentheses around the prepositional phrases in the following sentences, and underline the word each phrase modifies. Then write *adj.* above the phrase if it is used as an adjective or *adv.* if it is used as an adverb. (Add 20 points for each correct sentence.)

1. The colonies along the south Atlantic coast gained their income from tobacco and rice plantations.

2. With their new and sometimes persecuted religious beliefs, the Quakers needed the religious freedom of the New World.

3. Colonies were not established in Georgia until the eighteenth century.

4. In 1733 General Oglethorpe arrived in Georgia with a group of settlers and named the area after the British king.

5. The Pilgrims landed at Plymouth in 1620 and sought the friendship of the Wampanog tribe.

C. The following paragraph contains sentence fragments and run-on sentences. Correct the errors by adding or crossing out periods, commas, and capital letters as necessary. (Add 10 points for each correct answer.)

147

THE HERO OF SHERWOOD FOREST

1   Robin Hood is a legendary figure of English folklore his story can be
2   traced back to the fourteenth century. When writers first mention his
3   name. He has been identified with various real people. Among them a
4   twelfth-century earl. The Earl of Huntingdon. It is more likely that he was
5   simply a fictional character. There are many English folk songs about
6   Robin Hood, he was supposed to be a great archer who lived with his men
7   in Sherwood Forest. Near Nottingham, England. They robbed the rich
8   and gave money to the poor. As everyone knows. Thanks to modern
9   versions of the legends, members of the band are familiar figures, today
10   most young people have read about Friar Tuck, Little John, and Robin
11   Hood's other ''merry men.'' The story will remain forever fresh. While
12   there are new readers. To enjoy it.

D. The following paragraph contains comma and capitalization errors. Correct
these errors. (Add 4 points for each correct answer.)

A CAREER IN BRIEF

1   William E. b. Du Bois was born in Great barrington Massachusetts, on
2   February 23 1868, three years after the civil War. After High School, he
3   won a scholarship to Fisk university. As Editor of the school paper the
4   *Fisk herald* he called on his fellow students to organize a crusade to wipe
5   out racial prejudice. In 1888 harvard university awarded him a scholar-
6   ship and Du Bois proudly accepted. At harvard, he studied Philosophy
7   and History. Du Bois was one of the founders of the National association
8   for the advancement of colored people. He wrote over twenty books.
9   Among them was *The souls of black folk*.

Building Vocabulary: Antonyms

Simply knowing a new word is of no use unless you can make it part of your *active* vocabulary—so that you can recall it readily and use it correctly to say what you mean. It helps to think of words in pairs or groups. You think of words with similar meanings *as a group*. You can also think of words with *opposite* meanings as a group.

Antonyms are words that have nearly opposite meanings.

EXAMPLE   The newspaper charged that the chief of police was not *honest*.
The newspaper charged that the chief of police was **corrupt**.

In this example, *corrupt* and *honest* are antonyms—they have nearly opposite meanings. Notice that *corrupt* makes a more forceful statement than merely saying *not honest*.

Besides being useful for expanding your vocabulary, antonyms can also help you to explain word meanings briefly and clearly. Many words do not have close synonyms. For example, it is rather roundabout to say that *passive* means "enduring without offering resistance," but if you say that *passive* means "not active" or is "the opposite of *active*," the meaning is at once clear.

Study the following word meanings and try to think of a suitable antonym for each word.

brevity /brév ə tē/, *n.*   The use of few words to express something.

confirm /kən fə́rm/, *v.*   To say or prove that a doubtful statement is true.

dismal /díz məl/, *adj.*   Dark and gloomy; miserable.

disperse /dis pə́rs/, *v.*   To scatter or to go away to different places.

dubious /dú bē əs/, *adj.*   Doubtful; not sure of the outcome of something.

fickle /fík əl/, *adj.*   Not sticking to things; likely to change.

lenient /lḗ nē ənt/, *adj.*   Not harsh or severe; easygoing in matters of discipline.

predecessor /préd ə sés ər/, *n.*   One who has gone before someone in a job or an office.

tactful /tákt fəl/, *adj.*   Careful about doing and saying the right thing to others.

transient /trán shənt/, *adj.*   Lasting for only a short time.

EXERCISE. Underline the antonym (the word that has nearly the opposite meaning) for each italicized word. (Add 10 points for each correct answer.)

1. *Brevity* is not usually one of a politician's notable qualities.
   antonym: (a) friendliness   (b) intelligence   (c) wordiness

2. The government would not *confirm* the news of the new space program.
   antonym: (a) approve   (b) deny   (c) release

3. A pessimist can usually see the *dismal* side of any situation.
   antonym: (a) cheerful   (b) easy   (c) inexpensive

4. The mayor stood on the steps of city hall and asked the crowd to *disperse* and return to their homes.
   antonym: (a) continue   (b) gather   (c) agree

5. Carmen was extremely *dubious* about the outcome of the game.
   antonym: (a) certain   (b) happy   (c) fearful

6. During the fall, the weather tends to be *fickle*.
   antonym: (a) weak   (b) hard-working   (c) constant

7. Mr. Agnew is inclined to be too *lenient* with his class.
   antonym: (a) strict   (b) unkind   (c) serious

8. Our principal's *predecessor* was the author of several textbooks.
   antonym: (a) enemy   (b) successor   (c) co-worker

9. A *tactful* person would not have mentioned my poor grade on the test.
   antonym: (a) unkind   (b) stupid   (c) offensive

10. Fortunately, the lion's interest in Martha Magnuson was *transient*.
    antonym: (a) eager   (b) permanent   (c) hostile

REVIEW EXERCISE. In the space to the left of each word group, write the letter of the best meaning for the italicized word. (Add 10 points for each correct answer.)

.... 1. Two events may *coincide*.   a. sure to happen

.... 2. a *fantastic* idea   b. to destroy completely

.... 3. an *intricate* plan   c. strange, odd, fanciful

.... 4. The Huns *annihilated* the army.   d. the act of giving in

.... 5. a *haughty* person   e. a complete disaster

.... 6. an *aversion* to cats   f. proud, showing contempt for others

.... 7. engaged in an *altercation*   g. strong dislike

.... 8. a *concession* to weakness   h. to happen together

.... 9. the tragic results of the *catastrophe*   i. angry argument

.... 10. an *inevitable* result   j. extremely complicated

Spelling: Does It End with -cle or -cal?

When writing words such as *miracle* or *comical,* do you find yourself hesitating when you get to the *-c* near the end of the word and wondering whether to use *-cle* or *-cal?* These endings *sound* alike, so your ear is of no help in deciding. There is a way, however, that will help you to choose the correct ending for such words.

Examine the two lists of words below. All the words in list *1* end in *-cle;* all those in list *2* end in *-cal.*

1		2	
article	bicycle	musical	physical
icicle	tentacle	medical	political
popsicle	obstacle	logical	practical

Besides their endings, what else do the words in list *1* have in common? What do those in list *2* have in common? All of the words in *1* are nouns; all those in *2* are most commonly used as adjectives. To prove this, try using each word in a sentence.

Therefore, if the word you want to spell is a noun, you can be fairly certain that *-cle* is the correct ending. If the word is used primarily as an adjective, then you are right if you spell its ending *-cal.* In fact, *-cal* (actually *-ical*) was the ending used in Latin to turn a noun into an adjective. This helps explain why our English words that end in *-cal* are generally adjectives, and why there is usually a noun form for every adjective that ends in *-cal.* The adjective *musical* has the noun form *music;* the adjective *political* has the noun form *politics;* the adjective *logical* has the noun form *logic.*

EXERCISE A. For each of the following nouns, there is a related adjective ending in *-cal* (or *-ical*). In the blanks provided, write the related adjectives. If you need to, use your dictionary. (Add 10 points for each correct answer.)

EX.   grammar. *grammatical* . . . .

1. alphabet . . . .   6. method . . . .

2. critic . . . .   7. tropics. . . . .

3. rhythm . . . .   8. Bible. . . . .

4. mathematics. . . . .   9. myth . . . .

5. magic . . . .   10. poet. . . . .

EXERCISE B. Complete each unfinished word part in the following sentences by writing *-cle* or *-cal,* whichever is right, in the blank. Decide whether the incomplete word is used mainly as a noun or as an adjective; then apply the information you have learned. (Add 10 points for each correct answer.)

1. A tricycle is a vehi . . . . with three wheels.

2. That doctor performs surgi . . . . operations.

3. A trillion dollars is an astronomi . . . . sum of money.

4. A wastepaper basket is a recepta . . . . for trash.

5. My sister has a very mechani . . . . mind.

6. The sunset was a gorgeous specta . . . . to see.

7. Celia and Jennifer are identi . . . . twins.

8. The lists are arranged in numeri . . . . order.

9. On the lens of the microscope was a tiny parti . . . . of dust.

10. First draw a horizontal line and then a verti . . . . one.

EXERCISE C. Use any five of the adjectives you made for Exercise A in separate, original sentences. (Add 20 points for each correct answer.)

1. . . . .

2. . . . .

3. . . . .

4. . . . .

5. . . . .

REVIEW EXERCISE. Study the words below, and be prepared to write them from dictation. Remember the two easy rules about adding the suffixes -ly and -ness to a base word. (Add 4 points for each correct answer.)

1. thinness	10. angrily	18. plainness
2. daily	11. suddenness	19. sincerely
3. stubbornness	12. stingily	20. completely
4. coolly	13. kindliness	21. duly
5. tardiness	14. naturally	22. hoarseness
6. beautifully	15. weariness	23. heavily
7. drowsiness	16. cruelly	24. messiness
8. truly	17. finally	25. generally
9. strangeness		

CHAPTER 9

Using Verbs Correctly

Verbs express action, and action takes place in time—in the past, in the present, in the future. When you want to connect a particular action with a particular time, you can do so by adding a helping verb or by changing the form of the verb itself or by both together. Knowing which form of a verb to use and when to use it is often vital to clear and effective communication. In this chapter you will study the rules for using the various verb forms.

LESSON 76

How Verbs Show Time

The verbs in English can express past, present, and future time and a great many variations of these as well. The time expressed by a verb is called its *tense:* present tense, past tense, future tense. All the tenses which a verb needs to express can be made by means of four basic verb forms.

The four basic forms of a verb are the infinitive, the present participle, the past, and the past participle. These basic forms are called the principal parts.

INFINITIVE	PRESENT PARTICIPLE	PAST	PAST PARTICIPLE
walk	(is) walking	walked	(have) walked
hope	(is) hoping	hoped	(have) hoped
study	(is) studying	studied	(have) studied

As you can see, the present participle of a verb always ends in *-ing* and is always used with some form of *to be* as a helping verb. The present participle (plus its helping verb) is used to express action occurring now.

The past participle (plus some form of *to have* as a helping verb) is used to express past action.

The helping verb *to be* is also used with the past participle of some verbs to show that the subject *receives* the action of the verb.

EXAMPLES   The lesson was learned.   The wood has been burned.

The verb *to do* is used as a helping verb with the infinitive form (also called the *present*) in questions and for emphasis.

EXAMPLES   **Did** you study the assigment?   Honestly, I **did** study it!

The past principal part expresses past time all by itself, without the aid of a helping verb. It is sometimes called the *simple past,* to distinguish it from the past tense formed from the helping verb *to have* plus the past participle. Notice the difference in meaning between the two past tenses.

SIMPLE PAST
Yesterday I **studied** my assignment. (completed past action)

PAST WITH HELPING
I **have studied** the assignment, but I still don't understand it. (past action still affecting the present)

EXERCISE. The verbs in the following sentences are printed in italics. In the space to the left of each sentence, write *present* if the sentence is about action taking place in the present time or *past* if the sentence is about action taking place in past time. (Add 5 points for each correct answer.)

.... 1. Skiing *demands* skill and concentration.

.... 2. We *watched* the Winter Olympics on television.

.... 3. The downhill racer *fell* on the course.

.... 4. We *have seen* some terrible spills today.

.... 5. Fortunately, this skier *is* not hurt.

.... 6. The ski jumpers *are soaring* into the air.

.... 7. They *control* the flight of their jumps.

.... 8. Who *has seen* the longest jump of the day?

.... 9. On the ice rink the figure skater *was applauded* loudly.

.... 10. She *glides* over the ice gracefully.

.... 11. The judges *were posting* their marks.

.... 12. They *decide* the winner of a gold medal.

In the remaining sentences, change the italicized verb to the present tense if it is in the past tense or to the past if it is in the present. Write the verb in the space to the left of the sentence.

.... 13. Julia Child *baked* a superb dessert.

.... 14. I *pour* too much milk on my cereal.

.... 15. We *enjoy* our new book by Virginia Hamilton.

.... 16. A few *used* rancid butter to keep the mosquitoes off.

.... 17. At my desk I *work* on my homework assignment.

.... 18. Celia *visited* Mexico in the winter.

.... 19. Natalia Makarova *dances* beautifully.

.... 20. Annette *plays* a good chess game.

154

SEE and COME, DO and GO

The verbs that you studied in the preceding lesson are called *regular verbs*. All regular verbs form their past and past participle in exactly the same way—by adding *-d* or *-ed* to the infinitive form of the verb.

The verbs that you are now going to study do not form their past and past participle according to this simple rule. Because they do not follow the rule, these verbs are called *irregular verbs*. Some of the most common and most useful verbs in English are irregular verbs. Notice how the principal parts of the four verbs below differ from those of the regular verbs. (Since the present participle of *all* verbs is formed by adding *-ing* to the present form, the present participle is omitted from this table of irregular verbs.)

INFINITIVE	PAST	PAST PARTICIPLE
see	saw	(have) seen
come	came	(have) come
do	did	(have) done
go	went	(have) gone

People sometimes mistakenly use the simple past when they should use the past participle (I have *went* home). A more common mistake is the use of the past participle for the simple past. A past participle can act as the verb of a sentence only if it has a helping verb.

NONSTANDARD	We *seen* Jacqueline at the movies.
STANDARD	We saw Jacqueline at the movies.

The example can also be corrected by the insertion of a helping verb, although the sentence would then have a slightly different meaning.

ALSO STANDARD   We have seen Jacqueline at the movies. (The sentence now suggests that seeing Jacqueline is still important in some way, even though it happened in the past.)

The main thing to remember is that a past participle by itself cannot be the verb of a sentence.

NONSTANDARD	I *come* back from camp yesterday.
STANDARD	I came back from camp yesterday.

NONSTANDARD	Julius *done* all his homework last night.
STANDARD	Julius did all his homework last night.

NONSTANDARD	Mark *seen* the parade.
STANDARD	Mark saw the parade.

EXERCISE A. For each of the following items, fill in the blank with the past participle of the italicized verb when there is a helping verb, or with the simple past if there is no helping verb. (Add 5 points for each correct answer.)

1. *See:* I have ....
2. *Do:* They ....
3. *Come:* He has ....
4. *Go:* You ....
5. *See:* She ....
6. *Go:* We have ....
7. *Come:* They ....
8. *Come:* You ....
9. *See:* He was ....
10. *Do:* It was ....

11. *Come:* I have ....
12. *Do:* I ....
13. *See:* We ....
14. *Do:* It has been ....
15. *See:* You have ....
16. *Come:* We did ....
17. *Come:* I ....
18. *Do:* She has ....
19. *See:* We were ....
20. *See:* It has been ....

EXERCISE B. Write the correct past form of the verb in parentheses in the blank that follows it. Use the past participle after any form of the helping verb *to be* or *to have*. (Add 10 points for each correct answer.)

A TRIP TO THE AQUARIUM

1   Marcia's science class (go) .... on a trip to the aquarium. Most of

2   the class had (go) .... to the aquarium last year, but they hadn't (see)

3   .... all of the creatures there. The science teacher and two parents

4   (come) .... along on the trip. They (see) .... a baby whale, called

5   a calf, that weighed about fourteen thousand pounds. One of the parents

6   who had (come) .... on the trip explained that the calf might double

7   its size within a year. Marcia said that she had (do) .... a report on

8   whales last year. According to her research, some whales have been (see)

9   .... to reach maturity within three years. The class left the aquarium

10   and (go) .... back to school at about two o'clock. Most of the class

11   felt that of all the things they had (do) .... that year in school, they

12   had enjoyed the trip to the aquarium the most.

156

Sorting Out the Problem Verbs

Many of the irregular verbs fall into groups because they form the simple past and the past participle in a similar way. The verbs in this lesson, with two exceptions, form the simple past by changing the vowel *(e, i, o,* or *u)* to *a.* They form the past participle by changing the vowel to *u.*

INFINITIVE	PAST	PAST PARTICIPLE	INFINITIVE	PAST	PAST PARTICIPLE
begin	began	(have) begun	drink	drank	(have) drunk
run	ran	(have) run	ring	rang	(have) rung
sing	sang	(have) sung	swim	swam	(have) swum

A common error in using these verbs is to confuse the past participle with the simple past. To be sure of avoiding this error, memorize the three principal parts of the irregular verbs listed above. As you repeat these principal parts to yourself, always say the helping verb *have* with the past participle as a reminder that the past participle can never be used alone as a verb. It must have a helping verb with it.

NONSTANDARD	STANDARD
It *begun* to rain.	It began to rain.
He *run* all the way home.	He ran all the way home.
She *sung* beautifully.	She sang beautifully.

Less often, people make the opposite error, using the simple past in place of the past participle.

NONSTANDARD	STANDARD
We have *drank* our milk.	We have drunk our milk.
Someone has *rang* the bell.	Someone has rung the bell.
They have *swam.*	They have swum.

The verb *to bring,* the seventh verb in this lesson, is one of the two exceptions mentioned above.

INFINITIVE	PAST	PAST PARTICIPLE
bring	brought	(have) brought

Because *bring* rhymes with *sing* and *ring,* we sometimes make the mistake of thinking that its principal parts follow the same pattern. In standard English, however, there are no such words as *brang* or *brung.*

NONSTANDARD	Carol *brang* the book back.	She has *brung* it back too soon.
STANDARD	Carol brought the book back.	She has brought it back too soon.

157

Another common and important irregular verb, *to think*, works in the same way as *to bring*, even though it rhymes with *drink*. There are no such words as *thunk* or *thinked*.

INFINITIVE	PAST	PAST PARTICIPLE
think	thought	(have) thought

EXERCISE A. For each of the following items, fill in the blank with the past participle of the given verb when there is a helping verb, or with the simple past if there is no helping verb. (Add 10 points for each correct answer.)

1. They (swim) . . . .
2. It was (drink) . . . .
3. We (run) . . . .
4. She has (ring) . . . .
5. They (sing) . . . .
6. They were (begin) . . . .
7. It (ring) . . . .
8. He (drink) . . . .
9. It was (sing) . . . .
10. I have (swim) . . . .

EXERCISE B. For each of the following sentences, write the correct past form of the verb given in parentheses before each blank. Remember to use the past participle after a helping verb. (Add 10 points for each correct answer.)

1. The ballet instructor has just (begin) . . . . her lesson.

2. A small bear (drink) . . . . water from the pail that we left outside.

3. We have (bring) . . . . you many souvenirs from Florida.

4. The lifeguard had (swim) . . . . six laps a day as part of her training.

5. Who has (sing) . . . . this song before?

6. Volunteers had (ring) . . . . every doorbell on our street, but no one was home.

7. My sister (think) . . . . about the question before she replied.

8. The track team (run) . . . . in a dual meet yesterday.

9. Every carton of milk was (drink) . . . . during lunch.

10. My brother (begin) . . . . taking music lessons before he was ten.

Nine Problem Verbs

All of the irregular verbs in this lesson have past participles that end in *-en*, and all of them form their simple past by changing their vowel (or vowels) to a long *o*. These verbs fall into two groups, depending on whether the past participle is formed from the present or from the simple past.

INFINITIVE	PAST	PAST PARTICIPLE	INFINITIVE	PAST	PAST PARTICIPLE
break	broke	(have) broken	choose	chose	(have) chosen
speak	spoke	(have) spoken	freeze	froze	(have) frozen
steal	stole	(have) stolen			

The most common error in the use of these verbs consists of putting the simple past in place of the past participle.

NONSTANDARD	STANDARD
The clock was *broke*.	The clock was broken.
They have *chose* Ben.	They have chosen Ben.
My nose was *froze*.	My nose was frozen.

The second group forms the past participle by adding *-n* to the present. In three of these past participles, the vowel changes from long to short to make it easier to pronounce.

INFINITIVE	PAST	PAST PARTICIPLE	INFINITIVE	PAST	PAST PARTICIPLE
drive	drove	(have) driven	ride	rode	(have) ridden
write	wrote	(have) written	take	took	(have) taken

NONSTANDARD	We have *drove* twelve miles.	Janet has *rode* on a camel.
STANDARD	We have driven twelve miles.	Janet has ridden on a camel.

EXERCISE A. For each of the following sentences, write the correct past form of the verb given in parentheses before each blank. Remember to use the past participle after a helping verb. Check all answers against the tables of verbs given above. (Add 5 points for each correct answer.)

1. The shovel was (break) . . . . in two.

2. He had (choose) . . . . three books to read during vacation.

3. The pond was (freeze) . . . . the next day.

4. After the leader has (speak) . . . . , we will all leave.

5. Pearl Bailey had (steal) . . . . the show.

6. The birds were (drive) . . . . away by the cats.

7. Ynes Mexia (ride) .... a balsa raft on one of her botanical expeditions.

8. Sylvia has (take) .... the lead in the race.

9. The winning paper was (write) .... by someone I know.

10. Armand dropped his watch and (break) .... it.

11. They have (chose) .... three people to make the trip to Canada.

12. The ice cubes (freeze) .... in fifteen minutes.

13. The lecturer had (speak) .... on the same subject before.

14. Peter had (steal) .... the hearts of his admirers.

15. They (drive) .... the cattle along the Chisholm Trail.

16. Pia has even (ride) .... on an elephant's back.

17. Demetrius has (take) .... first prize for cooking.

18. Louisa May Alcott (write) .... many stories before *Little Women* was published in 1868.

19. By November the pond will have (freeze) ....

20. Maxine was (drive) .... to the party.

EXERCISE B. In the following paragraph, underline the correct verb of the two verb forms in parentheses. (Add 10 points for each correct answer.)

1   When the box was finally (broke, broken) into, it was obvious that
2   someone had already (stole, stolen) everything of value. A list of the
3   contents was (wrote, written) inside the cover and made it clear that the
4   thieves had (took, taken) only the important things. Each of us (chose,
5   choosed) something from the things that were left, but Paul (spoke,
6   speaked) for all of us when he said that it was a great disappointment. The
7   box itself was (took, taken) back to base camp. We left the area and (rode,
8   ridden) towards home. We had (rode, ridden) hundreds of miles through
9   this wilderness, and the trip had (took, taken) the whole year, all for
10   nothing.

More Problem Verbs

Verbs like *to tear* (past participle: *torn)* and *to blow* (past participle: *blown)* seem at first glance to have little resemblance to the other irregular verbs you have studied so far. In fact, however, they are not really so different. The verbs in this lesson form their simple past by a vowel change and their past participle by adding *-n* or *-en* either to the infinitive or to the simple past.

INFINITIVE	PAST	PAST PARTICIPLE	INFINITIVE	PAST	PAST PARTICIPLE
blow	blew	(have) blown	fall	fell	(have) fallen
know	knew	(have) known	give	gave	(have) given
throw	threw	(have) thrown			

The typical error in using *give* is the use of the present form for both the simple past and the past participle.

NONSTANDARD	STANDARD
Yesterday, Dad *give* me a lecture.	Yesterday, Dad **gave** me a lecture.
I have *give* too much time.	I have **given** too much time.

There is a tendency to treat *blow, know,* and *throw* as if they were regular verbs (adding *-ed* to form the past and the past participle). In standard speech and writing, however, you should use only the forms shown in the table below.

NONSTANDARD	We *knowed* all along.	Jerry has *throwed* it away.
STANDARD	We **knew** all along.	Jerry has **thrown** it away.

The second group of verbs consists of troublesome verbs. Both form the past participle by adding *-n* to the simple past, omitting the final *e.*

INFINITIVE	PAST	PAST PARTICIPLE	INFINITIVE	PAST	PAST PARTICIPLE
tear	tore	(have) torn	wear	wore	(have) worn

NONSTANDARD	STANDARD
The letter was *tore* in little pieces.	The letter was **torn** in little pieces.
I have *wore* my new shoes.	I have **worn** my new shoes.

EXERCISE A. Write in the blank the correct form (the past or the past participle) of the verb in parentheses. Remember to use the past participle after a helping verb. (Add 10 points for each correct answer.)

1. The hurricane has (blow) . . . . down dozens of trees.

2. I have (know) . . . . the professor for many years.

3. He had (throw) . . . . the ball without looking carefully.

4. They have (give) . . . . me real encouragement.

5. The pencil was (wear) . . . . down to a stub.

6. They have already (throw) . . . . out all the old papers.

7. Her sudden appearance (give) . . . . me a great shock.

8. I certainly (know) . . . . that he wasn't feeling well.

9. They all (blow) . . . . on their hands to keep them warm.

10. Carlos suddenly (throw) . . . . him a curve ball.

EXERCISE B. Some of the italicized verbs in the following sentences are in the correct form and some are not. Draw a line through each incorrect verb, and write the correct form above it. (Add 4 points for each correct answer.)

1. For years Mom refused, but at last she *give* in.

2. The wind *blowed* down a large tree and *tore* a hole in the fence.

3. If I had *knowed* you were coming, I would have *give* a party.

4. Mike has *fell* from his horse and has *tore* his shirt.

5. The outfielder had *threw* the ball to the pitcher, who then *threw* it home.

6. Vera has *blowed* out all the candles on her birthday cake.

7. His little joke has *throwed* the meeting into an uproar.

8. The thorns have *tore* a hole in Alice's sock.

9. I *knew* I should have *wore* blue jeans.

10. They had *gave* the address to Laura, but she *throwed* it away.

11. Mrs. Dougherty has always *gave* challenging homework assignments.

12. The wind, apparently, had *blew* the car out of control.

13. If Archie had *knew* about the branches, he would not have *torn* his slacks.

14. They *give* me the book about a month ago.

15. The woman had *tore* the letter in little pieces and had *threw* it away.

16. If Jerry had *knowed* how high he was, he might have *fell*.

Using <u>SIT</u> and <u>SET</u> Correctly

Do you *sit* in a chair or *set* in a chair? Do you *sit* a package down on the counter or *set* it down? The problem here is not one of mixing up the correct forms of a verb but of confusing two different irregular verbs which sound alike and have somewhat related meanings. In order to use *sit* and *set* correctly, you must be clear about how they differ in meaning.

The verb <u>sit</u> means <u>to sit down</u>, <u>to occupy a seat</u>, or <u>to rest</u>.

These are the principal parts of *to sit*.

INFINITIVE	PRESENT PARTICIPLE	PAST	PAST PARTICIPLE
sit	(is) sitting	sat	(have) sat

The verb <u>set</u> means <u>to place</u> or <u>to put something down</u>.

These are the principal parts of *to set*.

INFINITIVE	PRESENT PARTICIPLE	PAST	PAST PARTICIPLE
set	(is) setting	set	(have) set

As a rule, *to set* must have a direct object to complete its meaning. *To sit,* on the other hand, usually does *not* take a direct object.

SET   Conrad set the pan on the stove. Set me down, please.

SIT   Barnaby sat and sat. The pan is sitting on the stove.

EXERCISE A.   In the space to the left of each sentence, write the letter *a* or *b* to show the meaning of the italicized verb or participle:

> *a*—means *to sit down, to occupy a seat, to rest*
> *b*—means *to place* or *to put something down*

If in doubt about which verb is which, look at the lists of principal parts for *sit* and *set* above. (Add 10 points for each correct answer.)

a .... EX. The paint bucket was *sitting* on the highest shelf.

b .... EX. We will *set* the Ping-Pong table here.

.... 1. Mrs. Petersen *sits* in this chair while she reads.

.... 2. Annie Peck, the first to climb Mount Coropuna in Peru, *set* a ''Votes for Women'' pennant on its summit.

.... 3. We *set* the roses in the vase on the table.

163

.... 4. "Someone," said the bear, "has been *sitting* in my chair!"

.... 5. Please *set* the costume on my bed.

.... 6. Floyd *set* his glasses on the end of his nose and went to work.

.... 7. Imagine our surprise when we found a small kitten *sitting* in the back yard.

.... 8. I couldn't have *sat* there another minute.

.... 9. We *sat* in the waiting room for two hours.

.... 10. Sam *sets* his books on the sofa.

EXERCISE B. Underline the correct one of the two verbs in parentheses in each sentence. Determine what meaning the verb must have in the sentence. (Add 5 points for each correct sentence.)

1. My dog (sits, sets) in the shade in the afternoon.

2. Hearing a floorboard creak, Meredith (sat, set) up in bed.

3. (Sitting, Setting) down the tools, the plumber relaxed for a moment.

4. I suppose the books will just (sit, set) there until I put them away.

5. Dad (sat, set) Andrea on her feet and told her to walk.

6. This machine (sits, sets) the pins up automatically.

7. Norman and Beatrice had (sat, set) down on the porch swing.

8. They were still (sitting, setting) there an hour later.

9. The first one to (sit, set) a dime on its edge will win.

10. The two of us (sit, set) in the front of the class.

In the remaining sentences, cross out *set* if it is used for *sit* or *sit* if it is used for *set,* and write the correct form of the proper verb above the error. Write C above any form of *sit* or *set* used correctly.

11. You can't expect to solve the world's problems while setting in an easy chair.

12. After dinner Uncle Marc sets in his favorite chair and reads the paper.

13. Just sit the cup on the table, set down, and stop worrying.

14. Mildred sat in a stiff chair, and I set next to her.

15. She sat the hat on her head again, but it still did not set properly.

16. After sitting the coffeepot back on the stove, Nancy set down to talk.

Using <u>LIE</u> and <u>LAY</u> Correctly

Like *sit* and *set*, *lie* and *lay* sound alike and have somewhat similar meanings. To keep this troublesome pair straight, you must pay attention to the difference in meaning and know the principal parts.

The verb lie means to recline or to remain lying down.

These are the principal parts of *to lie*.

INFINITIVE	PRESENT PARTICIPLE	PAST	PAST PARTICIPLE
lie	(is) lying	lay	(have) lain

The verb lay means to to put down or to place something.

These are the principal parts of *to lay*.

INFINITIVE	PRESENT PARTICIPLE	PAST	PAST PARTICIPLE
lay	(is) laying	laid	(have) laid

Like the verb *to set*, *to lay* usually needs a direct object to complete its meaning. The verb *to lie*, on the other hand, usually does *not* have a direct object.

OBJECT   Lay the package on the counter. She laid her book aside.

NO OBJECT   The package lies on the counter. The book lay in a chair.

EXERCISE A. In the space to the left of each sentence, write the letter *a* or *b* to show the meaning of the italicized verb or participle:

> *a*—means *to recline* or *to remain lying down*
> *b*—means *to put down* or *to place something*

If in doubt, notice whether the verb has a direct object and is therefore a form of *to lay,* meaning *to put down.* If the verb does not have a direct object, it will usually be a form of *to lie,* meaning *to recline.* (Add 10 points for each correct answer.)

a. EX. On Saturdays I often *lie* in bed until ten o'clock.

b. EX. The contractor is already *laying* the foundation for our school.

.... 1. Isabella *lay* on the sand and watched the waves.

.... 2. Alex *laid* his sunglasses on the sand and went for a swim.

.... 3. The movers were *laying* the carpet in the wrong room.

.... 4. Terri left her bike *lying* in the snow until it had rusted.

.... 5. The donkey has *lain* down and will not get up.

.... 6. The children had *laid* their stockings by the fireplace.

.... 7. The farmhouse *lies* at the foot of the next hill.

.... 8. In the evening Miles *lays* out his clothes for the next day.

.... 9. The laundry will have *lain* there for a week when we finally get around to collecting it.

.... 10. The orderly saluted and *laid* the message on the general's desk.

EXERCISE B. Underline the correct one of the two verbs in parentheses. To make sure, decide what meaning the verb must have in the sentence, and check the lists of principal parts on the preceding page. (Add 5 points for each correct answer.)

1. If George (lies, lays) there any longer, he will catch cold.

2. Mother and I had already (lain, laid) our plans for the party.

3. (Lying, Laying) her book aside, Ms. Nesbitt looked expectantly at the class.

4. On a hot day (lying, laying) down in the shade feels good.

5. The clothes had (lain, laid) too long in the sun and were faded.

6. After the cyclone, broken furniture (lay, laid) all over the room.

7. We shall (lie, lay) our flowers on the monument.

8. At the bottom of the hole (lay, laid) a tin box of old papers.

9. A heap of rusty metal was (lying, laying) beside the barn.

10. Ambrose would get sunburned if he (lay, laid) in the sun.

In the remaining sentences, fill each blank with the correct past form of *to lie* or *to lay*.

11. The inn .... near where the village store once stood.

12. I. M. Pei, the architect, ... out the plans for the building.

13. The lion .... down its prey and .... down beside it.

14. The bugle still .... where Lee had .... it.

15. You should have .... aside that silly project long ago!

16. Shirley .... out her clothes for the next day before she .... down in bed.

17. The smog .... over the city.

166

Chapter Review

EXERCISE A. Write the simple past and the past participle of each of the verbs below. Some of them are regular verbs. (Add 4 points for each correct item.)

	PAST	PAST PARTICIPLE		PAST	PAST PARTICIPLE
1. see	....	....	14. write	....	....
2. give	....	....	15. throw	....	....
3. lie	....	....	16. take	....	....
4. come	....	....	17. blow	....	....
5. fall	....	....	18. bring	....	....
6. go	....	....	19. wear	....	....
7. freeze	....	....	20. set	....	....
8. drink	....	....	21. swim	....	....
9. run	....	....	22. lay	....	....
10. speak	....	....	23. begin	....	....
11. steal	....	....	24. do	....	....
12. drive	....	....	25. choose	....	....
13. ride	....	....			

EXERCISE B. In the following sentences, cross out the incorrect one of the two verb forms given in parentheses. (Add 4 points for each correct answer.)

1. The guests have (drank, drunk) two gallons of apple cider.

2. She (saw, seen) you coming out of the auditorium.

3. The children have (ran, run) around the block twice.

4. Charlie's aunt has (drove, driven) here from Chicago.

5. She has (tore, torn) two pages out of the notebook.

6. The coat (lay, lie) where he had (throwed, thrown) it.

7. They apparently (did, done) the same thing last week.

8. The three trucks (came, come) in at the same time yesterday.

9. The wind has (blew, blown) the shutter open.

10. We had (rode, ridden) overnight on the bus.

11. Maybelle has (went, gone) to buy some juice.

12. The courageous woman has (swam, swum) all the way across Lake Erie.

13. I have for once (wrote, written) all the details in my report.

14. When have you (sang, sung) the national anthem?

15. They have certainly (took, taken) their time about it.

16. The picture was (stole, stolen) some time before 11:00 P.M.

17. We were (lying, laying) under the tree, sound asleep.

18. Why don't you (sit, set) down and stay awhile?

19. Have you (brung, brought) the paper in yet?

20. The boys were already half (froze, frozen), and then it (began, begun) to snow.

21. Near the fire Brenda (sat, set) the shoes she had (wore, worn).

22. The vase has (fell, fallen) off the table.

EXERCISE C. Cross out each incorrect verb form in the following paragraph, and write the correct form above it. (Add 10 points for each correct answer.)

A CRAFT SHOW

1   We had went to the craft show hoping to learn some new skills. We

2 brung our own materials for the crafts in which we were interested. Chris

3 wanted to learn how glass is blew. Laurie had began hooking a rug and

4 wanted to pick up some tips on how colors should be chose for the best

5 effect. Angela come to the show to learn about stained glass construction.

6 She had already made two small pieces that she lay proudly on the table.

7 We seen a silkscreen artist at work. After the membership committee had

8 spoke, we accompanied the artists to their work areas. They done their

9 best to help us. Some gave us samples of their work.

Cumulative Review

A. In the following paragraph, indicate the part of speech of each italicized word, using these abbreviations: *n.* for noun; *pron.* for pronoun; *adj.* for adjective; *v.* for verb; *adv. for* adverb; and *prep.* for preposition. (Add 4 points for each correct answer.)

1 Our Student Council *proposed* that *student* volunteers *help* with *this*
2 year's United Fund Drive. *They posted* a notice on all the *school* bulletin
3 boards. *Several* students came and *asked* how they could help. *At* the
4 *headquarters* of the Fund Drive, *helpers* were *needed for* the *card* files,
5 and *some* of the students came in *for* an *hour* and worked *hard*. A *few*
6 students worked as messengers on *weekends*. All these volunteers *were* a
7 big help. *Afterward,* the director *officially thanked* the students for their
8 help.

B. Underline every direct object in the following sentences, and circle every subject complement. (Add 10 points for each correct answer.)

1. Dad is sleeping better, but he still does not look well.

2. After the summer we sent a crate of oranges to Grandma in Montreal.

3. Grant will eat a hamburger, a baked potato, and a salad.

4. Every car performed well in the race except ours.

5. The cat tasted its food cautiously but would not eat it.

6. The action seems foolish and unnecessary.

C. In the following paragraph, there are errors in capitalization and comma usage (omitted commas, unnecessary commas). There are also sentence fragments and run-on sentences. Correct all these mistakes. (Add 4 points for each correct answer.)

PROTECTING THE ENVIRONMENT

1 The environmental movement in the united states. Began not very long
2 ago. Large numbers of Scientists expressed alarm over the growing
3 pollution of air Water and soil. Clean air in cities was turning into smog
4 some rivers had turned into sewers fertile farm land was quickly
5 disappearing. the U.S. congress approved the environmental protection

6   agency, and gave it the power to enforce antipollution laws. Throughout
7   the country. Since the agency began, every state has made progress
8   against pollution. The government predicts clean air for u.s. cities by
9   1988, the greatest source of air pollution is the automobile, congress
10 expects auto makers to meet strict clean-air standards. The quality of the
11 country's water supply has also improved. City state and federal
12 authorities are spending billions of Dollars on water pollution control.
13 Most states now have laws protecting the soil from erosion the wasteful
14 runoff of valuable topsoil into streams. Much work still needs to be done
15 industry, private citizens and the government must all work together or
16 our air, water, and crops will be in danger.

D. In the following sentences, cross out the incorrect one of the two verb forms in parentheses. (Add 10 points for each correct answer.)

1. Everybody in both countries (was, were) pleased by the treaty.
2. The hinges for the right-hand door (was, were) taken off.
3. Both their car and their radio (was, were) made in Germany.
4. The house and the garage at the end of the street (was, were) damaged.
5. We (wasn't, weren't) in the mood for a party.
6. There (was, were) knots in it when you first got it.
7. At the back of the house (stand, stands) a toolshed and a garage.
8. Inside the box (lie, lies) a mother cat and her four kittens.
9. Either the station wagon or the truck (has, have) to turn.
10. Somebody from one of the classes (has, have) to find it.

Building Vocabulary: Choosing the Precise Word

An unabridged dictionary lists approximately six hundred thousand English words, and even that large number probably does not account for all the words we have in English. With so many words to choose from, you can find words that say precisely what you want to say.

In choosing among words with similar meanings, choose the one that says precisely what you want to say.

EXAMPLES   When his friend finally offered help on the project, Randolph spurned his offer.

After he won the contest without Jake's assistance, Randolph shunned every place where there was a chance of meeting him.

From the context, you can tell that *spurned* and *shunned*, the words printed in red, must be fairly close in meaning—*to reject* or *to treat unkindly*. The difference in meaning is important, however. *Spurn* means "to refuse something that has been offered and to do so with contempt." *Shun* means "to avoid completely." Which word you choose depends on precisely what you want to say.

Spurn and *shun* both carry a good deal of meaning. Very often, a single, precise word can replace a long phrase. Compare these two sentences, both of which have much the same meaning.

FLABBY   The candidate *aroused strong feelings of opposition* in his listeners.

PRECISE   The candidate antagonized his listeners. (*Antagonized* replaces all the italicized words in the preceding example.)

Study the following definitions. In the exercise that follows, be ready to use the words correctly.

contemplate / kón təm plāt/, *v.*   To consider carefully and thoughtfully: *The artist stood back from her painting to contemplate the effect.*

counteract /koún tər ákt/, *v.*   To act so as to keep something from happening: *The doctor's prompt treatment counteracted the poison.*

potential /pə tén chəl/, *adj.*   Possible but not yet developed; having the power to do or to become something: *Your careless driving is a potential menace to the community.*

shun /shun/, *v.*   To avoid completely.

spontaneous /spon tá nē əs/, *adj.*   Happening naturally, without forethought or outside cause: *Laura's decision to rescue the drowning child was entirely spontaneous.*

spurn /spərn/, *v.*   To refuse with contempt.

technique /tek nēk/, *n.*   The method or procedure needed to do something well: *Marion has improved her piano technique through much practice.*

tumult /tū mult/, *n.*   Noisy confusion, as of the voices of many people milling around: *When the Eagles tied the score, the tumult in the grandstand was deafening.*

turmoil /tə́r moil/, *n.* A bothersome confusion of movement or thought, not necessarily noisy (compare with *tumult*, which always involves noise): *In the turmoil after the game, I lost my hat.*

vigilance /víj ə ləns/, *n.* Keen and careful watchfulness, as for danger: *Only the guard's vigilance prevented the burglars from escaping with the company's money.*

EXERCISE. In the space to the right of each sentence, write the one word from this lesson that could replace the group of words in italics. (Add 10 points for each correct answer.)

1. Scientists have devised a new *method of production* for making artificial diamonds.   1. . . . .

2. The detective *studied* the photograph *carefully and thoughtfully* for a clue to the crime.   2. . . . .

3. Gabriel's reaction to the suggestion was, I'm sure, *without forethought*.   3. . . . .

4. Last-minute cramming cannot *keep* a semester of laziness *from taking effect*.   4. . . . .

5. As the study hall quieted, the teacher's *careful watchfulness* gradually relaxed.   5. . . . .

6. Sara's *possible but not yet fulfilled* talent as an artist seems very great.   6. . . . .

Complete the blanks in these sentences with words presented in this lesson. Study the context carefully, and be sure to use the word with the precise meaning for the context.

7. The crowd set up a great tu. . . . . at midnight, and in the

tu. . . . . the boy became separated from his parents.

8. After what he had done, the soldiers decided to s. . . . . the traitor

and to s. . . . . his attempts at friendliness.

REVIEW EXERCISE. To the left of each italicized word, write the letter of the best meaning from the list at the right. (Add 20 points for each correct answer.)

. . . . 1. a *colossal* statue

. . . . 2. *renounce* a privilege

. . . . 3. a *potent* force for good

. . . . 4. a *dismal* personality

. . . . 5. *disperse* one's efforts

a. to give up formally

b. huge, gigantic

c. gloomy, miserable

d. powerful, mighty

e. to scatter

172

Spelling: Homophones

Have you ever written *brake* when you meant *break?* Or *sent* instead of *scent?* Mistakes of this kind are fairly common because both pairs of words *sound* alike. Therefore, your ear cannot help you to choose between them. They may *sound* alike, but they differ in both spelling and meaning.

Such words are called *homophones.* The best way to master the correct use of homophones is to learn their spelling and meaning at the same time. You must simply memorize them by studying them in meaningful sentences.

Here are some of the more troublesome sets of homophones—each with a sentence illustrating correct meaning and spelling. Try to memorize them.

altar—alter	The priest faced the *altar*.	I will *alter* the hem.
brake—break	Release the *brake*.	You *break* the eggs.
capital—capitol	Lima is the *capital* of Peru.	We saw the *capitol* dome.
course—coarse	Vi has an art *course*.	His beard is *coarse*.
here—hear	Let's meet *here*.	Can you all *hear* me?
meet—meat	I'll *meet* you later.	Rover eats only *meat*.
principle—principal	My main *principle* is charity.	Mr. Ray is our *principal*.
sent—scent	Sue *sent* us a gift.	I like the *scent* of roses.
stationary—stationery	The desks are *stationary*.	Her *stationery* is blue.
through—threw	I see *through* him.	Who *threw* that ink?

EXERCISE A. Indicate the correct definition of each word in list *1*, by writing the *letter* of the proper definition from list *2*. (Add 10 points for each correct answer.)

1	*2*
.... 1. coarse	a. the edible flesh of animals
.... 2. stationary	b. a guiding rule
.... 3. alter	c. a mechanism for stopping a machine
.... 4. meat	d. rough
.... 5. hear	e. transmitted
.... 6. principal	f. official seat of government
.... 7. break	g. in this place
.... 8. scent	h. writing paper
.... 9. capital	i. a series of lessons in a subject
.... 10. through	j. to smash or shatter
	k. the head of a school
	l. to change
	m. not moveable
	n. to receive sounds
	o. an odor
	p. having finished successfully

EXERCISE B. Underline the correct word from the pair in parentheses. (Add 10 points for each correct answer.)

1. Name the (capital, capitol) of India.

2. When you are (threw, through) with the paints, may I use them?

3. Find out when we are supposed to (meat, meet).

4. Always apply the (break, brake) gently.

5. Our high school offers a (coarse, course) in Russian.

6. The (scent, sent) of apple blossoms came drifting in the window.

7. The Aztec priest stood before the stone (alter, altar).

8. Come (here, hear) immediately!

9. Plain white (stationary, stationery) is always in good taste.

10. Who is the assistant (principal, principle) of Pierson Junior High School?

EXERCISE C. On a separate piece of paper, use each of the words *not* underlined in Exercise B in a brief sentence that clearly shows its meaning. (Add 10 points for each correct sentence.)

REVIEW EXERCISE. Complete each unfinished word part below by writing -*cle* or *cal*, whichever is correct, in the blank. (Add 10 points for each correct answer.)

1. alphabeti. . . . .

2. identi. . . . .

3. obsta. . . . .

4. mechani. . . . .

5. politi. . . . .

6. practi. . . . .

7. vehi. . . . .

8. magi. . . . .

9. specta. . . . .

10. ici. . . . .

CHAPTER 10

Getting Your Pronouns Straight

A pronoun is a word used in place of a noun or of more than one noun. The few pronouns in English that have different forms to show person are called *personal pronouns*. Except for *you,* every personal pronoun has both a singular and a plural form. Except for *you* and *it,* every personal pronoun also has a nominative and an objective form.

Personal Pronouns

NOMINATIVE CASE		OBJECTIVE CASE	
I	we	me	us
you	you	you	you
he	they	him	them
she		her	
it		it	

The correct form of a pronoun is determined by its use in a sentence. The subject form is used for subjects and for subject complements; the object form is used for objects. In this chapter you will study the various situations in which pronoun problems arise.

LESSON 87

Pronouns as Subjects

To find the subject of a sentence, you first find the verb and then ask *who?* or *what?* The answer to this question will be the subject.

EXAMPLE Did they leave you behind again? (*Who* did leave? *They* is the subject.)

Only the nominative forms of the personal pronouns may be used as the subjects of verbs: I—we; you; he, she, it—they.

Most mistakes in the use of pronouns in the nominative case occur when the pronoun is part of a *compound subject*—two or more connected subjects that have the same verb. You naturally select the correct pronoun form when one pronoun is used as the subject of a sentence (She runs. We talk.—*not* Her runs. Us talk.) When the pronoun is connected with another noun or pronoun, however, you might not be sure about which form to use. The solution is to try the pronoun out by itself.

| NONSTANDARD | *Him* and *me* went to the movies last night. |
| STANDARD | <u>He and I</u> went to the movies last night. (*He* went, *I* went; therefore, *He* and *I* went) |

The pronoun *they* is the only one with which people often have trouble when it is not part of a compound subject. *Them* is the objective form of the pronoun and cannot be used as the subject of a verb.

| NONSTANDARD | *Them* are the trees I told you about. |
| STANDARD | <u>They</u> are the trees I told you about. |

Notice that in a compound subject the pronoun *I* comes at the end—it is considered impolite to mention oneself first.

| AWKWARD | *I,* Mary, and Ruth will bring some records. |
| BETTER | <u>Mary, Ruth, and I</u> will bring some records. |

EXERCISE A. Write a suitable personal pronoun in each blank, according to the meaning of the sentence. Use a variety of pronouns, but do *not* use *it* and *you,* which never change. If in doubt, try the pronoun by itself with the verb. (Add 10 points for each correct answer.)

1. Why can't Grace and . . . . see eye to eye about Mr. Rowley?

2. In my opinion, ... and Clayton were both mistaken.

3. . . . . and . . . . are tied for first place.

4. Last week, Pia and . . . . played a joke on my sister.

5. . . . . and their silly questions make me tired.

6. . . . . and . . . . always forget their books.

7. Danny and . . . . lost our way, but our teacher and . . . . found us.

EXERCISE B. Underline the correct one of the two pronouns in parentheses. (Add 10 points for each correct answer.)

1. (She, Her) and Roberta Linsky left for Florida last night.

2. Norman, Claude, and (I, me) camped out overnight.

3. Are you or (she, her) planning to go to college?

4. Maggie, Miss Klein, and (they, them) are traveling together.

5. Why, in heaven's name, should Deborah, (she, her), or (I, me) go on another of those silly picnics?

6. (He, Him) and (I, me) are going to have a serious talk.

7. (She, Her) and (I, me) were wearing identical hats.

176

Pronouns as Subject Complements

A *subject complement* is a noun, a pronoun, or an adjective that follows a linking verb. It describes or explains the simple subject. When it follows some form of the linking verb *to be,* a personal pronoun may be used as a subject complement. The name, *subject* complement, should help you to remember the correct pronoun forms to use.

Use the nominative forms of the personal pronouns when they follow any form of the verb to be: I—we; you; he, she, it—they.

EXAMPLES The man in the back of the bus was he

It must have been they at the front door.

A pronoun subject complement points to the same person or thing as the subject. For this reason, sentences like those in the examples can usually be turned around and still make perfectly good sense. To make sure which pronoun is right after a form of the verb *to be,* turn the sentence around and try the pronoun out as the subject of the verb.

NONSTANDARD   This year's prize winner will probably be *him.* (= *him* will be)

STANDARD   This year's prize winner will probably be he. (= *he* will be)

You need to be especially careful when the subject complement is compound. You can usually solve the problem by trying each pronoun by itself as the subject complement.

NONSTANDARD   Was it Lynn, *her,* or *me* who was supposed to report?
STANDARD   Was it Lynn, she, or I who was supposed to report?

(Was it *she,* Was it *I;* therefore, Was it *Lynn, she,* or *I*)

The expression *it's me* is usually permissible in informal speech and writing, even though it does not follow the rule. In formal situations—and in the exercises in this book—you should use the subject form *I* as the subject complement.

INFORMAL   The person waiting at the door was me.
FORMAL   The person waiting at the door was I.

EXERCISE. In the following sentences, underline the correct form of the personal pronoun in parentheses. (Add 5 points for each correct answer.)

1. The club president next year will be (she, her).

2. The last guests to arrive were Julius and (her, she).

3. The winners were (them, they) and (we, us).

4. Must the showoffs in this class always be (he, him) and Nick?

5. The finalist might be either you or (her, she).

6. The two fastest runners have usually been (she, her) and (me, I).

7. The founders of the Journalism Club were (them, they) and (us, we).

8. It will be (he, him), (her, she), or (I, me) who will be chosen.

9. It might possibly have been (him, he) whom you met.

10. Was it Anders or (she, her) who was ahead?

11. In this class the practical jokers are usually (they, them).

12. Whatever anyone says, it is (us, we) who will take the blame.

13. It might have been you or (I, me) in that show, Nan.

14. Was it (she, her) or Rebecca that you talked to on the train?

15. Must it always be (us, we) who do all the work?

REVIEW EXERCISE. The following paragraph contains all the kinds of personal pronoun constructions you have studied up to this point. Correct any pronoun error by drawing a line through it and writing the proper pronoun form above it. (Add 10 points for each correct answer.)

DISASTROUS FUN

1   Barney Haskell and me have been good friends for years, and anyone

2   would think he'd have better sense. It was him, not I, you see, who

3   suggested that we take Charlotte and Melissa to the Riverside Amusement

4   Park. Him and me had saved our money over the summer and gotten our

5   parents' permission. So, when that fateful Saturday arrived, us and the

6   girls set out with high hopes. Right away, the trouble started. Melissa and

7   Charlotte and I wanted to try all the different rides, but we discovered that

8   Barney—then he told us!—is afraid of high places. That ruled out the

9   Jackrabbit, the Moon Rocket, and the other rides that the girls and me had

10   come for. Him and Charlotte discussed the other rides, and it was him, of

11   course, who suggested a rowboat ride instead. Just as us and them were

12   getting in, it began to rain. And that was that!

Pronouns as Direct Objects

The direct object of the verb is a noun or pronoun that receives the action of the verb or shows the result of the action. It answers the question *whom?* or *what?* after an action verb.

Only the objective forms of the personal pronouns may be used as the objects of verbs: me—us; you; him, her, it—them.

EXAMPLES Harold lost them at the supermarket.

     They drove me to the party in their car.

Do not confuse a direct object with a subject complement, which requires the subject form of a personal pronoun. Remember that since a direct object receives the action of the verb, it must come after a verb that shows action—an *action* verb. A subject complement, on the other hand, comes after a form of the linking verb *to be*, which does not show action.

DIRECT OBJECT   Wendell introduced us to the Dexter boys. (action verb)

SUBJECT COMPLEMENT It might have been they who told us. (linking verb)

If the direct object is compound (made up of two or more objects joined by *and, or,* or *nor),* try each pronoun separately, as you learned to do with compound subjects.

NONSTANDARD The coach trained Otis and *he* patiently.

STANDARD   The coach trained Otis and him patiently. (trained *Otis,* trained *him;* therefore, trained *Otis* and *him)*

NONSTANDARD They invited neither May nor *I* nor any of our friends.

STANDARD   They invited neither May nor me nor any of our friends. (invited *May,* invited *me;* therefore, invited neither *May* nor *me)*

EXERCISE A. Fill each blank with a suitable personal pronoun, using each of the personal pronouns at least once. (Do *not* use the pronouns *you* and *it.*) All the pronouns needed are used as direct objects. (Add 10 points for each correct answer.)

EX. Driving all day across the flat prairie wears Bill and . . . . *me* . . . . down.

1. Mary's parents spoil her little sister and . . . .

2. The old man rowed Jerry and . . . . across the lake.

3. We didn't see their friends or .... at the game.

4. The pass play fooled the coach and ....

5. Before the performance Ms. Julkins taught .... and us our lines.

6. I signaled Carry and .... from the next hill.

7. The salesclerk told Lucille and .... that the book was no longer in stock.

8. Phyllis photographed Gardner and .... standing in front of the school.

9. During the night, mosquitoes kept Marty and .... from sleep.

10. Mr. Salisbury will take .... or the Mansons to the game.

EXERCISE B. All of the following sentences need a complement of some kind, but some of the complements are direct objects and others are subject complements. In the space to the left of each sentence, write *LV* if the verb of the sentence is a *linking verb* (requiring a subject complement) or *AV* if it is an action verb (requiring a direct object). Underline the correct one of the two pronoun forms in parentheses. (Add 10 points for each correctly marked sentence.)

A.V. EX. The storm hit both the Lacases and (we, <u>us</u>).

L.V. EX. It could have been (<u>they</u>, them) or the Henleys, of course.

.... 1. Mrs. Lowell praised Louis and (I, me) for our work.

.... 2. No, the storm did not worry (she, her) or (I, me).

.... 3. It was (she, her) and Andrea who left early.

.... 4. It never leaves (he, him) alone for a minute.

.... 5. The UFO frightened both (he, him) and (I, me).

.... 6. The only girls who saw it were (she, her) and Eve DeAngelis.

.... 7. Vinnie Orlando invited Sheila and (I, me) to the rehearsal.

.... 8. It will upset either (they, them) or Ruth, I think.

.... 9. It might have been (he, him) at the door.

.... 10. Neither Shirley nor Seymour had seen (her, she) before.

Pronouns After Prepositions

The noun or pronoun that comes after a preposition is called the *object of the preposition*. When the object of a preposition is a pronoun, you must be careful to use the objective form of the personal pronoun.

Only the objective forms of the personal pronouns may be used as the objects of prepositions: me—us; you; him, her, it—them.

EXAMPLES   Martha borrowed the music from us. (*Us* is the object of the preposition *from*.)

A teacher like him would inspire anyone. (*Him* is the object of the preposition *like*.)

Errors in usage often occur when the object of a preposition is compound. To be sure about which pronoun form to use, try the pronoun separately with the preposition.

NONSTANDARD   The Jacksons came after Maxwell and *I*.

STANDARD   The Jacksons came after Maxwell and me. (After *Maxwell*, after *me*; therefore, after *Maxwell* and *me*.)

EXERCISE A. In each of the following sentences, underline the prepositional phrase, and circle the correct one of the two pronouns in parentheses. (Add 5 points for each correct answer.)

EX. I have been talking to Emilio and (he, (him)).

1. My aunt brought gifts for my brother and (I, me).

2. We were sitting behind Olivia and (he, him).

3. Did you go with Ellen or (her, she)?

4. Has anyone heard from the Morgans and (they, them)?

5. The bus left without our teacher and (us, we).

6. I have confidence in the coach and (them, they).

7. We agreed to stay near the guide and (she, her).

8. The others arrived before Terry and (me, I).

9. With Jane and (she, her) went the relatives.

10. Between Silvio and (me, I) there was no agreement.

EXERCISE B. Some of the personal pronouns in the following sentences are in the subject form when they should be in the object form. Cross out any incorrect pronoun, and write the correct form above it. (Add 4 points for each correctly marked sentence.)

1. Nothing was too difficult for Russell and I.
2. Shelly got along without Ann and I very nicely.
3. The present was delivered to me but was really for he or Dave.
4. We kept the secret among Bernadette, Esther, and I.
5. Below, Clyde and I saw three men in a rowboat.
6. Nicky and she suddenly arrived with both of them.
7. Except for the Russoffs and we, nobody knew the hiding place.
8. Seymour sat down between Mickey and I.
9. Behind Walt and she came a string of cars.
10. Before Kiki and she stood a police officer and I.
11. The two dogs were past Wallace and I.
12. The Furukawas and they live near Jill and me.
13. Gary and he took a position against him and I.
14. The rain poured down like a waterfall on Rosa, Madeline, and I.
15. The whole argument is beneath Larry and he and I.
16. The Ogilvies and she finally arrived.
17. Like Harry and I, Ida and she do not care much for fishing.
18. With Mavis and I came Hal and he.
19. Dad and he were saving the game for Uncle Godfrey and they.
20. Everyone enjoyed the performance, except for Dita Ruiz and I.
21. Concerning Clara and she, I have nothing further to add.
22. Riding in the ski lift were Mandy and she.
23. What could I tell Oliver and they to help explain the mix-up?
24. Karen wrote a story about Monica and she.
25. Between you and I, this service is awful.

Pronoun-Antecedent Agreement

Every pronoun refers to another word, called its *antecedent*. Whenever you use a pronoun, make sure that it agrees with its antecedent.

A pronoun agrees with its antecedent in number.

Pronouns, like nouns and verbs, can be either singular or plural. If the antecedent is singular, the pronoun should also be singular. If the antecedent is plural, the pronoun should also be plural.

EXAMPLES   Bob found his bat.

The students completed their assignment.

1. Use a singular pronoun to refer to each, either, neither, one, everyone, everybody, no one, nobody, anyone, anybody, someone, or somebody.

EXAMPLES   Anyone can bring his (*or his or her*) lunch.

Each girl has her own coat.

2. Two or more singular antecedents joined by or or nor should be referred to by a singular pronoun.

EXAMPLES   Mary or Susie will read her letter.

Neither Pete nor Steve has his mitt.

3. Two or more antecedents joined by and should be referred to by a plural pronoun.

EXAMPLES   The teacher and the students have their books.

Mike and Bob went to their music class together.

A pronoun agrees with its antecedent in gender.

Some singular personal pronouns have forms that show the gender of the antecedent. *He, him*, and *his* are masculine forms. *She, her*, and *hers* are feminine forms. *It* and *its* are neither masculine nor feminine.

EXAMPLES   Mark brought his guitar to the party.

Jean read her poem aloud.

The town held its annual parade last week.

EXERCISE. In the space in each sentence, write a pronoun that is in the same gender and number as its antecedent. Then underline the antecedent. (Add 10 points for each correct answer.)

EX. Patricia has ..... *her* ..... gloves.

1. The dancers and the singers took .... places.

2. Everyone has .... assignment.

3. Pete and Stu are riding .... bikes.

4. Neither Sally nor Lucy has .... guitar.

5. The teachers attended .... meeting.

6. Each girl knows .... lines.

7. Someone left .... umbrella here.

8. Dad likes .... new keychain.

9. The town will hold .... art festival tomorrow.

10. Each boy fixed .... own bike.

Chapter Review

EXERCISE A. Identify the use of each italicized pronoun by writing above it *subj.* for subject, *s.c.* for subject complement, *d.o.* for direct object, or *o.p.* for object of a preposition. (Add 5 points for each correct answer.)

1   *I* like studying about turtles, but my brother doesn't. Reptiles upset

2   *him*. *He* doesn't like observing crawling creatures. For *him,* any reptile is

3   repulsive. *I,* on the other hand, find *them* fascinating. The size of some

4   turtles interests *me*. Compared to their extinct relatives, some of *them*

5   seem extremely small. One museum displays the skeleton of an extinct

6   turtle. The guide told *us* that *it* must have weighed about three tons.

7   Nevertheless, turtles still grow very large today. The largest living

8   species consists of the leatherback turtles. *It* is *they* who achieve

9   enormous sizes. The hard plates covering the shells of the hawksbill turtle

10   are used by some of *us* for tortoise-shell ornaments. My mother has a

11   tortoise-shell comb that her mother gave to *her*. *She* finds tortoise shell

12   very beautiful. One day, *I* would like to travel to the Galápagos Islands

13   with my family. *We* could study turtles close up. *I* am sure even my

14   brother would be interested in turtles once *he* saw some of the more

15   remarkable species. If ever there were a born turtle-lover, it is *I*.

EXERCISE B. Fill the blank in each sentence with the correct one of the two pronouns printed in italics. (Add 5 points for each correct answer.)

he, him   1. Roxanne and . . . . rode horseback this morning.

he, him   2. It was . . . . with whom I saw you at lunch.

They, Them   3. . . . . were the kindest words the child had ever heard.

she, her   4. We were not expecting . . . . and Maxine for breakfast.

I, me   5. On Sunday Dad and . . . . are driving to Eastport.

we, us   6. Except for the Bernaths and . . . . , everyone has moved away.

they, them   7. We visited . . . . and Stephanie White in Butte last summer.

I, me　　　　8. Dr. Hernandez was extremely kind to my sister and
　　　　　　　. . . . .

we, us　　　　9. It was . . . . who wrote that editorial without any
　　　　　　　help from anyone.

he, him　　　10. Besides you and . . . ., there will be the Holden
　　　　　　　twins.

she, her　　　11. Mike and . . . . often gather driftwood along the
　　　　　　　beach.

she, her　　　12. Near . . . . and the bull was a man with a cape.

they, them　　13. Could it have been . . . . in the back seat?

we, us　　　14. They invited the Judsons and . . . . to see their
　　　　　　　slides.

I, me　　　　15. If it had been Jasper, Dinah, or . . . ., we would
　　　　　　　have been nervous.

I, me　　　　16. The man showed Don and . . . . to the door.

we, us　　　17. May the Dobrowskis and . . . . go to the movie
　　　　　　　now?

they, them　　18. We have all suffered from . . . . and their practical
　　　　　　　jokes.

he, him　　　19. Did Rusty let you or . . . . try out for the team?

she, her　　　20. Mr. Bugati thinks it was . . . . who sang the best.

EXERCISE C. Cross out any incorrect pronoun, and write the correct form
above it. (Add 20 points for each correctly marked sentence.)

EX. Slowly, the snake crept nearer to Michael and he.
　　　　　　　　　　　　　　　　　　　　　　him

1. Too late Ossie and me had realized what was the matter.

2. Someone is always making trouble for him and I.

3. Could the two boys in the back row have been they?

4. Her and Carol will notify the other members and they of the meeting.

5. Near Conrad and we stood she and her brother.

Cumulative Review

A. Above each italicized word, write its part of speech, using these abbreviations: *n.* (noun), *pron.* (pronoun), *adj.* (adjective), *v.* (verb), *adv.* (adverb), *prep.* (preposition). (Add 2 points for each correct answer.)

1   Pia and *I* rebuilt an *old* car *during* the *summer*. It *was* a 1931 Model A.

2   We *took* the car *apart* and *cleaned every* piece. *It* was a lot *of* work to get

3   the *old rust* and grease off. *Afterward, we hammered* the *dents* out of the

4   *fenders* and *repainted* the *body*.

In the rest of this paragraph, which follows, underline the subject of each sentence once and the verb twice. Circle each complement, and write above it the appropriate abbreviation: *d.o.* for direct object or *s.c.* for subject complement.

5   This was actually the easiest part of the job. My sister then found a rebuilt

6   engine for the car, and we replaced the window glass and bought a new

7   battery. At last the car ran perfectly. We brought the car to inspection and

8   it passed. Now we can drive around in our car. We have become the

9   objects of our friends' admiration. My sister and I have joined an

10   antique-car society. Next year we and a friend will restore a vintage Stutz

11   Bearcat.

B. The following paragraph contains sentence fragments, run-on sentences, and errors in commas and capitalization. Correct all these mistakes. (Add 4 points for each correct answer.)

1   Simon Bolivar a famous leader of the movement for independence in

2   south America was born in caracas venezuela on July 24 1783. His wealthy

3   parents. Died in his childhood. He was educated by tutors, for a while he

4   lived in paris. Later, in Caracas, he and other rebels drafted a venezuelan

5   constitution but the rebels were defeated by the spanish army Bolivar

6   assembled another army, but was again defeated and forced into exile. He

7   finally drove the spanish from Venezuela. After ten years of bitter fighting.

8   He achieved his final victory the battle of Ayacucho peru on december 9

9   1824.

C. The following sentences contain errors in agreement. Cross out any incorrect verb, and write the correct verb above it. (Add 10 points for each correct answer.)

1. The ducks in the pond was swimming in formation.

2. The lily pads on the surface of the water was huge.

3. The frogs near the edge of the water was croaking.

4. Here is three rare photographs of an eagle's nest.

5. This picture don't show the baby birds very clearly.

6. Everyone in our nature club want to save the bald eagle from extinction.

7. Over there is the picnic area and the boathouse.

8. Beth and her next-door neighbor is going to paint the dock.

9. Either of them are acceptable.

10. The energy level of all my classmates really amaze me.

D. Underline the correct one of the two verb forms given in parentheses. (Add 5 points for each correct answer.)

1. They (saw, seen) both pictures on the same program.

2. The flowers have all (fell, fallen) from the plants.

3. The speaker (lay, laid) the notes aside and began to talk.

4. The front doorbell has been (rang, rung) several times.

5. I have (went, gone) to California three years in a row.

6. The letter was (wrote, written) before I (saw, seen) you.

7. Bernie (sat, set) down and (drank, drunk) three bottles of soda.

8. They (came, come) into the valley last night through the pass.

9. The cat is (laying, lying) under the tree.

10. I was (laying, lying) on the sofa reading the plans you have (lain, laid.)

11. I have not (begun, began) my homework yet.

12. The winner was (chose, chosen) and (gave, given) the prize.

13. Sharon (brung, brought) the potato salad.

14. *Fifth Chinese Daughter* was (written, wrote) by Jade Snow Wong.

15. The students (sat, set) their pens on their desks.

16. Coretta has (gone, went) out.

Building Vocabulary: Choosing the Appropriate Word

The English language is rich in synonyms—words that have the same general meaning but that have subtle shades of difference between them. Choosing the right synonym is important when you are trying to write clearly and effectively.

Select the word that conveys the meaning and impression you want to give.

Compare the following sentences. See if you can work out from the context the meanings of the words in red and the impressions they suggest.

EXAMPLES   Mary McLeod Bethune, a founder of Bethune-Cookman College, was one of the eminent educators of her day.
Billy the Kid, the notorious bandit, died a violent death.

Both *eminent* and *notorious* have the general meaning of "famous or well known for some accomplishment." *Eminent,* however, means "famous for something good," while *notorious* means "famous for something bad." It would be just as mistaken to say that Bethune was a "notorious educator" as to say that Billy the Kid was an "eminent bandit." The impressions that the two words suggest are entirely different.

Study the following pairs of words, noting their similar meanings and the very different feelings that they suggest. Try to think of contexts in which each word would be appropriate.

disagree /dis ə gré/, *v.*   **wrangle** /ráng gəl/, *v.*   Both words mean to have a difference of opinion about something. *Disagree* suggests little feeling and is a good word for plain factual statement. Two friends might *disagree* about something without any bad feeling, but if they have a long, drawn-out, angry argument, unpleasant for them and everyone else, they are *wrangling.*

resolute /réz ə lūt/, *adj.*   **pugnacious** /pug nā́ shəs/, *adj.*   These words have similarities in meaning but are not close enough to be true synonyms. Both suggest great strength of purpose, a readiness to stand up for what one thinks right. *Resolute* suggests a good quality; *pugnacious,* a quality that is not so good. *Resolute* people have thought out their positions and feel deeply that they are right. *Pugnacious* people are always ready for a fight, though not usually without a good reason.

persistent /pər sís tənt/, *adj.*   **obstinate** /ób stə nit/, *adj.*   Both words mean sticking to something without giving up. *Persistent* means going on with some activity, carrying it through, if possible, to its conclusion. *Obstinate* suggests a quality that may not be good. An *obstinate* person will stick to an opinion to the point of being annoying about it, even if in the wrong.

aloof /ə lū́f/, *adj.*   **haughty** /háu tē/, *adj.*   Both words suggest excessive pride. *Aloof* people show their feelings of superiority by keeping away from other people. *Haughty* people show pride actively by treating other people with contempt.

tranquil /tráng kwil/, *adj.*   **meek** /mēk/, *adj.*   Both words suggest a calm, quiet disposition. *Tranquil* is used only with the "good" suggestion of untroubled, at peace with oneself. *Meek* means without anger or envy and strictly speaking is also a "good" word, but it is often used to mean overly submissive or lacking in spirit, too ready to give in to others.

EXERCISE. In each blank, write the word from this lesson that makes the most sense. Make sure that the suggested impression of the word as well as its basic meaning fit the context. (Add 10 points for each correct answer.)

1. Unfortunately, people often take advantage of Waldo's .... disposition.

2. Metcalf is so naturally .... that he cannot bring himself to join in any school activities.

3. Although I .... completely with you, I shall always defend your right to express your views.

4. Only an extremely .... person would have had the courage to face the angry mob single-handed and unarmed.

5. It was certain beforehand that two people as .... in their opinions as the governor and Mayor Laverty would immediately begin to .... over the new city budget.

6. After calming the .... demonstrators at City Hall, Mother was glad to return to the .... atmosphere of home.

7. Quietly .... as always, Lola finally persuaded us.

8. The company's .... president kept the salesclerk waiting for two solid hours.

REVIEW EXERCISE. In the space to the left of each italicized word, write the letter of the best meaning. (Add 20 points for each correct answer.)

.... 1. a *lenient* parent
.... 2. a *tactful* remark
.... 3. *spontaneous* liking
.... 4. *contemplate* an idea
.... 5. *shun* an enemy

a. careful about others' feelings
b. to avoid completely
c. not strict or severe
d. to consider deeply
e. without outside cause

Spelling: Silent Consonants

One of the results of its long and complicated history is that English contains a number of words that have "silent" or unpronounced consonants. Some English words with silent consonants are taken from Latin, and the Latin spelling does not correspond to the way we now pronounce the words. Among such words of Latin origin are

salmon	debt	solemn
alms	doubt	column

Many other words containing silent consonants are derived from Old English forms in which the consonants *were* pronounced. The word *knot,* for example, was pronounced with the letter *k* sounded as /k/.

Here is a sampling of some modern English words that still retain a silent consonant as a kind of reminder of the days when the English language was Old English and people still sounded these now silent letters.

limb	write	know
climb	sword	knee
Wednesday	half	listen
handsome	folk	often

EXERCISE A. Draw a circle around the silent consonant in each word below. Say the word softly, and consult a dictionary, if necessary. (Add 5 points for each correct answer.)

1. knife	6. rustle	11. wreck	16. knack
2. often	7. mortgage	12. stalk	17. handsome
3. wrinkle	8. handkerchief	13. condemn	18. honest
4. hymn	9. fasten	14. knowledge	19. write
5. thumb	10. subtle	15. raspberry	20. trestle

EXERCISE B. Fill in the blanks in each incomplete word below. The meaning of the word is given in parentheses. (Add 20 points for each correct answer.)

1. an . . . . . er (a reply)

2. . . . . . eumonia (a serious lung disease)

3. mu . . . . . le (a bundle of body tissue)

4. . . . . . ist (the joint connecting the hand and the arm)

5. ca . . . . . le (a large building with thick walls)

EXERCISE C. The silent consonant (or consonants) in each word below is printed in red. Look at each word carefully. Try to picture it, especially the silent consonant, in your mind. Then be ready to write the words as your teacher dictates them. (Add 10 points for each correct answer.)

1. scene
2. island
3. psalm
4. toward
5. ghost

6. gnaw
7. descend
8. almond
9. wrestle
10. corps

EXERCISE D. Review all of the words you have studied in this lesson. Look at the word; close your eyes and picture it; look at it again; write it; check your written word. Concentrate on those words you had trouble with. Now you should be ready to write all of the words correctly as your teacher dictates them to you one at a time. (Add 4 points for each correct answer.)

REVIEW EXERCISE. Underline the correct word from each pair in parentheses. (Add 10 points for each correct answer.)

1. My mother's favorite (sent, scent) is musk.
2. All of the bookcases in this room are (stationary, stationery).
3. We had only two hours in which to (altar, alter) the costumes.
4. The pitcher (through, threw) a fast ball.
5. Tim, did you (brake, break) the good news to them yet?
6. Let's all (meet, meat) at the bus stop at eight o'clock.
7. The rescuers could (hear, here) voices from deep inside the cavern.
8. This picture was taken right in front of the (capital, capitol).
9. What are the (principals, principles) of your club?
10. You must rub the paint off with (course, coarse) steel wool.

CHAPTER 11

Apostrophes and Quotation Marks

The two punctuation marks that you will study in this chapter are small, but they can make a great difference in meaning. For example, notice the difference between these two phrases:

all the boy's hats   all the boys' hats

The first example means all the hats that belong to *one boy*. The second example means the hats that belong to *all the boys*. The little apostrophe makes all the difference.

Now consider these two sentences:

Miss Masaro said she will give the test tomorrow.
Miss Masaro said, "She will give the test tomorrow."

In the first sentence, Miss Masaro is talking about herself. In the second, she is talking about someone else. The quotation marks make the difference.

In this chapter, you will learn when and where to use apostrophes and quotation marks so that they work to express your meaning clearly.

LESSON 96

Apostrophes Show Possession

The form of a noun or pronoun that shows possession or ownership is called its *possessive case—possessive* for short. With nouns, you use an apostrophe to form the possessive.

1. To form the possessive of a singular noun, add an apostrophe and an s ('s).

EXAMPLES   an <u>uncle's</u> reply   the <u>dog's</u> tail   <u>Charles's</u> answer

2. To form the possessive of a plural noun not ending in s, add an apostrophe and an s ('s).

EXAMPLES   the <u>children's</u> dad   the <u>oxen's</u> yoke   the <u>geese's</u> pond

3. To form the possessive of a plural noun ending in s, add only the apostrophe (').

EXAMPLES   the <u>girls'</u> ponies   the <u>foxes'</u> cubs   the <u>ladies'</u> wishes

EXERCISE A. In the space to the right of each pair of words, write the correct possessive form of the word that names the possessor with the word that names what is possessed. Notice that in items 1–5, the possessors are singular nouns, and in items 6–10 they are plural nouns. (Add 10 points for each correct answer.)

	Possessor	*What is possessed*	
EX.	the woman	hat	*the woman's hat*
EX.	the Johnsons	house	*the Johnsons' house*
1.	a dog	bone	....
2.	some person	job	....
3.	the rainbow	end	....
4.	the waterfall	roar	....
5.	the moon	orbit	....
6.	some books	titles	....
7.	the ships	funnels	....
8.	our players	uniforms	....
9.	my grandparents	home	....
10.	the Rubins	new car	....

EXERCISE B. Form the possessives of the following nouns by writing in each blank either an apostrophe and an *s* (*'s*) or just an apostrophe ('). (Add 4 points for each correct answer.)

1. the city.... mayor
2. many states.... governors
3. two schools..... principals
4. the navy.... flagship
5. any women.... organization
6. the stores.... managers
7. the store.... manager
8. an electricians.... union
9. a banker.... ideas
10. my mother.... job
11. the Joneses.... children
12. friends.... disagreements
13. the captain..... badge
14. the executive.... meeting
15. our group.... objectives
16. a politican.... word
17. the snakes.... nests
18. the people.... choice
19. the delegates.... hopes
20. several machines.... motors
21. Mr. De Marco.... friends
22. the magazine.... price
23. Willy.... newspapers
24. earth.... riches
25. the actor.... lines

Apostrophes for Contractions

Whenever you use a word like *don't* (for *do not*) or *I'm* (for *I am*)—as you do very often in conversation—you are using a contraction. A *contraction* is a word made by combining two words and leaving out some letters.

Use an apostrophe to show where letters or numbers have been omitted in a contraction.

The most commonly contracted words are *is, are, have, not,* and *will.* In the following examples, notice which letters in these words are replaced by the apostrophe.

IS	he's	here's	there's	who's		
ARE	we're	you're	they're			
HAVE	I've	you've	we've	they've		
NOT	isn't	aren't	haven't	don't	doesn't	didn't
	wasn't	weren't	couldn't			
WILL	I'll	you'll	we'll	they'll	who'll	

Are, have, and *will* are usually contracted only with personal pronouns (*we're, I've, she'll*), while *not* combines mainly with helping verbs. *Is* (*'s*), however, may be contracted with almost any noun or pronoun.

EXAMPLES   The work's (= work is) too hard.
Nothing's (= Nothing is) getting done.

Is and *has* both have the same contraction (*'s*). So do *had* and *would* (*'d*). With both pairs of contractions, you must be careful to make clear which word you mean. In writing, it is perhaps best to avoid these contractions, simply because they may not always be clear.

EXAMPLES   He's left now. = He is left now. *or* He has left now.

They'd run home. = They would run home. *or* They had run home.

Finally, notice these three contractions, which are a little different from the ones listed above.

EXAMPLES   Let us go. = Let's go.

They cannot = They can't.

She will not = She won't.

Standard English usage does not permit any contraction of *am not. Ain't* is nonstandard English. Do not use *aren't* with the pronoun *I.* This is perhaps one of the most common errors in standard English usage. Many of us say ''Aren't

I?'' Although this is acceptable in nonstandard usage, we should remember, especially when writing, that the correct form is "Am I not?"

NONSTANDARD   *Aren't* (= are not) I invited? I *ain't* worried.
STANDARD   **Am** I **not** invited? I**'m** (= I am) **not** worried.

EXERCISE A. Write the contractions of the following words, putting the apostrophe in place of the omitted letters. (Add 4 points for each correct answer.)

EX. you have   ...*you've*..   13. let us   ....

1. did not   ....   14. you would   ....

2. I am   ....   15. cannot   ....

3. we will   ....   16. who will   ....

4. is not   ....   17. here is   ....

5. who is   ....   18. we have   ....

6. have not   ....   19. you are   ....

7. we are   ....   20. Glenn is   ....

8. was not   ....   21. were not   ....

9. they have   ....   22. she will   ....

10. will not   ....   23. they are   ....

11. there is   ....   24. it has   ....

12. I am not   ....   25. it is   ....

EXERCISE B. The following sentences contain possessive nouns and contractions, but all the apostrophes are missing. Supply the omitted apostrophes. (Add 10 points for each correctly marked sentence.)

EX. Wholl take Ambroses place?

1. Mayas dog wont run out into the street any more.

2. Lets not go to the bowling match tonight.

3. Im not happy about the mayors decision.

4. She wasnt so sure before the teams winning streak.

5. Theyll use the students dining room.

6. She shouldnt put her skates there.

7. Theyve no reason to complain.

8. Dont be so sure that hell win.

9. Whos going to tell her about Jacks failure?

10. I wont repeat what youve said to me.

196

Apostrophes: Some DON'TS

1. DON'T confuse the possessive pronouns with the contractions that sound like them.

The personal pronouns have special possessive forms that show possession all by themselves, *without the use of the apostrophe.*

EXAMPLES   **His** friends are **ours**. **Its** habits are like **theirs**.

Some of the possessive pronouns sound just like contractions. *Whose,* which is used in asking questions, also sounds like a contraction. When in doubt, ask yourself whether the word is used as a possessive pronoun or as a contraction (a pronoun plus a verb).

INCORRECT   *It's* coat is shaggy. *Its* time to leave.
CORRECT   **Its** (possessive) coat is shaggy. **It's** (= *it* + *is*) time to leave.

INCORRECT   *Their's* looks better. *Theirs* the answer.
CORRECT   **Theirs** (possessive) looks better. **There's** (= *there* + *is*) the answer.

INCORRECT   *Who's* book is that? *Whose* coming with us?
CORRECT   **Whose** (possessive) book is that? **Who's** (= *who* + *is*) coming with us?

2. DON'T use an apostrophe with plural nouns that do not show ownership.

INCORRECT   The men's *hats'* blew off.
CORRECT   The men's **hats** blew off. (*Hats* is not possessive.)

3. DON'T misplace the apostrophe.

Remember that the purpose of the apostrophe is to show where letters are left out. Put the apostrophe only where letters have been omitted.

INCORRECT   You *ca'nt* do that again.
CORRECT   You **can't** do that again. (The apostrophe goes in place of *no* in the long form, *cannot.*)

EXERCISE A. Underline the correct form of the pair of words in parentheses in the following sentences. (Add 10 points for each correct answer.)

1. (Whose, Who's) book am I using?

2. (Your, You're) right about that stop sign.

3. Stop wiggling (your, you're) feet.

4. (Their, They're) ideas about football are all wrong.

5. (Its, It's) unreasonable of him to expect so much work.

6. (Their, They're) sure that set of tools belongs to them.

7. (Ours, Our's) is a happy class.

8. (Their, There's) the one that lost the license plate.

9. (Their, They're) all coming to visit us.

10. (Theirs, There's) no reason for all that noise.

EXERCISE B. If the italicized word or contraction is correct, write *C* in the appropriate space to the right. If it is not correct, write the word or contraction correctly in the proper space. (Add 5 points for each correct answer.)

1   "*Don't* you tell me *its* my turn again,"   ....*C*....   ....*it's*....

2   Carla insisted. "*I'm* sure *Ive* done it two   ....

3   nights in a row. *Is'nt* that so, Nora?"   ....

4   *Noras' stamps'* held her interest, and   ....

5   she *did'nt* answer. It was *Bill's* problem.   ....

6   "Oh, no," said Bill, "*youve* skipped   ....

7   twice. *Someone's* got to clean *it's* cage, ...

8   but I know it *ain't* my turn."   ....

9   "*Who's* hamster is it—*yours*," Dad   ....

10 asked, "or *Carla's* or *Noras?*"   ....

11 "*It's their's!*" each shouted at once, ...

12 pointing to the other two.

13 "Tonight," said Dad, "*its* all *yours*, ...

14 and now *your* all going to feed it."   ....

Punctuating Quotations

Compare these two sentences:

Anita said that it would be a sunny day.
Anita said, "It will be a sunny day."

In the first sentence the speaker's words are not quoted directly. However, in the second sentence, the speaker's words are quoted directly. When you give someone's exact words, you are *quoting* that person, and what you quote is called a *direct quotation—quotation* for short.

Use quotation marks to enclose a <u>direct quotation</u>—a person's exact words.

EXAMPLES "<u>Nothing can change my mind</u>," I told her.

The man replied, "<u>Haven't you said that twice already?</u>"

"<u>How do you spell *psychology?*</u>" asked Norman.

A direct quotation begins with a capital letter.

In other words, a sentence that is quoted begins like any other sentence.

EXAMPLE The officer said, "<u>L</u>et me see your license."

A direct quotation is set off from the rest of the sentence by commas.

EXAMPLES "<u>I'll see you at the game tonight</u>," Homer remarked.

Priscilla inquired, "<u>Do you think it will rain today?</u>"

Notice, in the examples above, how a quotation ends. The comma (period, question mark, or exclamation point) is place *inside* the closing quotation marks. The comma at the beginning of a quotation, on the other hand, is *outside* the opening quotation mark.

One other comma use comes up mostly, though not only, in direct quotations—the word of direct address. A word of direct address is whatever name or title is used when speaking to a person.

A word of direct address is set off by commas.

EXAMPLES Mr. Handford asked, "<u>Willy</u>, do you know the answer or not?"

"Please, <u>Senator</u>, give me your autograph," Joyce said.

Add capital letters, periods, question marks, commas, and quotation marks where they are needed for the direct quotations in the following sentences. Remember to put the beginning comma outside the quotation marks and the closing punctuation mark inside. (Add 10 points for each correctly marked sentence.)

1. We would like to plant a rooftop garden Aretha said

2. That sounds like a good idea the superintendent replied

3. Brenda asked could we use a small section of the roof on the south side

4. Aretha added we really wouldn't need too much space

5. I'm certain something could be arranged commented the superintendent

6. Then he added what are you planning to grow

7. We were thinking of growing tomatoes, lettuce, radishes, and cucumbers Aretha replied.

8. Brenda said and I was planning on setting aside a tiny section for herbs

9. I'll help to block off a small section this afternoon the superintendent responded

10. The friends cheerfully replied oh, thank you very much

EXERCISE B. Some of the following sentences need additional punctuation, and some do not. Supply the missing punctuation marks and capital letters. (Add 5 points for each correct answer.)

THE WINNER

1   Arlene asked me why I expected her to win. I admire your determination

2   I told her. Then I went on it's persistence that counts in sports. But she said

3   that she still wasn't convinced. I told her all the things I could think of to

4   cheer her up. And, of course, she won.

5   Afterward, she asked me did you really expect me to win?

6   She insisted that she couldn't believe it, and I retorted don't be so

7   modest champ.

8   She laughed and said well, I can't deny I practiced hard.

Working with Longer Quotations

Both for interest and clarity, you often interrupt a quotation with the words that tell who is talking—*he said, they replied,* and so on. When you interrupt a quotation in this way, you put a comma and quotation marks *after* the first part of the quotation and a comma and quotation marks *before* the second part of the quotation.

EXAMPLES   "We're so near now," he said, "that we ought to be home by eight at the latest."

"Come over here," shouted Mr. Bailey, "and explain what you were doing here?"

Notice that in a divided quotation, the second part of the quoted sentence begins with a small letter.

EXAMPLES   "Do you want to lie down," Gertrude suggested, "until you feel better?"

"I wonder," said Geraldine with a troubled sigh, "whether that will really help."

In telling a story, you often quote the conversation of two or more people. In writing, conversation of this kind is known as *dialogue.*

When you write the conversation of two or more persons, begin a new paragraph each time the speaker changes.

EXAMPLES   "I thought I saw you on Third Street yesterday," John remarked.

"Oh, no," said Susie, "I was out of town, so it must have been some other person."

"Where did you go, Susie?" John continued.

"Well, you see, Aunt Lila's been sick," Susie explained, "and we all drove over to see how she was getting along."

Often, you quote several sentences at a time. You may be reporting conversation, or you may be quoting sentences from a book.

When a quotation consists of more than one sentence, put quotation marks only at the beginning and end of the whole quotation, not around each sentence in the quotation.

INCORRECT   Leon shouted, "Can you still hear me, Jennifer?" "The whole house is going." "The roof will collapse any minute." "Hurry up!"

CORRECT   Leon shouted,   Can you still hear me, Jennifer? The whole
house is going. The roof will collapse any minute. Hurry up!

Too many quotation marks (in the first example) are confusing. They make
the reader think several people are talking instead of just one.

EXERCISE A. The commas and quotation marks have been omitted from the
following sentences. Put them in. Not every sentence requires punctuation.
(Add 10 points for each correctly marked sentence.)

EX. I wonder Margie Jenny sighed if we really ought to go.

1. Where the director inquired do you find such strange costumes?

2. We'll just stay a few minutes Jim I said and then we'll go home.

3. Gloria told Miss Stivik that she feared the worst.

4. Whenever you talk Toby laughed you sound just like Uncle Lenny.

5. Trust me the scout whispered to get you out of this mess.

6. In this region said Mr. O'Hare we have gold mines and sheep.

7. Julia said I bet I would have liked traveling in a covered wagon.

8. Next time said John take the train.

9. Marv had sworn to all of us that he was telling the truth.

10. But as for me shouted Teddy I just like talking to people!

EXERCISE B. Supply the missing punctuation marks in the following
dialogue. Use a paragraph sign (¶) to show where the speaker changes and a
new paragraph should begin. (Add 4 points for each correct answer.)

1   Racquel, have you developed the photographs for the school paper
2   yet? asked Cheryl.   We need them by noon.   ''Yes   said Racquel.   I
3   took them to Mrs. Ortega's office.   Cheryl inquired   ''How did they
4   turn out?   Was the lighting good enough?   I had some difficulty with the
5   three shots I took at night   Racquel responded,   but the rest are pretty
6   sharp.   Thats great!   said Cheryl.   After all our hard work, I almost
7   cant wait to see the first issue of the paper.

Chapter Review

EXERCISE A. Form the possessives of the following expressions by adding either an apostrophe and an *s* (*'s*) or just an apostrophe ('). (Add 4 points for each correct item.)

1. the sun. . . . rays
2. the trucks. . . . tires
3. the men. . . . hats
4. anyone. . . . promises
5. the stars. . . . twinkling
6. the house. . . . basement
7. the nations. . . . ambassadors
8. the children. . . . pets
9. this man. . . . hopes
10. some magazines. . . . articles
11. the bridge. . . . maintenance
12. nobody. . . . fault

Write the contractions of the following expressions, being careful to put the apostrophes in the right places.

13. will not . . . .
14. did not . . . .
15. who is . . . .
16. she will . . . .
17. cannot . . . .
18. it has been . . . .
19. has not . . . .
20. here is . . . .
21. could not . . . .
22. let us . . . .
23. you would . . . .
24. I shall . . . .
25. would not . . . .

EXERCISE B. In the following sentences, underline the correct word of the two in parentheses. (Add 5 points for each correct answer.)

1. (Whose, Who's) coat is this lying on the floor?
2. I think (your, you're) idea of hair styles is better than (theirs, their's).
3. (Its, It's) a pleasure to see you.
4. Afterward, (your, you're) going to cut the grass.
5. (Hers, Her's) was a very poor choice, but (ours, our's) was even worse.
6. (Their, They're) trip starts tomorrow, and (their, they're) going to Nova Scotia.
7. (Your, You're) never going to finish (your, you're) book.
8. I envy that cheerfulness of (hers, her's).
9. (Ours, Our's) is the first house on the block to get one.

10. (Its, It's) hind leg must be hurt.

11. During (their, they're) vacation, (their, they're) leaving the dog behind in a kennel.

12. Their boat lost (its, it's) mast, but (ours, our's) is all right.

13. (Whose, Who's) going to repair (yours, your's) for you?

EXERCISE C. Supply quotation marks, commas, and other punctuation marks. (Add 10 points for each correctly marked sentence.)

1. Your resistance to my plan he said is incomprehensible.

2. Im so anxious to get away she said that I can hardly wait.

3. Ms. Beame asked if the answer was right or wrong.

4. Wheres the fire asked the officer.

5. Theres an enemy patrol over the ridge Captain said the corporal.

6. What I want to know Mother she said is why are you going?

7. Did Mr. Parks really say that to Jerry she asked.

8. You studied hard he said and thats why you did so well.

9. Since its our day off, lets enjoy it said the pilot.

10. What chance he asked have you got against such odds?

EXERCISE D. Supply the commas, quotation marks, capital letters, and apostrophes needed in the following dialogue. Where a new paragraph should begin, put in the paragraph sign (¶). (Add 2 points for each correct answer.)

DON'T OPEN IT, CHARLOTTTE

1   Mom said Charlotte plaintively Im certain I heard a noise like the
2 opening of a spaceships airlock. Thats a fine idea, her mother replied but I
3 guess were all a little tired tonight. I think its in the back yard the girl
4 continued. Thats just fine murmured the girls tired mother. The young
5 girls voice sank to a frightened whisper as she said please, Mom, weve
6 got to do something. Theyre coming out. Theyve turned on their ray guns.
7 Watch out! Arent you listening Mom? Whats that youre saying her mother
8 inquired. How can you read your paper at a time like this? the girl
9 shouted. Wearily, Charlotte's mom said, Of course, but first would you
10 mind seeing whos at our front door?''

Cumulative Review

A. In each blank space below, add an appropriate word that will fit into the context of the sentence. Then indicate how each of these words is used by writing above it the appropriate abbreviation: *subj.* for simple subject; *v.* for verb; *s.c.* for subject complement; *d.o.* for direct object; and *o.p.* for object of a preposition. (Add 2 points for each correct answer.)

1. The snowball . . . . him on the . . . .

2. . . . . was almost certainly . . . . in that big black car.

3. The sky above . . . . was a brilliant . . . .

4. Will . . . . of . . . . help . . . . with the dishes?

5. Beyond . . . . and . . . . of empty road.

6. Actually, I rather . . . . a . . . . of their . . . .

7. The winners . . . . in the dance contest were Alicia and . . . .

8. Has . . . . by any . . . . the problem to him?

9. No one . . . . more than Mrs. Fraglin.

10. Black clouds of . . . . blocked his . . . . of them.

B. In the following paragraph, correct the capitalization, sentence fragments, and run-on sentences, and supply missing commas. (Add 2 points for each correct answer.)

FIREWORKS!

1   Long before the People of europe knew anything about gunpowder, the

2   chinese had found a variety of uses for it. Chinese rockets were crude

3   inaccurate and dangerous as weapons of war but they produced a splendid

4   bang and a brilliant light. Qualities that are highly desirable in fireworks.

5   Even today fireworks play a leading part. In the celebration of the chinese

6   new year. The United States however is the world's leading consumer of

7   fireworks. The campaign for a ''safe and sane'' fourth of July has of

8   course eliminated some of the fun along with the danger, however

9   Independence day would simply not be the same to most of us without a

10   public display of fireworks. On the other hand in england and in hawaii,

11 rockets and other fireworks are traditional. In the celebration of new
12 year's day. French Customs in the use of fireworks are similar to ours, the
13 french use rockets roman candles pinwheels and other devices to celebrate
14 bastille day the commemoration of the start of the French revolution July
15 14 1789. Editorial writers for the *new york Times* and other newspapers
16 may to be sure wonder whether fireworks are worth it or not but it seems
17 likely that people throughout the world will continue to enjoy their bold
18 nighttime display for a long time to come. Indeed fireworks displays
19 sponsored by local communities draw large crowds and an afternoon
20 picnic followed by an evening spent watching a fireworks display. Seems
21 to be the traditional way of spending independence day.

C. The following sentences contain errors in pronoun and verb usage and in subject-verb agreement. Cross out the incorrect words, and write the correct forms above. (Add 4 points for each correct answer.)

1. Her and I seen them coming and wasn't at all pleased.
2. Bill and her have lain the problem before Corinne and he.
3. Last night the Moskoffs come over and brought their pictures.
4. Don't he ever get tired of laying around doing nothing?
5. There was no blankets for Barry and I, and we begun to worry.
6. Several of the students give the same answers on yesterday's test.
7. One of them has always give trouble, but it isn't she.
8. Lisa and her often goes to the beach and set there for hours.
9. Every one of us has fell behind this term.
10. They must have knowed when Joel and him put up the notice.
11. It was she and him who done it, but they don't seem sorry.
12. They have took you and me for a ride and now they have run out.
13. If either of them has wrote, he should have spoken up about it.

Spelling: Review

EXERCISE A. Correctly join each prefix (or suffix) and base word. Write the new word in the blank. (Add 10 points for each correct answer.)

1. dis + similar = ...
2. final + ly = ...
3. mis + spelled = ...
4. thin + ness = ...
5. un + named = ...

6. kindly + ness = ...
7. due + ly = ...
8. angry + ly = ...
9. hoarse + ness = ...
10. true + ly = ...

EXERCISE B. Make a complete, correctly spelled word by writing the prefix *pre-*, *pro-*, or *per-* in the blank. (Add 10 points for each correct answer.)

1. ..... manent
2. ..... fessor
3. ..... dict
4. ..... nounce

5. ..... cedes
6. ..... mote
7. ..... mit

8. ..... serve
9. .... sist
10. ..... duce

EXERCISE C. Make a complete, correctly spelled word by writing *-cle* or *-cal* in the blank. (Add 10 points for each correct answer.)

1. mechani......
2. parti......
3. ici.....
4. criti......

5. practi......
6. bicy......
7. arti......

8. obsta......
9. musi......
10. comi......

EXERCISE D. Correctly complete each word by writing *ie* or *ei* in the blank. (Add 10 points for each correct answer.)

1. perc......ve
2. br......f
3. w......rd
4. y......ld

5. sl......gh
6. rec......ve
7. fr......nd

8. n......ghbor
9. w......ght
10. l......sure

EXERCISE E. Make each noun plural, or change the form of each verb by writing *s* or *es*, whichever is correct, in the blank. (Add 10 points for each correct answer.)

1. cough......
2. waltz......

3. approach......
4. brag......

5. fox......
6. glass......

7. youth......   9. accomplish......
8. gas......   10. church......

EXERCISE F. Mentally add -ing to each word. Write the new word in the blank. (Add 10 points for each correct answer.)

1. prove ....   6. dye ....
2. die ....   7. make ....
3. scare ....   8. ride ....
4. lie ....   9. write ....
5. promise ....   10. dine ....

EXERCISE G. Underline the correct word of the two in parentheses. (Add 10 points for each correct answer.)

1. Are you (through, threw) using the computer yet?

2. Let me (altar, alter) the sleeves of that jacket.

3. Aunt Clare sent Jennifer a box of beautiful yellow (stationary, stationery).

4. What is the (capitol, capital) of Alaska?

5. The weavers were making a (coarse, course) linen fabric.

6. He claims that a UFO landed (here, hear).

7. Some animals are (meet, meat) eaters.

8. This thunderstorm should (break, brake) the hot spell.

9. Our science teacher is studying to be a junior high school (principle, principal).

10. Do you like the (scent, sent) of this perfume?

EXERCISE H. Be prepared to write the following words from dictation. (Add 5 points for each correct answer.)

1. climb
2. ghost
3. knife
4. pleasure
5. appeal
6. often
7. teach
8. wrinkle
9. heaven
10. muscle
11. scene
12. column
13. steak
14. island
15. ready
16. scream
17. toward
18. salmon
19. sword
20. descend

Review

FRAGMENTS AND RUN-ONS. The following paragraph contains ten sentence errors—sentence fragments or run-on sentences. Correct these errors by crossing out or adding periods and by crossing out or adding capital letters as needed. (Add 10 points for each corrected sentence.)

LEAGUE OF THE IROQUOIS

1   Before the American Revolution. Five Native American tribes had
2   formed a democratic government, the five tribes were the Mohawk,
3   Oneida, Onondaga, Cayuga, and Seneca. All five tribes lived in New
4   York State. According to legend, Hiawatha, a Mohawk, convinced all five
5   tribes to join together in a league. Which gave every tribe an equal vote.
6   Later the Tuscarora joined the other five tribes, and the group became
7   known as the League of Six Nations, the total population of the League
8   was about 16,000. The League was the bitter enemy of the French. Who
9   were settling in the area. The League, however, was friendly with the
10 English, they later became strong allies in the French and Indian War.
11 Which pitted the English against the French. When the American
12 Revolution began, the League helped the English. And were defeated.
13 The Mohawk and Cayuga retreated to Canada, many of the others
14 remained in New York State. Today, the League is no longer powerful.
15 Although ceremonies are still held to celebrate its past glory.

CAPITALIZATION. Where a capital letter is omitted, cross out the small letter, and write the correct capital letter above it. If a word is capitalized and should not be, merely cross out the incorrect capital. (Add 5 points for each correctly marked sentence.)

1. Last Spring, mayor Forbes opened our centennial celebration.
2. The battle of lexington began the american Revolution.
3. Rachel Carson wrote a book called *silent spring*.
4. The united tube company had its meeting at lake tahoe.

5. Ms. Knightsmith, manager of the australian branch, was there.

6. She showed them some publicity from the *Sydney daily clarion*.

7. At the meeting, uncle Henry talked about plans for an office building in phoenix, arizona.

8. The orlando area has a great future, according to one florida magazine.

9. Some people belong to Churches, Synagogues, or Mosques, but others prefer to worship privately in their own fashion.

10. We heard a talk by major Calkins of the United States air force.

11. Mr. Trent, the chief of police, spoke about national crime prevention week.

12. *Modern fiction studies* has printed a review of all of Carson McCullers' fiction.

13. I saw judge Capp's picture in the *evening Call*.

14. Large areas now bangladesh were once pakistan.

15. The Oxhide Tire company manufactures most of its Tires in a single plant in the middle west.

16. Stonehenge, to the North of the british city of Salisbury, may have been used in the worship of the ancient celtic Gods.

17. Marissa Bergman is a Manager at the Textco manufacturing company.

18. The alliance of performing artists picketed the television show.

19. Sam Spade was a Private Eye in *the Maltese falcon*.

20. Many commuters who work in New York city but have homes in the Suburbs live in new jersey, connecticut, and long island.

SUBJECT-VERB AGREEMENT. Cross out any verb that does not agree with its subject, and write the correct form above it. (Add 5 points for each correct sentence.)

1. The choice of the delegates are between two candidates.

2. Here comes the two cousins I wanted you to meet.

3. The cartons of food were falling from the truck one by one.

4. Either Wendell or Lucy has a good chance of winning.

5. Everyone in the class are taking the same test.

6. Well, at least a few of the answers are going to be right.

7. A sandwich, a glass of milk, and an apple is a healthful lunch.

8. Near the gate stands a boy and his father.

9. Don't he ever get tired of waiting there?

10. They was hardly fair when they made that decision.

11. Is Carmela and Aunt Mia leaving for Los Angeles next week?

12. Several of Abner's friends have seen the movie, too.

13. There in the box lie the money in a heap of old rags.

14. If they don't come soon, one of us are going to regret it.

15. Either of the candidates are equally acceptable to the voters.

16. A few was lost but there's still several to choose from.

17. Doesn't both of them want to help?

18. Do Ned or one of his friends want to come?

19. A few of the members of the gymnastics class wants to learn to do butterflies.

20. Several of the artists in the exhibition has sold some of their paintings.

VERB USAGE. In the appropriate spaces, write the missing principal parts of the following verbs. (Add 4 points for each correct answer.)

INFINITIVE	SIMPLE PAST	PAST PARTICIPLE
1. drink	. . . .	. . . .
2. ring	. . . .	. . . .
3. choose	. . . .	. . . .
4. freeze	. . . .	. . . .
5. drive	. . . .	. . . .
6. ride	. . . .	. . . .
7. speak	. . . .	. . . .
8. write	. . . .	. . . .

Underline the correct one of the two verb forms in parentheses.

9. We (saw, seen) them when they first (came, come) here.

10. When Jill had (did, done) the work, she (took, taken) it to the study and (lain, laid) it on the desk.

11. The cow has (went, gone) into the cornfield again.

12. Ethel had (tore, torn) her coat before the start of the game.

13. If I'd (knowed, known) you were in a hurry, I'd have brought the book back promptly.

PRONOUN USAGE. In the following sentences, underline the correct form of the pronoun given in parentheses. (Add 10 points for each correct answer.)

1. The person at the foot of the stairs was (she, her).

2. The twins and (he, him) have made all the plans.

3. (He, Him) and (we, us) are in agreement.

4. They will almost certainly give the jobs to George and (he, him).

5. I have asked Mr. Hunter and (he, him) about the matter.

6. The book was written by Dr. Miles in collaboration with Mr. Rawls, Mrs. Lucas, and (he, him).

7. Sandra and (she, her) were the basketball team's cocaptains.

8. Between you and (I, me) Pat knows who did it.

9. Peter saw both Geraldine and (she, her).

APOSTROPHES AND QUOTATION MARKS. Supply the missing quotation marks, commas, and apostrophes in the following dialogue. Where the improper word is used, cross it out and write the correct word above. Use the paragraph sign (¶) to show where the speaker changes and a new paragraph should begin. (Add 2 points for each correct answer.)

TO THE MOVIES

1   "Mac old buddy said Casper brightly howd you like to see that show at
2   the Palace tonight? Whats in it for you, Casper Mac cautiously asked.
3   Looking slightly hurt, Casper said Gosh, Mac I thought youd enjoy seeing
4   *A Martians Revenge* with me. Its got Vaughan Tender in it. Wouldnt it be
5   fun to go together?" "Youre making it sound pretty good, Mac admitted,
6   "but how are we going to get to the Palace? That very thought had
7   occurred to me," said Casper smoothly and I thought of your generous
8   brothers car." All right, said Mac with a weary sigh after Jim drives us
9   downtown, whose going to pay for the show? Casper went on briskly Im
10 just coming to that. Who's money should we borrow this time, Jim's or
11 your's? Where, asked Mac would a boys money go if it weren't for his
12 friends?"

CHAPTER 12

Sentence Combining

If you play tennis, football, or any other sport, you know you have to practice regularly in order to improve your skills. The same is true of writing. Just as you warm up before playing a sport, you do exercises to become a better writer. In this chapter you will study some of the ways you can avoid repetition and gain variety in your writing by combining sentences containing related ideas.

Combining with Adjectives and Adverbs

COMBINING WITH ADJECTIVES

Sometimes you may think of ideas separately and write them down the way you think of them, when actually they are related and belong in the same sentence.

EXAMPLE   Mark has a dog.
           The dog is big and friendly.

Notice that these two sentences can be combined by leaving out unnecessary words and placing the adjectives next to the word they modify.

           Mark has a dog.
           The dog is big and friendly.
           Mark has a big and friendly dog.

An **adjective** is a word used to modify a noun or pronoun. It makes the meaning of a noun or pronoun more specific. The adjectives *big* and *friendly* tell us what kind of dog Mark has. Remember that adjectives must be placed as close as possible to the nouns and pronouns they modify.

EXERCISE A. Combine each group of sentences into one sentence, eliminating unnecessary words and placing the adjectives next to the words they modify. Follow the example (Correct answers may vary. Add 10 points for each correct sentence.)

EX. Lobstering is a business.

It is an exciting business. .... *Lobstering is an exciting* ....
business. ....

1. Captain Sewell goes out in the boat.
   The boat is large. . . . .
   . . . .

2. There is a winch on the boat.
   The winch is electric. . . . .
   . . . .

3. The winch pulls up the lobster trap.
   The lobster trap is heavy.
   The winch is powerful. . . . .
   . . . .

4. Captain Sewell takes the lobster from the trap.
   The lobster is live. . . . .
   . . . .

5. She uses meat or fish heads to catch the lobster.
   The meat is old.
   The fish heads are smelly. . . . .
   . . . .
   . . . .

6. She then drops the trap back to the bottom.
   The trap is baited.
   The bottom is rocky. . . . .
   . . . .

7. The lobster smells the bait in the trap.
   The lobster is greedy.
   The bait smells delicious. . . . .
   . . . .

8. The lobster crawls into the trap and eats the bait.
   The lobster is hungry.
   The trap is open.
   The bait appears appetizing. . . . .
   . . . .
   . . . .

9. However, the lobster cannot crawl out of the passage in the trap.

   The lobster is well-fed.

   The passage is one-way. . . . .

   . . . .

   . . . .

10. The captain sells the lobster, and it becomes a dinner.

    The captain is enterprising.

    The lobster was large.

    The dinner is excellent.

    It is a seafood dinner. . . . .

    . . . .

    . . . .

COMBINING WITH ADVERBS

An **adverb** is a word used to modify a verb, an adjective, or another adverb.

EXAMPLES   Linda walked slowly up the hill.   (modifies verb)

She was unusually tired.   (modifies adjective)

Linda plays tennis very well.   (modifies adverb)

In combining with adverbs, you can use the same procedure that you use with adjectives. However, it is not always necessary to put the adverbs next to the words they modify. They may be placed where they are most effective.

EXERCISE B.   Combine each of the following groups of sentences by writing one complete sentence on the lines provided. Follow the example given. (Correct answers may vary. Add 20 points for each correct sentence.)

EX. Carlos came from Puerto Rico.

Carlos came here.

He came recently.   *Carlos recently came here from Puerto Rico.*

1. Carlos speaks two languages.

   He speaks them well. . . . .

   . . . .

2. He listens when his mother speaks Spanish.

   He listens very carefully. . . . .

   . . . .

3. In school Carlos speaks English.

   He speaks English daily. ....

   ....

4. Carlos has been teaching English to his grandmother.

   He has been doing this lately. ....

   ....

5. Speaking two or more languages is a valuable skill.

   Speaking languages fluently is valuable.

   It is extremely valuable. ....

   ....

   ....

Combining with Prepositional Phrases

The preposition and its noun or pronoun together are called a **prepositional phrase.**

EXAMPLES   She put the car in the garage.   (modifies a verb)

Jim has a horse with long ears.   (modifies a noun)

Prepositional phrases are useful because whole groups of words can be used as a single part of speech. If the phrase modifies a noun or pronoun, it is called an **adjective phrase.** If it modifies a verb, adjective, or adverb, it is called an **adverb phrase.**

It is just as possible to combine sentences with adjective and adverb prepositional phrases as it is with adjectives and adverbs.

EXAMPLE   Jim bought a dog.

He bought it after school.

It is a dog with black and white spots.

After school, Jim bought a dog with black and white spots.

When you are combining sentences with prepositional phrases, be sure to insert adjective phrases as close as possible to the words they modify. With adverb phrases, as with adverbs, you can use your judgment. They often fit well at the beginning of the sentence.

EXERCISE. Combine each of the following groups of sentences by writing one complete sentence on the lines provided. (Correct answers may vary. Add 10 points for each correct sentence.)

1. Marguerite lives on a ranch.

   The ranch is in Colorado. . . . .

   . . . .

2. Marguerite's father inherited the ranch.

   He inherited it from his grandfather. . . . .

   . . . .

3. Marguerite's father raises sheep.

   He raises them on the ranch. . . . .

   . . . .

4. The sheep eat grass.

   The grass is on the foothills.

   The sheep eat the grass in summer. . . . .

   . . . .

   . . . .

5. The sheepherders are from the Basque region.

   The Basque region is in Spain. . . . .

   . . . .

6. Marguerite likes to help the herders.

   She helps them with the baby lambs. . . . .

   . . . .

7. Sometimes the weather is very cold.

   It is cold in the mountains.

   It is cold at lambing time. . . . .

   . . . .

   . . . .

8. Unless the lamb stays with its mother, it will die.

   It will die during the first few days after birth.

   It will die from starvation. . . . .

   . . . .

   . . . .

9. Marguerite rides her horse.

   She rides it around the ranch.

   She rides it on errands. . . . .

   . . . .

   . . . .

10. Marguerite goes to school.

    She goes after breakfast.

    She goes by bus.

    She goes to school in a nearby town. . . . .

    . . . .

    . . . .

Combining with Compound Subjects and Compound Verbs

COMPOUND SUBJECTS

When two (or more) connected subjects in a sentence have the same verb, the two (or more) of them together are called a **compound subject.** Compound subjects are connected by *and, or, both . . . and, either . . . or,* or *neither . . . nor.* These words are called **conjunctions.** It is important to decide which conjunction or pair of conjunctions makes the most sense when you are writing a sentence with a compound subject. You must also be careful that the verb agrees with the compound subject.

EXAMPLES   Hank <u>or</u> Eric <u>knows</u> the combination for this lock.

(Singular subjects joined by *or* take a singular verb.)

Hank <u>and</u> Eric <u>know</u> the combination for this lock.

(Subjects joined by *and* take a plural verb.)

Singular subjects joined by *either . . . or* or *neither . . . nor* take a singular verb. Subjects joined by *both . . . and* take a plural verb.

These two sentences can be combined by using a compound subject:

EXAMPLE   Travis went water-skiing on Mobile Bay.
His sister went too.

There are two equally good ways to combine these sentences:

Travis <u>and</u> his sister went water-skiing on Mobile bay.

or

<u>Both</u> Travis <u>and</u> his sister went water-skiing on Mobile Bay.

When there are more than two parts to a compound subject, commas can be substituted for all but the last connecting word.

EXAMPLE   Bob likes soccer better than football.
Johann likes it better too.
So do I.

Bob<u>,</u> Johann<u>, and</u> I like soccer better than football.

COMPOUND VERBS

When two (or more) connected verbs in a sentence have the same subject, the two (or more) of them together are called a **compound verb.**

EXAMPLE   Nick hit a line drive to left field.
He dashed for first base.

Nick hit a line drive to left field and dashed for first base.

To make compound verbs, you use the same connecting words that you use to make compound subjects. You can also use the word *but*.

EXAMPLE   Allison ran well at the start of the race.
She grew tired near the finish line.

Allison ran well at the start of the race but grew tired near the finish line.

EXERCISE. Combine each of the following groups of sentences by writing one sentence with a compound subject, compound verb, or both compound subject and verb on the lines provided. (Add 20 points for each correct answer.)

1. Marcie has red hair.

   Joan has red hair. ....

   ....

2. The shop sells bicycles.

   The shop repairs bicycles. ....

   ....

3. Hurricanes cause severe damage.

   Tornadoes cause severe damage.

   Blizzards cause severe damage. ....

   ....

   ....

4. Armand might bring the canoe down to the lake.

   Paul might bring the canoe down to the lake. ....

   ....

   ....

5. Bianca wants to become a musician.

   Linda wants to become a musician.

   They have been studying music at school. ....

   ....

   ....

Combining Sentences into Compound Sentences

Often, two short sentences can be combined in a compound sentence. A **compound sentence** consists of two or more simple sentences usually joined by a conjunction.

> EXAMPLE   We picked wildflowers on our hike.
> Margaret arranged them in a beautiful bouquet.
>
> We picked wildflowers on our hike, and Margaret arranged them in a beautiful bouquet.

When you combine short sentences into a compound sentence, you use a conjunctions and place a comma before the conjunction.

The conjunctions for compound sentences are *and*, *but*, and *or*. Each conjunction gives the combined sentence a different meaning. Be sure to use the word that best shows the relationship between the parts of the sentence.

> EXAMPLE   Kevin is not very heavy.
> He is the best football player on the team.

There is a contrast between the two ideas; therefore *but* is the best conjunction.

> Kevin is not very heavy, but he is the best football player on the team.

Remember the rule about commas in compound sentences. Use a comma before *and*, *but*, or *or* when it joins the parts of a compound sentence.

EXERCISE. Combine each pair of sentences by writing one compound sentence on the lines provided. Add commas where necessary. (Correct answers may vary. Add 10 points for each correct sentence.)

1. Climates vary in the United States.

   Different plants grow in each climate. . . . .

   . . . .

   . . . .

2. Some plants thrive in hot and humid weather.

   Other varieties prefer a cooler, drier climate. . . . .

   . . . .

   . . . .

3. Gardeners plant tulip bulbs in the early fall.

   In the early spring small sprouts appear. ....

   ....

   ....

4. Pine trees can grow almost anywhere.

   Varieties of these evergreens fill the forests of North America. ......

   ....

   ....

5. The loblolly pine is a familiar sight in the South.

   In the North, other types of pine are more common. ....

   ....

   ....

6. Keep the Norfolk Island pine near sunlight.

   This unusual house plant will wither. ....

   ....

   ....

7. Cactus fruits are berries.

   The larger ones are sometimes edible. ....

   ....

   ....

8. Rain forests thrive in tropical weather.

   Not all rain forests are in the Tropics. ....

   ....

   ....

9. Marigolds might have bright orange flowers.

   They might have yellow flowers instead. ....

   ....

   ....

10. A day-lily blossom usually lasts only twenty-four hours.

    Most lily blossoms last more than a day. ....

    ....

Combining Sentences with Other Conjunctions

There are many other conjunctions besides *and, but,* and *or* that can be used to combine ideas in a single sentence. In this lesson, you will learn about five of these conjunctions: *after, as, until, if,* and *because.* Each of these conjunctions shows a different relationship between two ideas in a sentence.

EXAMPLE   The Spanish-American War was declared.
An American ship had been destroyed.

No words have to be left out in combining these two sentences, but the correct conjunction has to be chosen to indicate their relationship.

After an American ship had been destroyed, the Spanish-American War was declared. *(After* is the right choice because we want to show the order in which these two events occurred.)

Study the following examples. Note how the relationship between the ideas is expressed by the conjunctions.

EXAMPLES   As the rain began to fall, we got out our umbrellas.

Ginny had to wear a life jacket on the boat until she learned how to swim well.

Enrique will win the spelling contest if he can spell *pneumatic.*

Because we were late, we missed the movie.

Note where a comma is used in the examples above. When sentences begin with *after, as, until, if,* and *because,* use a comma to separate the introductory words from the rest of the sentence.

EXAMPLES   Until the parade starts, fireworks are not allowed.
Because we needed the exercise, we jogged around the park.

EXERCISE. Combine each pair of sentences by writing one complete sentence using *after, as, until, if,* or *because.* Add commas where necessary. (Correct answers may vary. Add 10 points for each correct sentence.)

1. There are different seasons.

   The earth tilts as it spins around the sun. . . . .

   . . . .

2. Some problems are solved.

   Solar energy will heat this house. . . . .

   . . . .

3. You stand on the moon at night.
   You can read a book by "earthlight." ....

   ....

4. We saw outlines of animals.
   We were looking at the stars. ....

   ....

5. No one knew what was under Venus' clouds.
   A recent space probe solved the mystery. ....

   ....

   ....

6. Every day, newspapers showed the barren Venusian landscape.
   The space probe sent back pictures. ....

   ....

   ....

7. A spaceship tried to land on Jupiter.
   It might crash because of the force of gravity. ....

   ....

   ....

8. Astronomers search the solar system.
   They make new discoveries nearly every day. ....

   ....

   ....

9. Halley's comet reappeared in 1986.
   Scientists discovered new information. ....

   ....

   ....

10. Scientists depend on mechanical space probes.
    Space flights can take many, many years. ....

    ....

    ....

More Conjunctions

In this lesson, you will combine sentences by using the conjunctions *although, before, so that, when,* and *while*. Each of these words has a different meaning, so you must choose the word which makes the clearest connection between two ideas.

EXAMPLE   The temperature is very hot.
The breeze keeps us comfortable.

<u>Although</u> the temperature is very hot, the breeze keeps us comfortable. (*Although* shows that there is a contrast between two facts.)

Study the following examples. Note how the relationship between the ideas is expressed by the conjunctions.

EXAMPLES   The snowstorm began <u>before</u> we arrived home.

Maureen worked after school <u>so that</u> she could earn money.

<u>When</u> Martin visited Canada, he learned some French.

<u>While</u> you are peeling potatoes, I will start the fire.

Notice where a comma is used in the preceding examples. When a sentence begins with *although, before, so that, when,* or *while,* use a comma to separate the introductory words from the rest of the sentence.

EXAMPLE   Before the referee arrived, angry players argued.

EXERCISE. Combine each pair of sentences by writing one complete sentence using *although, before, so that, when,* or *while*. (Correct answers may vary. Add 10 points for each correct answer.)

1. Andy works in Washington, D.C.

   He spends much time in South America on business. . . . .
   . . . .
   . . . .

2. Julie's parents went to the sales convention.

   Julie went with them. . . . .
   . . . .
   . . . .

3. Rachel decided to take the course.

   She could learn Spanish. . . . .

   . . . .

   . . . .

4. They arrived at the mountain camp.

   They had to climb over two mountains. . . . .

   . . . .

   . . . .

5. The United States is over two hundred years old.

   Many Europeans think of it as a young country. . . . .

   . . . .

   . . . .

6. Jason walked up the steep streets.

   He had to take deep breaths. . . . .

   . . . .

   . . . .

7. The light bulb was invented.

   Homes used hundreds of candles each year. . . . .

   . . . .

   . . . .

8. We were on our way down the mountain.

   Felice spotted a beautiful waterfall. . . . .

   . . . .

   . . . .

9. Tony's family visited the Gold Museum.

   They could see many treasures. . . . .

   . . . .

   . . . .

10. Brilliant fireworks lit up the sky.

    The band played "The Star-Spangled Banner." . . . .

    . . . .

    . . . .

Review of Sentence Combining

Here are two paragraphs to help you review what you have learned about sentence combining. The sentences in each paragraph are short and choppy, and they do not show the relationships among the ideas in the paragraph. Rewrite each paragraph, combining sentences with the methods you learned in this chapter. You will need to leave out unnecessary words and do some rearranging to make the paragraphs read smoothly. Do not be afraid to make the changes you think are necessary, but do not leave out any ideas. Do not hurry to get through.

EXERCISE A. Rewrite the following paragraph.

Benita Begay is a Navajo Indian. She is a young Navajo. She lives in a house. It is near Kirtland, New Mexico. She lives there with her family. Benita's favorite pastime is soccer. She often plays soccer at home with her brothers and sisters. Benita wants to play professional soccer. It is necessary for her to practice dribbling, passing, and shooting every day.

. . . .
. . . .
. . . .
. . . .
. . . .
. . . .
. . . .
. . . .
. . . .
. . . .
. . . .
. . . .
. . . .

EXERCISE B. Rewrite the following paragraph.

Richard likes to go fishing. He fishes in Lake Michigan. For bait, he finds worms. He finds several. He finds them in the vacant lot. This lot is beside his house. He usually fishes from the dock. The dock is next to the steel mill. He fishes very early in the morning. His friends never catch a thing there. Richard can catch at least six perch. He can do this every time. Richard's father sometimes fishes with him. Richard's father tells stories about catfish. The catfish are in the Mississippi River.

CHAPTER 13

Composition

As you develop the skills discussed in this chapter, you will have a chance to apply what you have learned in previous chapters about writing clear, correct sentences. Clarity and correctness are basic to good writing.

Equally important, however, is the ability to make what you say interesting and effective. Effective writing requires careful planning and organization. An organized plan is often called a *process*. The *writing process* consists of prewriting, writing, revising, proofreading, and preparing the final version.

Prewriting is all the thinking you do when you are not actually expressing your ideas in sentences and paragraphs. Most prewriting will occur before you begin your first draft; however, you will be using prewriting skills throughout the writing process. These skills include: determining your purpose, identifying your audience, gathering information, choosing a limited subject, and ordering your facts and ideas.

Writing the first draft will require your using punctuation, grammar, and usage to create sentences and paragraphs that express your ideas clearly. During this stage you will write your statement of purpose and develop it through the introduction, body, and conclusion of your composition. (If you are writing a paragraph, you will write your topic sentence and develop it with supporting sentences.)

Revising means looking back over your writing to make sure that your sentences and your words best express your ideas. At this stage you will also want to check your facts to be certain that they are correct and are organized to support your ideas clearly.

Proofreading is the stage in which you search through your composition for mistakes in grammar, usage, and mechanics (spelling, punctuation, and capitalization) and make corrections.

Preparing the Final Version completes the writing process. In this step you will prepare a clean copy of your composition according to correct manuscript form and your teacher's directions.

Although the writing process has five separate stages, you will move back and forth among these stages whenever you are writing. By carefully applying the skills you learn in the writing process, you will be able to organize and present your ideas effectively in a written composition.

What Is a Paragraph?

A *paragraph* is a series of sentences that present and develop one main idea about a topic.

That word *one* is important. A good paragraph presents just *one* main idea, not several. The paragraph that follows below is a poor one precisely because it contains too many different ideas, each of which might be developed in a separate paragraph. In the first sentence, the paragraph seems to be starting out to tell how the books are arranged in the school library, but then the paragraph goes off in different directions.

THE BOOKS IN THE LIBRARY

The books in the school library are arranged by subject. Some public libraries in large cities have many branches. In the little town in Arizona where my aunt lives, there is no public library at all. Once a week a truck called a bookmobile arrives from Phoenix, loaded with books. In the summers, my aunt comes home to Milwaukee, where she grew up.

A good paragraph presents one main idea and *develops* this idea. It takes several steps to develop a roll of film, and it also takes several sentences to develop an idea.

None of the one-sentence "paragraphs" in the following example is really a paragraph at all—none says enough to *develop* an idea. (Notice, however, that the second, third, and fourth sentences all help to explain, or develop, the idea presented in the first sentence. Put together in one paragraph, the four sentences would make an acceptable paragraph.)

USING COLOR EFFECTIVELY

When you decorate a room, it is advisable to plan the color scheme carefully in advance.

A chair covered in purple is not likely to look like much beside that bright green couch that seemed so handsome by itself.

On the other hand, too many browns or grays make a room lifeless and uninteresting, even though they all go well together.

The colors that you choose for your room should fit well together, but they should also have enough variety to give life and interest.

EXERCISE. Two groups of sentences follow. Decide which group below you think is *not* a good paragraph, and write an X on the line next to the word group. If the group of sentences is a good paragraph, leave the line blank.

SURPRISES

1. . . . . Everybody at our house loves surprises. Sometimes we make up our own, instead of waiting for something to happen. For instance, my brother Tom wanted to surprise us at Easter. Instead of buying toy bunnies, he bought our family real ones. Everyone was delighted.

HOLIDAYS

2. . . . . Most people wait for holidays to come. Each week there is something that is interesting for us to do at our house. Sometimes it is just a special chore, but sometimes it is getting ready for a friend's visit. July Fourth is fun because of the firecrackers. Actually, I am hoping for a visit from someone interesting right now. In the summer the buses get very hot. That is why we like to travel around Christmastime.

Note: Following the lessons that include writing assignments in this chapter, you will find specific directions and hints about using the writing process. Many of these directions and hints will apply to all writing assignments. Consequently, before you begin doing the exercises in this lesson, look through the rest of the chapter to pick up helpful tips that you can start using right away.

The Topic Sentence

The topic of a paragraph is stated in one sentence in the paragraph. This sentence is called the <u>**topic sentence.**</u>

The topic sentence is one of the signs of a well-written, well-organized paragraph. Usually the topic sentence is placed first in a paragraph so that the reader will know at once what idea the paragraph is going to present and develop. The topic sentence in the following short paragraph is printed in red. Notice how the remaining sentences help to explain this main idea.

DAWN

Dawn comes slowly over the ocean. At first, while it is still night, the sky and sea are both equally dark. Then gradually the sky becomes transparent, as if the gray light were leaking through a sieve, but the sea remains as dark as night. As light fills the sky, the waves begin to sparkle. At last you see the sun rising slowly and majestically over the rim of water. A new day has dawned.

EXERCISE A. In each of the following paragraphs, the topic sentence is in italics. Among the other sentences in each paragraph is one that does not belong there. Find and underline the sentence that does not help to develop the main idea in the topic sentence.

1. *Automobile racing officially began in 1906 with the first Grand Prix race held by the Automobile Club of France.* Within a short period of time, the sport became so popular that other countries in Europe began their own Grand Prix races. Another internationally popular sport is skiing. The principal teams competing in Grand Prix races were usually owned by large, established automobile companies. Among these were the Alfa Romeo team and the Mercedes-Benz team. The Ferrari team was one of the few independently owned teams. Today, Grand Prix teams tend to be smaller and more independent of automobile companies.

2. *The general direction of weather movement is from west to east.* New Yorkers can be reasonably sure that the weather in Chicago today will have moved on to the East Coast by tomorrow. The change is not always in a straight line, of course. Since many weather systems rotate, winds from the north or the south may cause extreme changes. It often gets very hot in Texas.

Nevertheless, New Yorkers may be sure that the weather over Europe is of less interest than the weather over North Dakota.

3. *Reading can be a profitable occupation, or it can be a waste of time.* We can read for pleasure and derive a lively sense of reward from our book, or we can read merely to escape from the world, in which case we are likely neither to enjoy what we read nor to forget successfully the world around us. Under such circumstances a book becomes nothing but a time-killing device. Many new books have appeared in bookstores in recent days.

EXERCISE B. In paragraph 1, find and underline the topic sentence. Read paragraphs 2 and 3 carefully, and then circle a suitable topic sentence in the list provided after each paragraph. Remember that the topic sentence should state the main idea, developed in the paragraph.

1. It was a remote and beautiful island. Hundreds of kilometers south and east lay Tahiti, from which the steamer came once a month with supplies and mail. Out of the South Pacific, the island rose straight and high, like a castle, and its cliffs were draped with waterfalls. Wild goats on the crags and small pigs in the forest furnished most of the island's meat.

2. The old-fashioned diving suit, with its great weight and its attached air and safety lines, severely limited the exploring that divers could do under water. Today, however, equipped only with a tank of oxygen and a pair of flippers on their feet, adventurous divers can move freely at depths as great as 60 meters. With a small submarine, people have descended nearly five kilometers, to the deepest underwater regions known on earth.

A. Exploring underwater has never been very safe.
B. Improvements in underwater equipment have enabled us to dive deeper than ever before.
C. People enjoy diving beneath the water.

3. The grizzly is the only other large meat-eating animal that is almost the size of the giant Alaska brown bear. The brown bear's claw marks have been measured four meters up a tree, high enough to reach into a second-story bedroom window. Its neck alone may be 150 centimeters around. A full-grown male weighs close to 480 kilograms, and a few specimens have been taken that weighed nearly a metric ton.

A. The grizzly bear is a big, tough, meat-eating animal that roams the wastes of Alaska and Canada.
B. No one wants to play around with bears.
C. The Alaska brown bear is the largest meat eater in the world.

Choosing a Subject

To write a satisfactory paragraph or a composition of any length, you must first choose a subject in which you are interested and about which you know something, either from firsthand experience or from information gained through reading, talking with others, etc. Otherwise, your chances of producing a satisfactory piece of writing are slight. What, for example, do you think is wrong with the following paragraph?

Baseball has a long history. It has been a popular game for over eighty years, and during that time there have been important changes in the rules of the game. Crowds have grown larger. More cities have major league teams now than ever before. Houston has the Astrodome, a stadium with a roof. During the past eighty years there have been many great players. They have been noted for different achievements. Some of them have set records which have stood for many years.

This paragraph is very dull because the writer has offered only a series of general statements, none of which tell readers anything they did not already know. There are no specific details. The subject is too large to treat in one paragraph. Each of the supporting sentences could become the topic for a paragraph or even for a longer composition. When you write anything you expect others to read, remember that readers expect something from you. It may be information, a fresh viewpoint, or even entertainment. Communicate your interest. Almost any subject can be made interesting to others if you are interested in it yourself.

1. Choose a subject about which you know something from firsthand knowledge or experience.

Here are a few very general subjects, each of which might offer many good subjects for a paragraph. In how many of these areas do you have some special interest? The answer may surprise you!

GENERAL SUBJECTS
hobbies	cooking	fashions	history	art
literature	music	mythology	sports	travel

All of these subjects are, of course, too big, too general for a short composition. Within each subject, however, you can find many limited subjects, or topics, about which you may have the kind of knowledge and experience that will enable you to write an interesting and informative paragraph. For example, do you ski or go trout fishing or collect all-time baseball records? Do you play a musical instrument? Have you visited one of the historic battlefields of the American Revolution or the Civil War? When you ask yourself questions like these about any general subject, you are taking the next big step in planning a composition.

2. Limit your subject so that it can be treated adequately within the limits of your composition.

When your readers finish reading something that you have written, they want to feel that you have adequately covered your topic. They should not be left with the feeling that you have overlooked some aspects of your topic. In planning a paragraph, you need to limit your subject to a topic that could be properly developed in four or five sentences.

Suppose, for example, that you are planning a paragraph about hobbies. This large, general subject contains many limited subjects that might be suitable for a paragraph. By asking yourself questions, you can limit the subject to a topic for a paragraph.

1. What hobbies have I had experience with?
2. What one hobby do I know most about?
3. What was my most successful hobby project?

With each question, you limit your subject further until finally you reach one that you can present adequately within a paragraph. Because you will write from your own special knowledge and experience, you have a good chance of holding the interest of your readers and telling them some things they may not have known before—of keeping your end of the writer-reader agreement.

GENERAL SUBJECT	hobbies
LIMITED SUBJECTS	photography, model-making, gardening, stamp collecting
MORE LIMITED SUBJECTS	train models, ship models, model airplanes
TOPIC FOR A PARAGRAPH	building a model schooner

Here is the one-paragraph composition that might be written on this limited subject. Notice the italicized topic sentence, which states the main idea that the paragraph is going to develop about its topic.

BUILDING A MODEL SCHOONER

Using a plastic model kit, you can build a realistic scale model of one of the classic American schooners, perhaps even the America *itself.* The kit will provide all the main parts of the ship, a detailed diagram for assembling them, and the special cement needed to hold the plastic parts together. You will furnish thread for the rigging, model paint, and the patient hours of enjoyment that will be needed to build your model. You will have to follow the diagram to the last detail. For the beginner, the nine sails, ranging from the big and billowing mainsail on the mainmast to the little fore gaff-topsail on the foremast, may be a problem. Rigging the ship—putting on the yards of thread that represent the lines and cables of the original schooner—also requires nimble fingers. When the last tiny knot is tied, however, and the ship is painted to your taste, you will have a handsome and satsifying trophy for your efforts.

In the process you will have learned a surprising lot about one of the great sailing ships.

EXERCISE A. In each of the following sets of subjects, all but one are too broad to be treated in a single paragraph. Check the one subject in each group that you think might be a good one for a paragraph. Be ready to discuss your reasons for choosing it.

1.

.... A. The first television show broadcast via satellite

.... B. A history of television

.... C. The American broadcasting industry today

2.

.... A. Making a movie

.... B. A movie star's life

.... C. The brightest new star in movies

.... D. How cable television has changed the movie industry

3.

.... A. The smaller animals of North America

.... B. A chipmunk's nest

.... C. American rodents

.... D. Varieties of squirrels

4.

.... A. The benefits of sports

.... B. Swimming long distances

.... C. Our team's best game this season

5.

.... A. Popular singers of today

.... B. Building a record collection

.... C. Rock music instruments

6.

.... A. The purpose of a school newspaper

.... B. After-school activities

.... C. Getting the most out of school

.... D. Organizing a school glee club

.... E. Our school sports program

7.

.... A. The modern Olympic Games

.... B. Winter sports

.... C. How a ski jumper prepares to jump

.... D. Olympic record holders

8.

.... A. Cities of Europe

.... B. The European city I would most like to visit

.... C. Career opportunities in the field of travel and transportation

EXERCISE B. For each of the following general subjects, list three limited subjects, or topics, that would be suitable for a one-paragraph composition. Compare your lists with those of your classmates, and see if they agree with your choices.

Family activities: 1. .... 2. ....

.... 3. ....

City activities: 1. .... 2. ....

.... 3. ....

Musical instruments: 1. .... 2. ....

.... 3. ....

Reading for pleasure: 1. .... 2. ....

.... 3. ....

Conserving energy: 1. .... 2. ....

.... 3. ....

WRITING ASSIGNMENT. Choose one of the suitable paragraph topics from Exercise B, and develop it into a paragraph. If none of the topics interests you, choose another one.

Prewriting. Be sure you choose a topic about which you know something. Brainstorm (think about the topic and write down ideas as they come to you) to gather ideas about your topic. Then, select three or four of those ideas that directly relate to the topic.

Writing. Write your topic sentence at the beginning of the paragraph. Write a sentence for each of the ideas that relates to the topic. Use transitional words and expressions, where appropriate, to link these sentences.

Revising. Reread your paragraph. Ask yourself questions such as the following ones: Is the topic limited enough for the paragraph? Does the topic sentence state the main idea about the topic? Do the other sentences develop the main idea? Are these sentences linked with transitional expressions, where appropriate?

Below is a sample revised paragraph to help you recognize how to revise your own writing.

Attics can be full of fascinating things. I know ours is. One day *when* my parents were away from home, I spent the whole day in our attic looking at *old* things. I found *funny* old magazines, some books my parents had when they were children, and even some old furniture. There were boxes full of *long old-fashioned* dresses, hats, and *delicate-faced china* dolls that Mom and Dad had saved from a long time ago. I had such a good time looking at things, that I didn't even realize it when they came home.

The next time I have a chance, I'm going to spend another day in the attic.

Proofreading. Use a blank sheet of paper to cover the lines below the one you are proofreading. Check each line for errors in usage, capitalization, punctuation, and spelling. Use a dictionary to help you with the spelling.

Preparing the Final Version. Here are several manuscript guidelines that are widely used and accepted: (A *manuscript* is any word-processed, typewritten, or handwritten paper as distinguished from a document printed on a printing press.)

1. Use lined composition paper or, if you type, white 8½ × 11-inch paper.

2. Write on only one side of a sheet of paper.

3. Write in blue, black, or blue-black ink, or typewrite.

4. Leave a margin of about two inches at the top of a page and margins of about one inch at the sides and the bottom. The left-hand margin must be straight; the right-hand margin should be as straight as possible.

5. Always follow your teacher's instructions for any particular guidelines, such as where to place your name, the class, the date, and the title of your manuscript.

238

Selecting Your Ideas

You are now acquainted with the importance of choosing a subject that you know something about and then limiting it for a paragraph. If you choose your subject carefully, you will probably know a good deal about it and will easily be able to find any additional information you may need. But, once you have your limited subject, how do you select the details for it? First, decide what the *purpose* of your paragraph will be, and then decide which points or facts will best express that purpose to your readers.

1. **Decide on the purpose of your paragraph.**
2. **Makes notes on the points you want to cover in your paragraph.**

When you have determined your purpose, jot down a few brief notes on the ideas you have. This will help you spot points that do not belong in your paragraph because they are not part of the purpose, or main idea, that you want to develop. Since the notes are for your own use, they can be brief, sometimes just a word or two for a point.

If, for example, you are planning to describe an acting class at the local center, you might list points like these in your notes.

1. location of class
2. time of class
3. teacher's name
4. teacher's background
5. size of class
6. background of students
7. the thrill of acting
8. stage exercises

All of these notes are part of your knowledge of the class, and they could be part of a description of the class. However, if you are limiting your composition to one paragraph, you cannot possibly include all of them. You must eliminate those points that are not essential to your purpose. For example, if your purpose is to give essential information about the acting class, you would leave out points 7 and 8.

Sometimes, the ideas you jot down may cause you to change your purpose. You may even find it better to jot down the ideas about your topic *before* you have clearly determined your purpose. If you do, you may find that the ideas themselves will suggest a purpose to you.

In writing about the acting class, your purpose may be to *inform* your readers, giving them important facts. Or it might be to get your readers to *share your feelings and ideas* about the class.

Your purpose in writing determines your choice of points to cover and the emphasis you will give to each. Your enjoyment of certain exercises, for example, might not be important in an informative account of the class, but it could have a lot to do with how you feel about the class.

Let's suppose that you are writing a one-paragraph description of the acting class. Your purpose is to give essential information to readers who have little or no knowledge of the class, and your personal feelings will not be so important. For this purpose, the list of facts that you already have is about right—minus points 7 and 8.

Here is a paragraph written with the purpose of giving information. Notice that the first few sentences arouse the reader's interest, the topic sentence occurs near the beginning of the paragraph, and the rest of the sentences follow in a logical order.

ACTING AT THE CENTER

Have you wanted to play Long John Silver? Was the role of Eliza Doolittle written just for you? Would you be perfect for a part in *Our Town*? Well, aspiring actors take note. *The local youth center offers a class in acting techniques on Saturday afternoons.* The class is taught by Glenda Perkins, a director who has had shows both on and off Broadway. Ms. Perkins has studied with Lee Strasberg at the Actor's Studio in New York, and she emphasizes method acting in her classes. In order to ensure that each student will receive individual attention, the classes are limited to fifteen students. Ms. Perkins has said that prospective students do not need any previous experience. In fact, she prefers to train them from scratch.

With a different purpose, you might use the same basic points as the paragraph above, but they would not have the same importance. Suppose, for example, that your main purpose is to arouse interest in the class. Most of the facts about the class would still be there, but the emphasis would be different in order to create the feeling of excitement for your readers.

ACTING AT THE CENTER

It is Saturday, early afternoon. A group of teen-agers sit on a bare stage. Their eyes are closed. The lights are dim. The voice of Glenda Perkins drones softly in the background. All attention is focused on the voice. She creates a scene—a beach in May. The young actors are to remember such a scene from their own experiences. They are to recall not only the setting but also the way they felt at the time. They are to come in contact with their feelings. *This is a stage exercise for method acting during a drama class at the youth center.*

Notice that in this paragraph the italicized sentence at the end gives the main idea and serves as a topic sentence. The writer holds off the main point in order to arouse the interest of readers and hold their attention.

EXERCISE. Listed below are six topics suitable for one-paragraph compositions. Each is followed by a list of points that might be used in developing the topic, but one of these points is less important or less closely related than the others and should be omitted. Read each group carefully, and decide which

240

point to omit. Place a check in the space to the left of the point that should be eliminated.

1. How to be a good baby sitter
.... A. Take along something to do
.... B. Don't eat or use anything without permission
.... C. Have a number to call in case of emergency
.... D. How much fun it is to telephone friends!
.... E. If you use the television, keep the volume down

2. Taking care of a pet
.... A. The kind of food it needs
.... B. What animals make good pets
.... C. How often it should be fed
.... D. How often the pet needs to be cleaned

3. Training to be a gymnast
.... A. Disciplining the body through exercise
.... B. Famous gymnasts
.... C. Eating a proper diet
.... D. Developing new skills slowly
.... E. Working out on the parallel bars

4. Improving your stamp collection
.... A. Knowing which stamps are most valuable
.... B. Knowing people to trade with
.... C. Learning about the printing of stamps
.... D. Specializing in the stamps of one country

5. First steps in skiing
.... A. Reading about champion skiers
.... B. Getting the feel of wearing skis
.... C. Controlling your movements
.... D. Choosing the right equipment
.... E. Learning the snowplow

6. Our city's recreation facilities
.... A. Parks and bridle paths

.... B. Beaches and swimming pools

.... C. Stadiums and sports arenas

.... D. Concert halls, auditoriums, and theaters

.... E. Bus terminals, train stations, and airports

WRITING ASSIGNMENT. Choose one of the topics from the exercise, and develop it into a paragraph. If none of the topics in the exercise appeals to you, choose one of your own or one from the following list. When you have finished the paragraph, give it a title that will arouse the interest of your readers.

PARAGRAPH TOPICS

1. Foreign foods I have liked
2. An unusual pet
3. A secret ambition
4. My favorite comic strip
5. Learning to ride a horse
6. Building a cabinet
7. My favorite music group
8. Playing a guitar
9. Why I like camping
10. Why I'm glad I'm a Scorpio (Cancer, Aquarius, etc.)

Prewriting. Once you have selected your topic, decide on your purpose. Are you going to explain your topic to your audience, or are you going to describe how you feel about your topic? Then, make a list of details that are related to your topic and are appropriate for your purpose.

Writing. Depending on the purpose of your paragraph, you may decide to begin your paragraph with a topic sentence or place the topic sentence at the end of the paragraph. Be sure that your other sentences develop or lead up to the main idea of the topic sentence.

Revising. With your teacher's permission, exchange papers with classmates to find out whether they can spot any inappropriate or unrelated ideas and whether you can spot any in theirs.

Proofreading. As in revising, it is often useful to have someone else look over your paper to help spot mistakes you miss.

Preparing the Final Version. Write legibly and neatly. If you are typing, do not strike over letters or cross out words.

Writing a Good Beginning

How a paragraph begins is important. You cannot force your readers to read what you have written. You must persuade them by showing them right at the beginning that there is some reason for them to go on. For this reason, the beginnings of paragraphs are worth a little extra attention on your part, and the same thing is even truer of longer compositions.

How can you persuade readers to go on with your paragraph? Very often, the best way of doing this is simply to tell them in the first sentence what the main idea about your topic is going to be. This is why many paragraphs, and particularly those meant to inform, begin with the topic sentence, which states the main idea of the paragraph.

When the purpose of your paragraph is to inform, the topic sentence often makes the strongest paragraph opening.

EXAMPLES   One day, high-frequency sound waves may be used to perform many common household tasks.

Modern rockets are based on principles of jet propulsion discovered by the Chinese more than a thousand years ago.

What are considered good manners in one country may be bad manners in another.

Quite often, the topic sentence reveals the writer's attitude—or purpose in writing—as well as the topic. If your topic sentence shows that you are strongly against something that the readers are strongly in favor of, they may read no further. On the other hand, a challenging topic sentence may arouse readers to go on, if only so that they can prove that you are wrong.

EXAMPLES   Over the years, our school's athletic program has been destroyed, bit by bit, by the indifference of the students and the penny-pinching of the school board.

The so-called sport of boxing, which has improved little since the days of the Romans, should be prohibited by law.

The following paragraph opens with the topic sentence, which is printed in italics. Notice the two functions of the topic sentence here: It states the main idea of the paragraph, and it suggests the writer's purpose (to explain).

Every piece of clothing worn by the cowhand of the old West had a thoroughly practical purpose. The heavy silk bandanna which he wore around his neck, for example, was not simply for decoration. It could be used as a dust mask, a blindfold for a calf, a towel, or a bandage—and it often was. The cowhand's shirt was of cotton and his trousers of heavy denim or some other tough material. His boots were knee high, and the heavy leather leggings that he wore over them served to protect his legs from thorns or rope burns. Spurs at the heels and a revolver on the hip completed the costume.

EXERCISE. In the space provided before each paragraph, write a suitable topic sentence. Your topic sentence should state the main idea of the paragraph and suggest the purpose of the paragraph.

1. . . . .

. . . .

A loaf of bread thrown together without a recipe can be awful. Foolhardy cooks who create bread dough as they go along may find themselves with nothing more than an exceedingly dirty oven or wall to clean after the explosion, and if they are lucky enough to achieve something that pleases the eye, they have no assurance that the taste will be judged as favorably.

2. . . . .

. . . .

At times the cars are so crowded that you stand no chance of getting a seat. In fact, that's just what you do—stand. The straps to hang on to are almost impossible to reach, especially if you are not above average height. Holding on doesn't really matter though. During rush hours, the trains are so tightly packed that you couldn't possibly fall down. Indeed, by the time you get to where you are going in the morning, you are often so tired you just want to go home. But you don't. That would mean you would have to get back on the subway.

WRITING ASSIGNMENT. Choose one of the topics from the list below, and develop it into a paragraph. If none of the topics in the exercise appeals to you, choose one of your own. When you have finished the paragraph, give it a title that will arouse the interest of your readers.

PARAGRAPH TOPICS

1. The seasons in our part of the country
2. The architecture of the buildings in our town
3. The different musical tastes in my family
4. My favorite holiday
5. The sounds of the night

Prewriting. Once you have selected your topic, decide on your purpose. Are you going to explain your topic to your audience, or are you going to describe how you feel about your topic? Then, make a list of details that are related to your topic and are appropriate for your purpose.

Writing. Write an effective topic sentence as the first sentence of your paragraph. Then write a sentence for each of the related ideas.

Revising. Reread your paragraph several times. Examine each sentence to make sure that it presents necessary information and sticks to your topic.

Proofreading. If you can, put your paragraph away for a day or so before you proofread it. Doing that will give you a chance to spot mistakes more easily.

Preparing a Clean Copy. Prepare a clean copy. Make sure you make the changes marked on your proofread copy. Then check your final copy for any new errors. Hand in a clean copy.

Supporting Your Ideas

When you have chosen a topic and limited it to the points that can be covered in one paragraph, you are ready to begin writing. The idea that you want to write about may be true and important, but that, by itself, is not enough. You must present your idea in such a way that your readers can see its truth and importance for themselves. When your purpose is to give information or to persuade someone to accept your viewpoint, there are three main ways of supporting your ideas.

Support your ideas by giving details, reasons, or examples.

Suppose you are writing about hiking trips near your home. You might support your main idea—that hikers should be cautious in the woods—with details, reasons, or examples.

DETAILS

Even short hikes in the woods can be dangerous. Unfamiliar terrain often hides crevices, rock faults, and cliffs with dense undergrowth. There are usually no guideposts, and forest trails can become an erratic, confusing maze. Dense, rocky, or wooded areas can also hide snakes. The wise hiker will take care to examine the terrain carefully and keep on the lookout for danger.

In this paragraph, details are used to expand the main idea. Each sentence adds another detail explaining why hikes can be dangerous. After all the details are given, a conclusion is drawn in the last sentence.

REASONS

Even short hikes in the woods can be dangerous. Many hikers are inexperienced and are not likely to recognize loose or unreliable rock formations on hillsides. Many hikers also have a hard time telling a dangerous snake, like a rattlesnake, from a harmless one. Only with experience or training will a hiker realize that a rock pile or a woodpile makes a perfect hiding place for a dangerous snake. It is important to be very cautious and very alert, even on short hikes.

This paragraph gives reasons telling *why* the woods can be dangerous rather then details showing *how* the woods can be dangerous. Reasons help to support a topic sentence. Details, on the other hand, help to expand a topic sentence and to make it clearer to the reader.

Even short hikes in the woods can be dangerous. We once stopped the car and walked off a short distance into a nearby woods and found ourselves lost. We became confused because nothing looked familiar and the sun was hidden by clouds. When I tried to climb up on a rocky hill to look around, I knocked out some stones and startled two gopher snakes. I was scared silly. I thought for sure they were rattlers, and I lost my balance and fell. Luckily I only sprained my ankle, but it took us two hours to find our way back to the car.

This paragraph gives an example. An example is an important fact or event that explains your topic sentence. The example in this paragraph tells "what happened to me once" to explain how hiking can be dangerous even on a short hike near home.

DETAILS, REASONS, AND EXAMPLES TOGETHER

Even short hikes in the woods can be dangerous. Unfamiliar terrain often hides crevices, rock faults, and cliffs with dense undergrowth. Any dense, rocky, or wooded area can also harbor snakes. Many inexperienced hikers have a hard time telling a dangerous snake from a harmless one. Once, for example, I tried to climb up on a rocky hill to look around, and I knocked out some stones and startled two gopher snakes. I was scared silly. I thought for sure they were rattlers, and I lost my balance and fell. When a hiker is unfamiliar with the terrain in a local woods, serious problems can result.

Mixing details, reasons, and examples is the way writers develop many of their paragraphs. In this paragraph, the second and third sentences are from the paragraph that was developed by using details. The fourth sentence comes from the paragraph developed by using reasons. And the next three sentences come from the paragraph developed by using examples.

EXERCISE A. Underline the topic sentence of each of the three following paragraphs. In the space next to each paragraph, tell whether the topic sentence is supported by details, reasons, or examples.

1. . . . . Morrisville is a very small town with only one main family. There is a single gas station, and it is operated by Jim Morris. The only other store in town is the grocery, which Bill Morris runs. Some of the fresh vegetables come from Fred and Wilma Morris' farm. The eight school-aged children take the bus every day to school in another town. Five of them are named Morris, like most of the folks in town. The Morrises settled this town in the last century. Today it is the smallest town in the state.

2. . . . . One should not always believe what people say about friends. Someone told me that Sheila had become unfriendly and would not

talk to anyone these days. But I remembered when Sheila was very talkative. So, when I saw Sheila, I asked her how she was doing. She wasn't stuck-up at all. She told me she was worried about her mother, who was going into the hospital. Then I realized that her worry had made her seem quiet and unfriendly.

3. . . . . If I had my choice, I would want to live in the country. The air in the country is much cleaner than in the city. The noises of the country are more gentle, more natural, and more soothing than the noises of the city. In the country you can find a swimming hole when it is hot or a skating pond when it is cold. There is always some place to explore, and I love to watch birds building nests or squirrels gathering acorns.

EXERCISE B.   Under each topic sentence, write a list of details, examples, or reasons that will support the topic.

1. Topic sentence: Every school newspaper has certain obligations it must meet.
   A. . . . .
   B. . . . .
   C. . . . .
   D. . . . .

2. Topic sentence: Being a good student is more than just getting grades.
   A. . . . .
   B. . . . .
   C. . . . .
   D. . . . .

3. Topic sentence: Planning a weekend hike can be very complicated
   A. . . . .
   B. . . . .
   C. . . . .
   D. . . . .

WRITING ASSIGNMENT.   Choose one of the following topic sentences to develop your own paragraph. Make an outline. Then, write the paragraph. (Depending on which list you choose your topic sentence from, you will develop your paragraph with details, reasons, or examples.)

DETAILS   1. My first visit to a baseball park was unforgettable.
2. A good swimming stroke is made in one fluid motion.
3. No game has a quicker pace than hockey.

248

REASONS	1. America's national pastime should be football rather than baseball.
	2. Sports are growing in popularity across the country.
	3. Many people like to keep fit by playing sports.
EXAMPLES	1. People in my family love to watch football.
	2. Most of the excitement during a game can happen in the stands.
	3. I know some people who are totally devoted to sports.

Prewriting. To generate ideas about your topic, try asking the *5 W-How?* questions: *Who? What? When? Where? Why? How?* For example, if your topic were *my first visit to a baseball park was unforgettable,* your questions might consist of the following ones: *When was the game? Where was it? Who was there? What happened in the game?*

Writing. Some writers find it useful to say their ideas out loud and then copy down what they have said. Write complete sentences, and try to make them as correct as possible, but remember: this is only your first draft. The important thing at this stage is to get your ideas clearly stated in writing. You will be going back over your paragraph during the next two stages of the writing process to make corrections and improvements.

Revising. When you read your paragraph, be critical. Ask yourself: Do these ideas make sense? Could someone who is not as familiar as I am with these ideas understand what I have written? Could I choose any better words to make my paragraph clearer? Have I left out any information?

Proofreading. Check your capital letters to make sure that they cannot be mistaken for lowercase letters.

Preparing the Final Version. Be sure you have written on your paper your paragraph's title, your name, and any other information required by your teacher.

Coherence in Paragraphs

A paragraph may have several details, reasons, or examples, and it is important to arrange them in a logical order. For example, a paragraph about how to shape and smooth wood with a drawknife will begin by telling you how to hold the instrument before explaining how to pull the blade. Paragraphs that are logically arranged are called *coherent* paragraphs.

Sentences in a paragraph can be arranged according to order of importance or chronological order (the order of time).

To hold a reader's interest, arrange the sentences in a paragraph in their order of importance, leading up to the most important detail, reason, or example—the one that readers are most likely to remember.

EXAMPLE We students should get involved with the political campaign this year. Working together for a candidate can build friendship and trust. It can teach us how the political process works. It can show us the meaning of democracy and the responsibilities of citizenship.

This writer gives three reasons, in their order of importance, for working in a political campaign. Building "friendship and trust" is one important reason. Learning "how the political process works" is another, more important reason. Discovering "the meaning of democracy and the responsibilities of citizenship," however, is the most important reason of all. It comes last in the paragraph.

Chronological order (the order of time) is another effective way of organizing the details in a paragraph. This is the order used in telling a story—what happened first, second, and so on.

EXAMPLE On Monday, everything went wrong, I woke up late because my little sister forgot to set the alarm. On my way to school, three letters dropped out of my bookbag and into a puddle. During art class, an easel fell over and wrecked my wire sculpture. As if all of this were not enough, at dinner Monday night my father told the family that, effective immediately, the television set would stay off until grades on our school work improved.

This writer has arranged the paragraph in chronological order, from early Monday morning to Monday evening. Chronological order is also helpful when explaining how to make or do something. It tells the reader exactly what to do first, what to do second, and so on.

EXERCISE. Decide whether the following groups of sentences should be arranged in *chronological order* or in *order of importance* (from least to most important). Then indicate the best order by writing the number 1, 2, or 3 in the space to the left of each sentence.

1.

.... Swing your right leg over the saddle of the bicycle.

.... Place your left foot on the left pedal of the bicycle.

.... Ride off on your bicycle

2.

.... People vote for the Presidential ticket on the first Tuesday in November.

.... The major parties select their candidates for President and Vice-President in the summer preceding the election.

.... The President of the United States is inaugurated in January.

3.

.... The colonies won their independence from Great Britain.

.... The settlers gradually spread westward from the sea coast.

.... The first American colonists settled along the Atlantic coast.

4.

.... When she was young, Elizabeth Blackwell taught school.

.... Blackwell was the first woman to receive a medical degree in America.

.... Blackwell established the New York Infirmary for Women and Children.

WRITING ASSIGNMENT. Choose one of the topics below (or one from the exercise), and develop it into a paragraph.

PARAGRAPH TOPICS

1. How to water-ski, wash a car, plan a meal, organize a picnic, prepare a homework assignment, study for a test, or do anything else that requires practice or special skill
2. Losing and finding a pet
3. First impressions of a new neighbor
4. Eating a meal in a restaurant (at home or in the school cafeteria)
5. The worst day in the week (for you)

Prewriting. Gather ideas for your topic by brainstorming or by asking the 5 W-How? questions. Then look over your ideas carefully, and select three or four that relate directly to your topic.

Next, decide whether you will use chronological order or order of importance. Put the ideas into this order. Finally, write a topic sentence that expresses your main idea about the topic and suggests the purpose of your paragraph.

Writing. Use your plan (topic sentence and list of related ideas) to help you write your first draft. First, write the topic sentence. Then, write a sentence for each of the related ideas. If any other ideas occur to you as you write your paragraph, pause to think about whether or not they will improve your paragraph. If they will, include them where they logically fit.

Revising. Check that your topic sentence expresses your main idea about the topic and that the other sentences develop the main idea.

Proofreading. Check your paragraph for sentence fragments and run-on sentences. Also proofread for usage and mechanics.

Preparing the Final Version. Be sure that you have made all the changes indicated on your proofread copy and that the final version is neat and free of errors.

Using Transitional Expressions

<u>Transitional expressions</u> **are words or phrases that show how an idea is related to other ideas in the paragraph.**

The topic sentence gives us the main idea of the paragraph. The rest of the sentences support that idea and take us further toward fully understanding it. A smooth and well-written paragraph, however, needs more than a string of sentences. Transitional expressions make good connectors between ideas. In the following examples, the first paragraph has no transitional words or phrases. The second paragraph has the transitional words and phrases underlined for comparison.

NO TRANSITIONS   Waiting is one of the hardest things to do. Watching for the next car or the next person to come around the corner is as frustrating as waiting for water to boil. It can be made enjoyable. Try watching other people as you wait. Imagine stories about them. Imagine them as characters in a play. Imagine what it would be like to talk to them. You will find the time passes quickly.

TRANSITIONS   Waiting is one of the hardest things to do. Watching for the next car or the next person to come around the corner is as frustrating as waiting for water to boil. <u>However</u>, it can be made enjoyable. Try watching other people as you wait. Imagine stories about them. See them, <u>perhaps</u>, as characters in a play. <u>Even</u> imagine what it would be like to talk with them. <u>As a result</u>, you will find the time passes quickly.

The transitional words and expressions are usually very short. They rarely add much information to your topic, but they can point out relationships and distinctions. Words such as *but, instead,* and *because* establish clear relationships between the elements of the paragraph.

Some of the most common transitional expressions are as follows:

however	although	on the other hand	also
too	nonetheless	therefore	finally
for instance	eventually	soon	as a result

One problem with transitional expressions is that they can be overused. A paragraph overladen with transitional words can be as difficult to read as one with no transitions.

EXERCISE A. In the following paragraph, the transitional expressions have been left out. Supply them in the blanks provided. Use the above list if you need to.

The magician Harry Houdini, was a magnificent performer on the stage;

.... he also wanted to prevent people from believing too much in magic. He devoted time, ..., to a study of fortune-tellers and miracle workers. .... he was able to show that most of these operators were fakes. He demonstrated .... that they were cheating people out of money. .... he exposed the fakers by publishing all of his findings.

EXERCISE B. The following sentences can form a good paragraph if they are reorganized. Look for the topic sentence of the paragraph; then rewrite the paragraph using at least three transitional expressions to show the relationships between the sentences.

It changed its shape every day, and this fact was thought to be very important.

The moon could do things no other light in the sky could do.

People used to worship the moon.

It did not appear in the sky at all on some evenings.

They thought it had special powers.

WRITING ASSIGNMENT. Use the following informal paragraph outline or one of your own to write a paragraph in which transitional expressions help connect the sentences. Underline the transitional expressions in the paragraph you write.

TOPIC   Preparing for a test
  1. Setting aside a time and place
  2. Gathering materials—textbooks, notes, papers, etc.
  3. Reviewing notes and other materials

Prewriting. As you organize your facts and ideas, pay close attention to how they are related. Do ideas follow one another in order of time? If so, use transitional expressions that show chronological order. Are facts and ideas linked together by cause and effect? If so, plan for transitions that show cause and result. Does an idea summarize facts and information? If so, plan a transition to indicate where the summary begins.

Writing. Most transitions require careful placement in the sentence. Be sure that your transitions clearly show the relationship(s) you are trying to express.

Revising. As you look over your paragraph, be sure you have included all the information needed to establish similarities, differences, and other relationships among your facts and ideas.

Proofreading. In addition to careful placement, transitions also require careful punctuation. Refer to the sections in your text dealing with parenthetical expressions, introductory clauses and phrases, connectives, and other lessons on comma usage.

Preparing the Final Version. Whenever you have more than one page, number all pages after the first one. Page numbers are usually placed in the center of the top line or in the upper right-hand corner. Number your pages according to your teacher's instructions.

Effective Conclusions

The word *conclusion* has two separate meanings, but both apply to the kind of conclusion we are concerned with in a paragraph or composition. On the one hand, a conclusion is whatever comes at the end—for example, the last, or concluding, sentence of a paragraph. But a conclusion is also an idea that we arrive at through careful thinking, an idea that takes account of all the steps in our reasoning. The conclusion of a paragraph should pull together the ideas presented earlier and leave the readers with the important point that you want them to remember.

The concluding sentence may be used to summarize or restate the paragraph's main idea.

The conclusion may restate in a different and more forceful way what has already been said in the topic sentence. More often, however, it will connect the topic with one or more of the important details presented in the paragraph. Notice the conclusion of the following paragraph.

TRAFFIC LIGHTS FOR SAFETY

At least two more traffic lights should be installed along East Main Street. The new Eastgate Shopping Center has attracted more traffic to that end of town than ever before, and traffic is especially heavy during the time when students are going to school. Since East Main passes just one block away from Harvey School, many students must cross it despite the heavy traffic. We will have a serious accident some day unless the city makes it easier to cross East Main. *For the protection of Harvey students, traffic lights should be installed on East Main at both Ninth and Fifteenth Streets.*

The paragraph is developed by giving reasons that support the idea stated in the topic sentence—reasons for installing new traffic lights on East Main Street. Notice that the italicized conclusion repeats the topic sentence, but it adds two points not found at the beginning of the paragraph: (1) The conclusion adds the most important of all the reasons that have been given for the traffic lights (''for the protection of Harvey students''); and (2) it makes the main idea of the paragraph more definite—it suggests not just two traffic lights but traffic lights at two particular places, Ninth and Fifteenth Streets.

There are probably as many ways of concluding a paragraph as there are paragraphs. Many paragraphs can benefit from a definite conclusion of some kind, especially paragraphs that present information or try to persuade readers to accept the writer's ideas. Without a concluding statement, the paragraph may simply trail off, leaving readers wondering what the point of it has been.

GOOD MANNERS

Good manners are a kind of social lubricant. Machinery requires lubrication to operate smoothly, and in the same way people who work together need good manners to help them get along. Good manners make difficult situations easier, especially when people who disagree or do not like each other must get along well whether they want to or not.

This paragraph is left hanging. It needs another sentence to act as a conclusion, to tell readers when the writer is through expressing opinions, and to remind readers what the point of the paragraph is.

When the topic sentence is placed at the end of the paragraph, it serves also as the conclusion of the paragraph.

THE BEST SEASONS OF THE YEAR

Some people like skiing and tobogganing, and some people like swimming and camping out. I belong in this last group. For me, swimming and tennis and camping out are the best sports of all. As I see it, winter is just a time to get through as quickly as possible, so that I can begin my favorite activities again. *That's why, so far as I'm concerned, summer is the best season of the year*.

In a paragraph as short and simple as this one, there is really no need for separate topic and concluding sentences. Although the topic sentence is at the end, the paragraph has a definite, strong opening. It starts in at once with the writer's reasons for liking summer better than winter. Since most people are interested in sports, this makes an effective paragraph opening.

Do not change the topic in the concluding sentence.

Notice how the last sentence weakens the effect of this paragraph.

WALKING IN THE RAIN

I love to walk in the rain. I can recommend it to anyone. Some people think I am crazy when I tell them this, but they don't know what they are missing. If you wear the right clothing, you can stay completely dry and comfortable, and see how different the world looks in the rain. *Walking in the country along back roads is also a delight.*

Disorganized conclusions are a sure mark of bad writing, for they cause a paragraph to lose its effectiveness. In this paragraph, after talking about walking in the rain, the writer has, in the last sentence, switched to a different topic. This leaves readers wondering what main idea the writer wanted to convey. Did the writer mean that walking in the rain is pleasant and that walking in the country, rain or shine, is pleasant also? Because the writer did not clearly conclude the main idea, the paragraph is not effective.

EXERCISE. In the space provided after each paragraph, write a suitable concluding sentence. Try to make your concluding sentence restate the idea in the topic sentence in a more effective way. In some paragraphs, you should build into the conclusion the most important supporting detail in the paragraph. Be careful, however, not to introduce any completely new material in your concluding sentences.

1.   Fine gardens take work. The most beautiful garden in our neighborhood belongs to Ms. O'Toole. She grows more different kinds of flowers than I have seen together anywhere except in parks. But she spends all her spare time working on her garden. As soon as she gets home from work, she goes out and works on her flowers. You could even say she was a slave to her garden.

Conclusion: ....

....

2.   Some people say they are afraid to fly in airplanes. They aren't afraid to take long trips in their cars, however. The truth is that many more people are injured in automobile accidents than in airplane crashes. Cars are much more dangerous than airplanes. No matter how careful drivers are, they can't protect themselves against the carelessness of strangers who may come speeding out of a side road at them.

Conclusion: ....

....

3.   It's hard to imagine today what our country looked like two hundred years ago. All of Indiana and Ohio were covered by forest, and in the great plains there were millions of acres of grass and gigantic herds of buffalo. Whole forests of huge pine trees which had taken centuries to grow were cut down in twenty or thirty years and can never be replaced.

Conclusion: ....

....

4.   Not many people realize how fast scientists have learned about the world we live in. Even though some basic discoveries were made long ago, most of our present scientific knowledge has been gathered during the twentieth century. It was only about a hundred years ago that doctors learned about disease-causing germs, and modern methods of cancer research could not have been imagined fifty years ago.

Conclusion: ....

....

WRITING ASSIGNMENT. You should now be prepared to write a well-developed, coherent paragraph with an interesting opening and an effective conclusion. Keeping in mind all of the suggestions given so far in this chapter, choose one of the topics below, and write a paragraph of several sentences on it. Remember that if the topic seems to you to be too broad, you must narrow it down to a more workable size. If none of these topics interests you, pick one that does. It should be something with which you have had some experience or of which you have acquired some knowledge.

PARAGRAPH TOPICS

1. One way for students to earn money
2. Getting acquainted in a completely new neighborhood
3. The thrill of long-distance running
4. The advantages of a particular hobby
5. What causes people, once friends, to stop liking each other

Prewriting. Once you have selected your topic, decide on the purpose for your paragraph. Gather ideas for your topic and purpose. Select those ideas that best relate to your topic and purpose. Then, put them in the most effective order for your paragraph. Next, write a topic sentence that expresses your main idea and that suggests the purpose of your paragraph.

Writing. Use your working plan (your topic sentence and list of details) to help you write your first draft. End the paragraph with a conclusion that is appropriate for your topic, purpose, and audience. Try writing a few before you decide on one.

Revising. Check to see that your topic sentence directly states your main idea, that the other sentences develop the main idea and are linked with transitional expressions, where appropriate, and that the concluding sentence restates or summarizes the main idea about the topic.

Proofreading. Proofread your paragraph for punctuation, capitalization, spelling, and sentence structure.

Preparing the Final Version. Copy your proofread copy, making all the changes indicated. If you must erase, do so neatly. If you type, do not strike over any letters or cross out any words. Reread your final version to make sure that you have not made any new errors. If you have, correct these neatly before handing in your paper.

Writing a Narrative Paragraph

The narrative paragraph tells a story or relates a series of events.

A narrative paragraph tells us *what happened*. The narrative paragraph supports its main idea with an account of events or things that have happened. Examples of narratives include the following incidents: When you tell how you get up every morning and get ready for school, when you tell how your family took a cross-country trip, or when you tell about how your best friend broke a leg. If something really unusual happens one morning, your narrative might be more interesting for the surprise event.

The opening statement of a narrative paragraph should arouse the interest of the reader. If you were to begin a narrative paragraph by writing "There is a deep mystery about the house on the hill," your readers would want to know about the house—what it looks like and who lives there. If you were to begin a narrative paragraph by writing "The last time I rode my bike down to the mall, I wound up being the hero of the day," your readers would want to know exactly what happened and why you became the hero of the day. Whether you are writing about events, about people, or about yourself, begin the narrative paragraph with a clear statement that will get your reader's attention.

Model Narrative Paragraph

DISCOVERING CARLSBAD CAVERNS

Story Begins

Details: What Happened When

One afternoon in late summer, some seventy years ago, a lone cowboy slowly loped across a Western prairie looking for strays. Suddenly he pulled back on the reins. In the distance he could see a cloud of heavy black smoke belching from a low-lying range of hills in the nearby Guadalupes. The cowboy touched spurs to his mount and headed in the direction of this peculiar phenomenon. As he approached the eerie spectacle he could see the mouth of a yawning pit; his ears caught the ceaseless beat of countless wings. The "black smoke" turned out be a tremendous flight of bats, pouring out of a cave. The cowboy watched the flight emerge for three hours, and when it had ended, he built a great bonfire, dropped flaming torches into the cave and saw them vanish into the darkness hundreds of feet below. He had discovered Carlsbad Caverns, an astonishing underground world hidden deep beneath the scorching desert of New Mexico.[1]

The Story Ends

[1] From "Nature's Big Tunnel in the Guadalupes" by Henry N. Ferguson. Originally published in *Gracious Living,* 1976. Reprinted by permission of Doris C. Ferguson.

This writer begins with the simple but effective opening: "One afternoon in late summer, . . ." It works. It tells us a story is coming and sets the time. The rest of the sentence establishes background, or why the cowboy was in the desert. A strong opening sentence can make the rest of the narrative flow smoothly.

A narrative should include these important facts:

1. Time. Ask yourself, *"When did this happen?"*
2. Place. Ask yourself, *"Where did this happen?"*
3. People. Ask yourself, *"Who was involved?"*
4. What happened. Ask yourself, *"What happened first? second? etc."*

Notice how the model narrative paragraph answers each one of these questions.

Paragraph Checklist. When you write your narrative paragraph, keep these points in mind:

Write a topic sentence that tells what your story is about.
Begin the story right away.
Focus on action.
Follow events as they happened.
Write a strong ending. Be sure you have told the whole story.

WRITING ASSIGNMENT. Write a narrative paragraph (150–200 words). Tell about something interesting that happened to you recently, or choose one of the topics below:

1. What you did at home last weekend
2. What made you late for school once
3. How you once helped a friend
4. The most frightening thing that ever happened to you
5. How you learned to swim (skate, dance, etc.)

Prewriting. To generate facts and ideas for a narrative paragraph, you need to ask *What happened?* When you have listed several specific items, stop and see how they are related. Will your narrative aim to entertain, to make a point, or both? When you answer this question, you will have the purpose of your paragraph. Make sure that all your facts and details help achieve your purpose; also fill in any additional information needed to tie together what you already have. Organize your information in an outline.

Writing. Present your facts to unfold the event or incident in a logical, interesting series of actions. Generally, narratives are best told in chronological order, ending with the climax.

Revising. Be sure that the sequence of actions is linked together with the right transitions. Make certain that no actions are out of place or unrelated to other actions in your narrative.

Proofreading and Preparing the Final Version. As with all other assignments, carefully check your paper for spelling, usage, and punctuation errors. During the revision and proofreading stages, you probably made a number of changes on your paper. If so, neatly recopy your paragraph before handing it in.

Writing a Descriptive Paragraph

The descriptive paragraph appeals to the senses of sight, sound, touch, taste, and smell.

A descriptive paragraph is full of sense appeal. It includes accurate details that give the reader an exact impression of an object, a person, a place, or an event. In other words, the aim of a descriptive paragraph is to make the reader see, hear, touch, taste, or smell what you, the writer, are trying to describe. If, for example, you are describing a walk on a freezing winter day, you will want the reader to feel the icy, crisp air, to see the mounds of snow piled deep beside the sidewalk, or to hear the wind as it blows through the trees. If, by contrast, you are describing a hot summer day, you will want the reader to feel the blistering sun's heat, to see children playing in a park, or to hear a panting, long-haired dog. Details in a descriptive paragraph come from close observation and a precise choice of words.

Good description relies on specific verbs, nouns, and adjectives that convey an exact sense of action. For example, the verb *amble* is more specific than the verb *walk,* since *amble* means "to walk in a leisurely way." The more specific your nouns are, the better. Instead of saying "the man," say "Lena's father," "the sergeant," or "Mr. Alverio." Specific adjectives are also important. Imprecise adjectives, such as "large," "amazing," "fantastic," "sensational," "important," can sometimes dull the effect of writing.

Model Descriptive Paragraph

AN EVENING AT MY UNCLE'S

Details:
Sight

    I can remember the bare wooden stairway in my uncle's house and the turn to the left above the landing, and the rafters and the slanting roof over my bed, and the squares of moonlight on the floor and the white cold world of snow outside, seen through the

Sound
Touch

curtainless window. I can remember the howling of the wind and the quaking of the house on stormy nights, and how snug and cozy one felt under the blankets, listening; and how the powdery snow

Sight

used to sift in around the sashes and lie in little ridges on the floor, and make the place look chilly in the morning and curb the wild desire to get up—in case there was any. I can remember how very dark that room was in the dark of the moon, and how packed it was

Sound
Atmosphere

with ghostly stillness when one woke up by accident away in the night, and forgotten sins came flocking out of the secret chambers of the memory and wanted a hearing; and how ill chosen the time seemed for this kind of business and how dismal was the hoo-hooing of the owl and the wailing of the wolf, sent mourning by on the night wind.[1]

[1] From *Mark Twain's Autobiography*, Volume One, by Mark Twain. Copyright 1924 by Clara Gabrilowitsch. Reprinted by permission of Harper & Row, Publishers, Inc.

In the model paragraph, Mark Twain describes a room in which he spent some cold evenings. He focuses on the appearance of the room, including its darkness. When he speaks of its darkness, he introduces the different sounds he heard. That, in turn, suggests what feelings he had in the room, and he describes them. He pays attention to details: the slant of the rafters, the "squares of moonlight" on the floor, the quaking of the house. It is almost as if we are there, too. Good description gives clear details that help the readers visualize the scene.

Paragraph Checklist. When you write a descriptive paragraph, keep these points in mind:

The topic sentence tells what you are describing.
Use specific verbs, nouns, and adjectives. Choose your words carefully.
Focus on one sense, such as sight, but include others as well.

WRITING ASSIGNMENT. Write a descriptive paragraph (150–200 words). Describe something or someone you know very well, or choose one of the following topics:

1. The room in your house where you spend the most time
2. The best-dressed person you know
3. The place where you and your friends meet
4. The most spectacular view you've ever seen
5. Your street at night

Prewriting. Think carefully about the person, place, or thing you will describe. List as many concrete and sensory details as you can. Decide on your main impression, and select the appropriate details from your list. Arrange the details in a logical order. Write a topic sentence that expresses the main idea about your topic.

Writing. Use your prewriting notes to guide you in your writing. Begin your paragraph with your topic sentence. Be sure to use vivid verbs, nouns, and adjectives as you write.

Revising. Check to see that your topic sentence conveys a main impression about your topic. Check that your details support the main impression and that they are arranged in a logical order. Be sure that you have used vivid verbs, nouns, and adjectives.

Proofreading and Writing the Final Version. Proofread for usage, capitalization, punctuation, and spelling. Eliminate any fragments or run-ons. Prepare a clean copy, making sure that you make all the changes indicated on your proofread copy.

Writing an Expository Paragraph

The expository paragraph explains how something works, how to do something, or why something happens.

An expository paragraph gives information. It may explain how an electric motor works, how to build a tree fort, or why bicycling is good exercise. Because the expository paragraph can do so much, it is probably the most important kind of paragraph you will write.

One of the most reliable ways of developing a good expository paragraph is to give important details that develop the main idea about your topic. Another way is to give reasons that support your main idea. A third method is to give an example—such as a personal experience—that can explain your topic very easily. A good expository paragraph may often have some details, some reasons, and some examples all working together.

Often, the best way to start an expository paragraph is by writing a topic sentence that clearly states your main idea and suggests the purpose of the paragraph.

Model Expository Paragraphs

WOODS FOR CARVING

The most common softwoods are balsa, basswood, sugar pine, white pine, buckeye, poplar, and butternut. Balsa is unique because you can dent it with your finger. The two other softest woods are basswood and sugar pine; they will not take a good polish but are fine for things that are to be painted or do not need a high finish. The rest of the softwoods will take almost as good a finish as the hardwoods. White pine must be of what is called "clear-select" or best quality, for the hard, dark streaks and knots in the other grades would spoil the appearance of most projects and be a nuisance to the carver.[1]

BLACK HOLES

Scientists are reasonably sure that strange phenomena called "black holes" exist in space. Black holes occur when a star begins to "die" or lose its energy. Without energy, the star cannot expand; powerful gravity in the star thus begins to pull and pull at all of the star's matter until this matter becomes compressed into an immeasurably small space. Even light cannot escape the irresistible tug of gravity in a collapsed star. Because all light is trapped inside, the former star becomes a black hole in space. Scientists are fearful that any object passing near a black hole would also disappear into its unknown depths.

[1] From *How to Make Whirligigs and Whimmy Diddles and Other American Folkcraft Objects,* by Florence H. Pettit. Copyright © 1972 by Florence H. Pettit. Reprinted by permission of Florence H. Pettit.

Paragraph Checklist. When you write an expository paragraph, keep these points in mind:

Write a topic sentence that states the main idea about your topic.

Give details, reasons, or examples to explain and support the main idea in your topic sentence.

WRITING ASSIGNMENT. Write an expository paragraph of 150–200 words. Choose one of the topics below, or make up one of your own.

1. The best pet
2. The best way to listen to music
3. The best way to learn how to swim
4. How to fix a flat tire (broken skate, shattered vase, etc.)
5. How to study for a test

Prewriting. Be sure to choose a limited topic for a paragraph. Think about your purpose and audience and how they will affect your choice of topic, the details you use, and the language you use. Gather information for your topic, and write a topic sentence that states the main idea about your topic. Make a working outline, or plan (topic sentence and list of related details in the most effective order for the paragraph).

Writing. Use your plan to help you write your first draft.

Revising. Use the following questions to help you revise your draft: (1) Does the topic sentence state the paragraph's main idea clearly and suggest the purpose of the paragraph? (2) Do the details support the main idea? (3) Are there enough details to explain the main idea to your audience? (4) Is the order of the details logical? (5) Is the language appropriate for your audience?

Proofreading and Preparing the Final Version. If possible, put your paragraph aside for a day. This will help you spot mistakes in usage, punctuation, capitalization, and spelling that you might otherwise miss. Then, make a final copy.

Writing a Persuasive Paragraph

A persuasive paragraph presents an argument to convince the reader that an opinion is true or to persuade the reader to do something.

A persuasive paragraph presents an argument.

The argument in a persuasive paragraph is made up of an opinion and the reasons or evidence to support it. It begins with a topic sentence that clearly and precisely states an opinion.

When you choose a topic for your persuasive paragraph, you should keep two things in mind. First, the topic should be one that people have differing opinions about. For example, since most people would agree that "Exercise is healthful," it would not be a good topic. The second thing to keep in mind is that the topic should not just be a matter of personal taste. For example, "Bicycling is the best sport" is a matter of personal taste and not suitable for a persuasive paragraph.

Once you have selected a serious, debatable topic, you need to gather reasons or evidence to support your opinion. You need convincing examples and accurate facts. Two or three strong reasons will support your opinion adequately.

The following persuasive paragraph uses reasons to convince the readers that the school day should not be extended one hour. Notice that the first sentence introduces the writer's opinion and the following sentences provide the reasons and details.

The school day should not be lengthened one hour. A longer school day would present a problem for those students who live far from school and need the time to travel home after school. It is also true that students are only able to handle so much "school" information in a day. At a certain point, they become too exhausted to think. Finally, and most important, lengthening the school day would shorten the time for other activities, such as art, drama, and athletics. Students would be deprived of an important part of their overall education. For these reasons, then, the length of the school day should not be lengthened.

WRITING ASSIGNMENT. Choose one of the following subjects or a subject of your own, and limit it by stating your opinion about it. Then, write a persuasive paragraph that develops an argument supporting your opinion.

1. Nonsmokers' rights
2. Admission fees for museums
3. Dress code for school
4. Allowances
5. Sharing household chores
6. Foreign language requirement in junior high school
7. Record album ratings
8. Extension of school day

Prewriting. Make a list of reasons to support your opinion. Be sure these reasons do not simply restate your opinion. Arrange your reasons in a logical order. You may arrange them with your most important reason last so that it stays in your readers' minds, or first, so that it catches your readers' attention.

Writing. Be careful that you do not word your opinions as facts and your facts as opinions. The verbs *should, ought to,* and *can* are used to express opinions. Adjectives that state judgments, like *good, bad,* and *worst,* also express opinions. If additional reasons come to you as you are writing, pause to determine if they will provide convincing reasons for your argument. If they will, include them where they logically fit.

Revising. Ask yourself the following questions to help you revise your persuasive paragraph: (1) Is the paragraph about a serious, debatable topic? (2) Is the topic limited enough for a paragraph? (3) Is the topic sentence developed with reasons that support the writer's opinion? Are the reasons convincing? (4) Are the reasons arranged in an effective order? (5) Remember that in a persuasive paragraph a logical and reasonable tone is the most convincing way to present your argument. Therefore, make sure that you have avoided name-calling, emotional appeals, and fallacies.

Proofreading and *Preparing the Final Version.* As you reread your paragraph several times, focus each reading on a different aspect, such as spelling, punctuation, or usage. Your final version should be clean, without smudges or extraneous marks on the page, as well as correct and neat.

Writing Friendly Letters

If friends have been away for a while, there is always plenty to talk about when you see them again. You ask where they have been and what they have been doing, and they want to know about your activities, too. This is also the sort of thing that you write about in a friendly letter. A friendly letter takes the place of conversation.

In a friendly letter, write about things that interest you and the person to whom you are writing.

A letter is a special form of writing, in which you will put to work the writing skills that you have been practicing in this chapter. In particular, your letters should be put together in interesting, well-organized paragraphs that do not jump around from topic to topic. Avoid the vague "I am fine, how are you?" kind of letter. Fill out the paragraphs of a friendly letter with definite details, including information about things you have been doing that will be of interest. Ask your friends what they have been doing. Then your friends will enjoy your letter as much as Julie did Sheila's letter.

1743 Brian Avenue
Buffalo, New York 14221
September 30, 1986

Dear Julie,

School started almost a month ago now, but I still can't get used to the idea. It doesn't seem as real to me as camp. And to think that just six weeks ago we were all together enjoying ourselves at a beautiful lake! My mother says I spend too much time daydreaming, but, really, I'm just thinking about us at camp.

Do you remember the cove where we had the picnic that day when it began to rain? For some reason, that's the place I think about most. Next summer, it will be the first place I head for when I get back to camp.

I hope you can visit us during winter vacation. If there's enough snow, we can go skiing, and of course there will be ice-skating and tobogganing. Maybe we can even arrange a sleigh ride. But be prepared for cold weather. We have many days when the temperature stays close to zero, even at noon.

I was so excited when I got your letter that I ran upstairs to show it to Mother. Write me again as soon as you get a chance. And don't forget to make plans for New Year's in Buffalo.

With love,
Sheila

Follow generally accepted rules for the form of a friendly letter.

The rules for the form of a friendly letter are matters of common sense. They are meant to make your letter clear and neat and easier to read.

In general, your letters should be written on white, unruled paper. Write in blue or black ink—not in pencil and not in an odd shade of ink, like red or green. (A typewritten letter is also acceptable, if you type well.) Center the whole letter on the page, with good margins all around. Follow the model letter below for letter form. Notice these points in particular.

1. Heading. Write your address in two lines, with a comma between the city and the state. Leave a little space, and then put your ZIP code number after the state. (See page 277 for additional information on ZIP codes and state codes.) There should be no comma between the state and the ZIP code number. Write the date on the third line, with a comma between the day of the month and the year. Put no punctuation at the ends of these lines. The heading is usually written in *block style,* meaning that the three lines are lined up at the left.

2. Salutation. Leave a little space between the heading and the salutation. Place the salutation at the left margin and put a comma after it.

3. Body. Indent the first line of the letter and of each new paragraph. Other lines should line up evenly with the left margin.

4. Closing. Capitalize the first word only. Begin the closing a little to the right of the center of the page. Put a comma after the closing. For someone whom you do not know very well, *Sincerely yours* is the most usual closing.

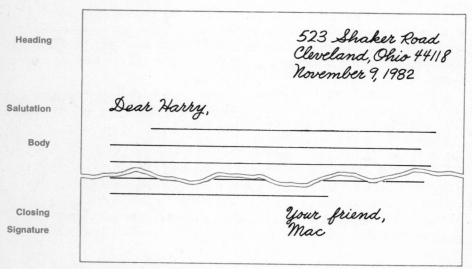

A Model for Friendly Letter Form

Other closings, such as *Love* or *Your friend* are better for close friends.

5. Signature. Line up your signature with the closing. If your name is short, it may be centered under the closing. It is best to sign your first and last name when you write to someone you do not know well.

6. Envelope. Follow the model below. The return address (your name, street, city, state, and ZIP code) should be in three lines at the upper left-hand corner. A comma is needed between the city and state. (Do not place a comma between the state and the zip code.) Center the address of the person to whom you are writing. Use a title (*Mr., Miss, Mrs., Ms., Dr.,* etc.) here but not in the return address. If it is not known whether a woman is married or single, you may choose to use *Ms.* as the title. Also use *Ms.* if it is known that this is the form of address the woman prefers.

Maxwell Shepherd
523 Shaker Road
Cleveland, Ohio 44118

Mr. Henry Duff
37 Locust Avenue
Lubbock, Texas 79404

A Model Envelope

WRITING ASSIGNMENT. Write a friendly letter, with its envelope, to a friend of yours or a relative. Write neatly in ink on suitable paper, and follow the other rules of form given in this lesson. Organize your letter in well-constructed paragraphs, and check it for errors before handing it in. The following questions may help you to think of interesting details to include.

1. What have you done recently that was unusual and that will interest your friend?
2. Have you read a book or seen a movie that you especially liked?
3. Have there been any odd or amusing incidents, at home or at school, that your friend would like to hear about?
4. Can you give news of other friends of yours that the person you are writing to also knows?

Writing Letters of Appreciation

A letter of appreciation is the special kind of friendly letter that we write when we wish to thank people for a kindness they have done us—for a present, an overnight visit in their home, or a particular favor of some kind. In form, a letter of appreciation is like any other friendly letter. The content of this kind of letter is determined by its purpose.

Follow these suggestions for the content of a letter of appreciation.

1. *Write promptly.* Delay in expressing your thanks for any kindness is discourteous. If someone has sent you a gift, a prompt letter shows that the gift has been received and appreciated.

2. *Write enough.* A letter of appreciation need not be long, but it should be long enough to say what you like about the present or visit and to express a personal interest in the person to whom you are writing.

3. *Be sincere.* No one likes an exaggerated expression of thanks that the writer does not really mean. Often, the best way of expressing your appreciation is to tell the person you are thanking one or two definite things that you like about the gift or about your visit. Like all other writing, a good letter of appreciation is built from clear, definite details.

The following letters of appreciation show how the suggestions above can be applied. The first letter thanks someone for a gift. The second letter (page 273) thanks someone for a visit. After you have stayed for a few days in someone's home, it is a thoughtful gesture to write a personal letter of thanks to your hosts.

27 Lewis Drive
Ogden, Utah 84404
December 29, 1986

Dear Aunt Margaret,

How could you possibly have guessed that a new stamp album was one of the things I'd been hoping to get for Christmas? Dad's been saving the stamps from his foreign mail, and my collection has completely outgrown the old book. I've spent most of my time since Christmas reorganizing my stamps in the new album.

I hope your Christmas has been as pleasant as ours. It's been cold here since the beginning of vacation, and Lonnie and I have gotten in a lot of skating.

Again, thank you for your very thoughtful present.

Sincerely yours,
Waldo

367 River Street
Boston, Massachusetts 02106
August 17, 1986

Dear Mr. and Mrs. Stetson,

I had a wonderful time during my visit. The week in Philadelphia seemed to go by in a flash, with something new and interesting to do every moment. The day I spent at the newspaper office with you, Mrs. Stetson, was extremely interesting. I had never considered being a reporter before, but watching you work made the field seem so exciting that I now think it is what I want to do.

I also want to thank you, Mr. Stetson, for the enjoyable tour of Temple University. I hadn't realized that it was quite so large. The library where you work particularly impressed me.

Mom and Dad tell me that they would be glad to have Marcia come and stay with us. They said they would get tickets to a play, and perhaps we could go to the shore. We might even take a ride up to Salem, the site of the witch trials. They will be writing more about this to you soon.

Sincerely yours,
Debra Timons

WRITING ASSIGNMENT. Write two letters of appreciation, one expressing thanks for a gift, the other for a visit to someone's home. If you wish, you may choose an imaginary situation like the ones listed below and write suitable letters, making up any additional details you may need. Follow the rules for the form of a friendly letter.

1. You have been given a hand-knitted sweater for a birthday present.
2. At Chanukah, you have been given a magic kit by an aunt and uncle whom you seldom see because they live so far away.
3. You have been sick in bed, and some friends have sent you a book which you read with great interest.
4. You went to visit friends in a big city, and they had something new and different planned for you every minute. For three days you were on the go constantly and scarcely had a chance to rest. But it was fun.
5. You have spent a week with a friend whose family has a cabin in the mountains. While you were there, you went fishing in a lake with ice-cold water, you went climbing up mountains, and one morning you got up early to see the dawn on the mountainside.

Writing Business Letters

We often have occasion to write a business letter—to place an order, perhaps, or to request help or information from some organization. Use the business letter below as a model for your own business letters.

Follow generally accepted rules for the form of a business letter.

1. Heading. Write your complete address and the date in three lines. Add commas only between the city and state (with its ZIP code) and between the day of the month and the year.

2. Inside Address. Put the inside address at the left margin. It should include the complete name and address of the person or organization (or both) that you are writing to.

3. Salutation. Notice that in a business letter the salutation is followed by a colon, not a comma. Your letter may be addressed to an individual within a company when the name is known (Dear Mr. Hudson: *or* Dear Ms. Prinz:). Otherwise, address the letter by title only (Sales Department:). If you are writing to a company in general, the traditional salutation is *Gentlemen* or *Dear Sir*. It is understood, of course, that the group you are writing to may be

Heading	41 Ryan Road Augusta, Georgia 30904 February 4, 1981
Inside Address	Durham Crafts Company 33 Lambeth Circle Durham, North Carolina 27705
Salutation	Sales Department:
Body	Please send me, by parcel post, the following items as listed in your latest catalogue:

```
                    1 leather tooling set   $2.25
                   12 lacing needles         1.50
                                            $3.75
         I am enclosing a money order for $3.75, plus 50¢
      to cover postage, a total of $4.25.
```

Closing	Yours truly,
Signature	*Harold Mason* Harold Mason

A Model Business Letter

composed of both men and women. Leave space between the inside address and the salutation.

4. Body. Leave extra space between the salutation and the body of the letter. Notice the indentation for the first line and each new paragraph (5 spaces in a typewritten letter).

5. Closing. Leave space below the body of the letter and begin the closing a little to the right of the center of the page. *Yours truly* or *Very truly yours* (followed by a comma) is the usual closing for a business letter. Only the first word is capitalized.

6. Signature. Write your name clearly. In a typewritten letter, the signature is typed below the written signature.

As you should have noticed, the *form* of a business letter differs from that of a friendly letter in a number of ways. These differences in form reflect differences in content that are even more important.

Follow these suggestions when you write a business letter.

1. *Be brief.* A business firm that does its business through the mail may receive thousands of letters and orders every day. If you clutter up your business letters with unnecessary details or personal comments, your request may be delayed or handled incorrectly.

2. *Be clear and complete.* Give all the necessary information, and arrange it (as in the order letter on page 275) so that it will be easy to follow. Be definite about what you want and whether you are placing an order or merely asking for information.

3. *Be neat.* If your letter is smudgy or messy, full of erasures and crossed-out words, it may not receive the kind of attention you want. Typing is preferred for a business letter, if you type well. This also makes it easy to keep a carbon copy of your letter. (On a carbon copy, the inside address provides a record of the person or organization to whom you wrote.) If your letter is handwritten, it should be in ink, and you should keep a copy or a summary for later reference. Use plain white paper only, preferably 8½ × 11-inch typing paper, whether the letter is typed or handwritten.

Notice how the letter on page 274 carries the various suggestions for business letters that have been made in this lesson.

WRITING ASSIGNMENT. Choose one of the letter ideas in each group, and write the appropriate business letter. Type the letters, or write them in ink, following the suggestions in the lesson. Prepare an envelope for each letter.

REQUEST LETTERS

1. Write to a book publisher asking for a catalogue of books on any subject that interests you.

2. Write to the director of a summer camp asking for information about camp next summer. Ask for definite information, such as dates, costs, transportation to the camp, activities, and special equipment needed.

ORDER LETTERS

1. From a newspaper or magazine, cut out an advertisement for something that you would like to order by mail. Write the letter ordering the merchandise, saying how you will pay for it (money order, C.O.D., etc.) and how you would like it sent. Attach the advertisement to your letter when you hand it in.

2. You have seen an advertisement for a six-foot surplus toboggan, at a price of $24.95 postpaid. Order this from Gateway Service Supply, 1927 Jennings Lane, Evansville, Indiana 47712. Indicate that you are enclosing payment.

The United States Postal Service recommends the use of two-letter codes for states, the District of Columbia, and Puerto Rico. The Service also recommends the use of nine-digit ZIP codes. When including these codes, the address should look like this:

EXAMPLE   Ms. Joanne Beebe
785 West End Ave.
New York, NY 10025–1813

The following is a list of two-letter codes for states, the District of Columbia, and Puerto Rico. Notice that the codes do not include periods.

Alabama AL	Louisiana LA	Ohio OH
Alaska AK	Maine ME	Oklahoma OK
Arizona AZ	Maryland MD	Oregon OR
Arkansas AR	Massachusetts MA	Pennsylvania PA
California CA	Michigan MI	Puerto Rico PR
Colorado CO	Minnesota MN	Rhode Island RI
Connecticut CT	Mississippi MS	South Carolina SC
Delaware DE	Missouri MO	South Dakota SD
District of Columbia DC	Montana MT	Tennessee TN
Florida FL	Nebraska NE	Texas TX
Georgia GA	Nevada NV	Utah UT
Hawaii HI	New Hampshire NH	Vermont VT
Idaho ID	New Jersey NJ	Virginia VA
Illinois IL	New Mexico NM	Washington WA
Indiana IN	New York NY	West Virginia WV
Iowa IA	North Carolina NC	Wisconsin WI
Kansas KS	North Dakota ND	Wyoming WY
Kentucky KY		

INDEX

Action verbs, 45, 46, 47, 51
Address, direct, commas in, 199
  inside, in business letter, 274
Adjective phrases, 63, 67
Adjectives, 29, 33, 51, 63, 151
  combining sentences with, 213
  defined, 23, 29
  proper, 119
Adverb phrases, 65, 67, 139
Adverbs, 29, 33, 51, 65
  combining sentences with, 215
  defined, 27, 29
Agreement, of verbs with subjects, 131,
    133, 137, 139, 143
Alter, altar, 173
Antonyms, 149
Apostrophes, for contractions, 195–96
  don'ts for, 197
  for possession, 193
Appositive phrases, 81–82, 99
Appositives, 81
Articles, defined, 23

Beginning of paragraph, 243–44
Body, in business letter, 274–75
  in friendly letter, 270
Brake, break, 173
Business letter, 274–75

Capital, capitol, 173
Capitals, for calendar items, 117
  for compass directions, 117
  for direct quotations, 199
  for geographical names, 117
  for names of organizations, 115–16
  for names of persons, 115, 119
  for names of products, 116
  for names of races, 117, 119
  for names of regions, 117
  for names of religions, 117, 119
  for names of seasons, 117
  for names of special events, 117
  for proper adjectives, 119
  for references to God, 119
  for school subjects, 119
  for titles, 121
Closing, in business letter, 274–75
  in friendly letter, 270
Coherence, in paragraphs, 250
Combining sentences, *see* Sentence
    combining
Commas, in addresses, 83
  for appositives, 81–82
  in compound sentences, 79
  before conjunction in compound
    sentence, 11
  in dates, 83
  in direct address, 199
  in direct quotation, 199
  for interrupters, 81
  for items in series, 77–78
  in quotations, 199, 201–202
  for separating parts of compound
    verb or subject, 9
Compass directions, capitals for, 117
Complements, 43–44, 45, 47
  defined, 43
  subject, 49, 179, 181

Composition, beginning a, 243
  choosing subject for, 234–35
  concluding a, 256–57
  friendly letter as, 269–70, 272–73
  planning a, 234–35
  rewriting a, 229, 238, 242, 244,
    249, 252, 254, 259, 261, 264,
    266
  See also Paragraphs
Compound sentences, 11, 79, 221
Compound subjects, 9, 43, 143, 177,
  219
Compound verbs, 9, 43, 219–20
Concluding sentence, in a paragraph,
  250, 256–57
Conjunctions, 9, 11, 33, 78, 79, 143
  in combining sentences, 223, 225
  with compound subjects, 219–220
  with compound verbs, 219–220
Context, verbal, 15, 39, 57, 89, 111
Contractions, 139, 141, 195–96
Course, coarse, 173

Dates, commas in, 83
Descriptive paragraph, 263–64
Development of paragraph, 246–47
Dialogue, 201–202
Dictionary, use of, 73, 89
Direct address, commas in, 199
Direct objects, 47, 179
Direct quotations, 199, 201
Don't, doesn't, 141, 195

Either, or, use of, 143
Envelope for letter, 271
Exclamation points, 1–2, 103, 199
Expository paragraph, 265–66

First draft, of composition, 229
Fragments, of sentence, 97–98, 99,
  101, 103, 105, 209
Friendly letter, 269–272

Geographical names, capitals for, 117
Good, well, use of, 52

Heading, in business letter, 274
  in friendly letter, 270
Helping verbs, 5, 26, 46, 155, 156, 157
Here, hear, 173
Here, there, use of, 139
Homophones, 173

Imperative sentences, 7
Indefinite pronouns, 137
Infinitive, 99
Infinitive phrase, as fragment, 101
Inside address, in business letter, 274
Interjections, 33
Interrupters, 81–82
Irregular verbs, 157, 159, 161, 163

Lay, Lie, use of, 165
Letters, of appreciation, 272–73
  business, 274–75
  friendly, 269–272
  order, 276
  request, 275–76
Lie, lay, use of, 165

Linking verbs, 25, 45, 46, 49, 51, 179

Meet, meat, 173
Modifiers, *see* Adjectives; Adverbs

Narrative paragraph, 260–61
Neither, nor, use of, 143
Nouns, 33, 151
 defined, 19
 number in, 131
 plural, 17, 131, 133, 135, 197
 proper, 115–16, 117
 singular, 131, 133, 135
Number, agreement in, between verbs
  and subjects, 131, 133, 135, 137,
  139, 143

Object pronouns, 179, 181
Objects, direct, 47, 179
 of prepositions, 181
Opening of paragraph, 243–45
Order letter, 276
Order of importance, in organizing
  ideas, 250
Organizations, capitals for, 115–16

Paragraphs, beginning of, 243–45
 choosing subject for, 234–35
 coherence in, 250
 concluding sentence in, 250, 256–57
 defined, 230
 descriptive, 263–64
 details, reasons, examples in,
   246–47, 250, 256, 265
 development of, 246–47
 expository, 265–66
 narrative, 260–61
 narrowing subject of, 234–35
 notes for, 239–40
 opening of, 243–45
 order of importance in, 250
 organization of, 250
 persuasive, 267–68
 planning, 234–35, 239–40
 purpose of, 239–40, 243, 246–47
 rewriting, 229, 238, 242, 244, 249,
   252, 254, 259, 261, 264, 267
 selecting ideas for, 239–40
 subject for, 234–35
 time order in, 250
 transitional expressions in, 253
Participial phrase as fragment, 101–102
Participles, 101, 155–56, 157, 159,
  161, 163
Past tense, 155–56, 157, 159, 161, 163
Periods, at end of sentence, 1
 in quotations, 103, 105, 199
Personal pronouns, 177, 179, 181, 197
Persuasive paragraph, 267–68
Phrase fragments, 99, 101
Phrases, adjective, 63, 67
 adverb, 65, 67
 appositive, 81–82, 99
 prepositional, *see* Prepositional
   phrases
 in series, 77
 -ing, 101
 See also Phrase fragments
Planning, paragraph, 234–35, 239–240

Plural nouns, 17, 131, 133, 135, 197
Plural pronouns, 131, 133, 137
Possession, apostrophes for, 193
Possessive pronouns, 197
Predicates, defined, 3
 simple, 5
Prefixes, 75, 91
Prepositional phrases, 61–62, 63, 65,
  99
 combining sentences with, 217
 defined, 32, 61, 99
 fragments, 67–68, 99
 and number of subject, 135
 placement of, 67–68
Prepositions, 31, 181
 defined, 31, 61
 list of, 31
Present participles, 153–54
Present tense, 153
Principal, principle, 173
Product names, capitals for, 116
Pronouns, defined, 21, 137
 agreement with antecedent, 181
 as direct objects, 179
 indefinite, 137
 number of, 131, 137
 object, 177, 179, 181
 personal, 131, 175, 177, 179, 181,
   183, 197
 plural, 131, 133, 137
 possessive, 197
 after prepositions, 181
 singular, 131, 133, 137
 as subject complements, 177
 as subjects, 175–76
Pronunciation, 17, 59, 73, 75, 191
Proper adjectives, 119
Proper nouns, 115, 119
Punctuation, *see* specific punctuation
  marks

Question marks, 1, 103, 105, 199
Question sentences, 139
Quotation marks, 193, 201–02

Regions of country, capitals for, 117
Regular verbs, 155, 157
Request letters, 275–76
Rewriting a composition, 229, 238,
  242, 244, 249, 252, 254, 259, 261,
  264, 267
Run-on sentences, 97, 105

Salutation, in business letter, 274
 in friendly letter, 270
School subjects, capitals for, 119
Seasons, capitals for, 117
Sent, scent, 173
Sentence bases, 43–44
 three-part, 43–44, 45, 47
 two-part, 43, 45
Sentence combining, into compound
   sentences, 221
 with adjectives, adverbs, 213, 215
 with compound subjects, compound
   verbs, 219–20
 with other connecting words, 223,
   225
Sentence fragments, 97–98, 99, 101,
  103, 105, 209

278

Sentences, completeness in, 103, 105
    compound, 11, 79
    concluding, 250, 256–57
    defined, 1–2
    imperative, 7
    predicates of, 3, 5
    question, 139
    run-on, 97, 105
    simple, 11
    subjects of, 3, 7, 43–44
    topic, 232–33, 239, 243, 253,
        256–57
    turned-around, 139
    variety in, 229, 238, 242, 244, 249,
        252, 254, 259, 261, 264, 266
Series, punctuation of, 77–78
Set, sit, 163
Signature, in business letter, 275
    in friendly letter, 271
Simple past, 153–54
Simple sentences, 11
Simple subjects, 7
Singular nouns, 131, 133, 135
Singular pronouns, 131, 133, 137
Sit, set, 163
Specific words, use of, 171
Spelling, *-cle* or *-cal* ending, 151
    ea and its three sounds, 59
    and final silent *e,* 113
    homophones, 173
    ie-ei rule, 41
    plural nouns, 17
    prefixes and, 75, 91
    pronunciation and, 17, 59, 73, 75, 191
    sibilants, 17
    silent consonants, 191
    suffixes and, 113, 129
Stationary, stationery, 173
Subject, for paragraph, 234–35
Subject complements, 49, 179, 181
Subjects, agreement of, with verbs,
        131, 133, 135, 137, 141, 143
    compound, 9, 43, 143, 175
    complete, 7

simple, 7, 43
    pronouns as, 175–76
    of sentences, defined, 3, 7, 43–44
Suffixes, 113, 129
Synonyms, 127, 189

Tense, 153–54, 155, 157–58, 159, 161,
    163, 165
There, here, 139
They, them, use of, 175–77
Through, threw, 173
Time order of events, 250
Titles, capitals for, 121
Topic, for composition, 239–40
Topic, sentences, 232–33, 239, 243,
    253, 256–57
Transitional expressions, in paragraph,
    253

Verbal context, *see* Context
Verbs, 33, 43–44, 45, 155–56
    action, 45, 46, 47, 51
    agreement of, with subjects, 131,
        133, 135, 137, 141, 143
    compound, 9, 43
    defined, 5, 25, 45
    helping, 5, 26, 46, 155–56
    irregular, 157, 159, 161, 163, 165
    linking, 23, 45, 46, 49, 51, 179
    principal parts, 153–55
    regular, 155, 157
    in series, 77
    simple, 5, 43
    tense of, 153–54, 155, 157–58,
        159, 161, 163, 165

Well, good, use of, 52
Words, appropriateness of, 189
    precise meanings of, 171
Writing process, 229, 234–35, 239–40,
    243–44, 246–47, 260–61,
    263–64, 265, 267

INDEX OF VOCABULARY WORDS

(Page numbers refer to definition in text)

abhor, 89
adhere, 39
adept, 73
agitate, 39
aloof, 189
altercation, 111
annihilate, 111
anonymous, 111
appalling, 90
appropriate, 111
aristocracy, 15
aristocrat, 15
ascertain, 111
aspiration, 111
asset, 58
audible, 73
aversion, 127

balmy, 15
banish, 89
blemish, 15
brevity, 149

catastrophe, 58
coincide, 58
colossal, 90
commend, 127
compensate, 58
competitor, 89
compute, 111
concession, 39

concise, 57
confirm, 149
congenial, 127
congregate, 127
consistent, 90
contemplate, 171
counteract, 171

disagree, 189
discord, 89
dismal, 149
disperse, 149
distort, 58
dubious, 149

eject, 58
eligible, 90
eloquent, 74
eminent, 189
exclude, 111
exquisite, 39
extinct, 57

fantastic, 74
farce, 15
fickle, 149
frivolous, 39
futile, 127

gaudy, 15

hamper, 74
haughty, 74, 189
humane, 39
hysterical, 90

inevitable, 127
inflammable, 57
intricate, 89

lenient, 149

meek, 189
mimic, 15
monopoly, 74

notorious, 189

obstinate, 189

persistent, 189
plausible, 90
potent, 127
potential, 171
predecessor, 149
protrude, 15
pugnacious, 189

ravenous, 15
rebuke, 74
refute, 57
renounce, 111

repel, 74
replica, 15
resolute, 189
restrict, 127
ruthless, 127

salient, 74
satire, 39
shun, 171
speculate, 39
spontaneous, 171
spurn, 171
submerge, 15
superfluous, 111

tactful, 149
technique, 171
thwart, 127
tolerate, 39
tranquil, 189
transient, 149
tumult, 171
turbulent, 39
turmoil, 172

vigilance, 172
vivid, 74

wrangle, 189

A NOTE ON SPELLING

Writing may be thought of as a way of recording the sounds of speech by the use of symbols that represent those sounds. The letters in our alphabet are the symbols we use to represent our speech sounds. If we had a different letter for each sound, spelling would be easy, just a matter of knowing which letter to use for each sound. Unfortunately, English spelling is not that simple. There are more sounds than there are letters in the alphabet to represent them, and so the task of learning to spell in our language is somewhat complicated.

The complications, however, may be partially overcome by becoming aware of, and learning, the many *spelling patterns* that do exist. These patterns involve the use of various combinations of letters to spell certain sounds.

To show the *sounds* of a word, rather than the letters, a special phonetic alphabet has been developed. Using this phonetic alphabet will help you understand the relationship between sounds and letters, and thereby help you to become a better speller.

On the next two pages are two charts. The first one, entitled "Consonant Sounds and Their Common Spellings," summarizes twenty-four main consonant sounds of English, the symbols used to represent these sounds, and common ways of spelling them. The *symbol* for each consonant sound is written between a pair of slanted lines. For example, the symbol /k/ stands for the sound of the first letter in the word *kit*, as you can see by looking at the chart. The sound /k/ may also be spelled by the letters *c* (as in *cold*), *ck* (as in *lick*), or *ke* (as in *like*).

The second chart, "Vowel Sounds and Their Common Spellings," shows the symbols for fourteen main vowel sounds and the vowel sound called a *schwa*. If you look at the vowel sound /ī/ on the chart, you will see the several patterns or ways in which this sound may be spelled. For example, in the word *line*, it is spelled with the letter *i* followed by a consonant (*n*), which, in turn, is followed by an *e*. (The letters **VCe,** standing for *vowel, consonant, e,* represent *one* of the ways or patterns in which the sound /ī/ may be written in English.) Other ways include *-igh,* as in *high; -y* as in *try; -ie* as in *die*.

The spelling patterns reflected in these two charts should help to balance the irregularities of English spelling. The point is, that *despite* exceptions and seemingly illogical spellings, our spelling system exists as it does for good historical reasons and is, on the whole, a predictable system.

Consonant Sounds and Their Common Spellings

Sound	At the Beginning	At the End
/p/	**p:** pie	**p:** rip; **pe:** ripe
/t/	**t:** ten	**t:** pet; **te:** date
/k/	**k:** kit; **c:** cold	**ck: lick; ke: like**
/ch/	**ch:** chin	**tch:** witch; **ch:** reach
/b/	**b:** bed	**b:** tub; **be:** tube
/d/	**d:** do	**d:** rid; **de:** ride
/g/	**g:** get	**g:** beg; **gue:** league
/j/	**j:** jet; **g:** gentle	**dge:** budge; **ge:** cage
/f/	**f:** fun; **ph:** phrase	**ff:** stuff; **fe:** life; **f:** beef; **ph:** paragraph
/v/	**v:** very	**ve:** save
/s/	**s:** see; **c:** center	**ss:** glass; **s:** bus; **se:** case; **ce:** rice
/z/	**z:** zoo	**z:** quiz; **zz:** buzz; **se:** rose; **ze:** sneeze
/sh/	**sh:** ship	**sh:** push
/zh/	**j:** Jacques	**ge:** rouge; (in the middle) **s:** treasure
/r/	**r:** run; **wr:** wrist; **rh:** rhyme	**r:** car; **re:** care
/l/	**l:** lose	**ll:** pill; **le:** smile; **l:** fail
/m/	**m:** move	**m:** Sam; **me:** same; **mb:** tomb
/n/	**n:** nose; **gn:** gnaw; **kn:** know	**n:** pin; **ne:** pine
/ng/		**ng:** strong; **n:** trunk
/th/	**th:** thick	**th:** path
/t͟h/	**th:** then	**th:** smooth; **the:** bathe
/y/	**y:** you; **u** /yū/: use	
/w/	**w:** will; **o** /wu/: one; **qu** /kw/: quick	
/h/	**h:** hat; **wh:** who	

Vowel Sounds and Their Common Spellings

Fourteen Vowel Sounds

Sounds	/i/	/e/	/a/	/u/	/o/
Spellings and Examples	**i:** hit	**e:** red **ea:** dead	**a:** cat	**u:** but **o:** son	**o:** top **a:** far

Sounds	/ī/	/ē/	/ā/	/ū/	/ō/
Spellings and Examples	**VCe:** line **igh:** high **y:** try **ie:** die	**VCe:** Pete **ee:** deed **ea:** heat **e:** he **ie:** chief **ei:** deceive	**VCe:** lame **ai:** wait **ay:** pay **ei:** weigh	**VCe:** June **oo:** root **ew:** few **ue:** Sue **o:** to	**VCe:** lone **oa:** goat **ow:** slow **oe:** hoe **o:** no

Sounds	/o͞o/	/ou/	/oi/	/au/
Spellings and Examples	**oo:** look **u:** push	**ou:** out **ow:** cow	**oi:** oil **oy:** toy	**au:** haul **aw:** flaw **a:** ball **o:** long **ough:** fought **augh:** caught

The Vowel Sound Schwa /ə/

	i	e	ea	u	o
In Words of One Syllable	stir girl	were her	learn earth	burn spur	world worse

	-er	-or	-ar
The Sound /ər/	runner maker father	actor orator navigator	beggar liar sugar

	-al	-le	-el	-ul	-ile	-il
The Sound /əl/	legal moral rural	steeple battle circle	camel satchel travel	beautiful useful helpful	fertile juvenile hostile	April evil council

	-en	-an	-ain	-in
The Sound /ən/	frozen deepen oaken garden	American orphan woman organ	captain curtain mountain certain	robin cabin basin cousin

Key to *English Grammar and Composition**

The following chart correlates lessons in *English Workshop, First Course* to the appropriate rules in the Liberty Edition of *English Grammar and Composition, First Course* and the Benchmark Edition of *English Composition and Grammar, First Course*.

Workshop Lesson	Text Rule	Workshop Lesson	Text Rule
1	1a, 13a/10a, 22a	67	8c/17c
2	1b, 1d/10b, 10d	68	8d–e/17d–e
3	1e/10e	69	8k/17k
4	1c/10c	70	8n/17n
5	1f–g, 3d/10f–g, 12d	71	8g–i/17g–i
6	7a–b/16a–b	74	27b/27b
8	28b/28b	76	9a–b/18a–b
9	29i/25i	77–82	9c/18c
10	2a/11a	85	28f/28f
11	2b/11b	87	10a/19a
12	2c/11c	88	10b/19b
13	3a/12a	89	10c/19c
14	3b/12b	90	10d/19d
16	3c/12c	91	8p/17p
17	3d–e/12d–e	94	28f/28f
21	28b/28b	96	15l–n/25l–n
22	29a/25a	97	15o/24o
24	3a, 4a–c/12a, 13a–c	99	14k, 15b–g/23k, 24b–g
25	4a/13a	100	15d, 15h–i/24d, 24h–i
26	3a, 4c, 11c/12a, 13c, 20c	104–105	17a/9a
27	11c/20c	106	17c–d/9c–d
32	5b/14b	107	17e/9e
33	5c/14c	108–109	17f/9f
34	5d/14d	111	20a/2a
35	11f/20f	112	20b/2b
38	27a–b, 28c/27a–b, 28c	113	19c, 19e, 20e–f, 23a–c/ 1c, 1e, 2e–f, 5a–b
40	14f–g/23f–g		
41	14h/23h	114	19a, 19f–k, 20h–i/1a, 1f–k, 2i
42	14k/23k		
43	14l/23l	115	20i–j/2i–j
46	27b, 28c/27a, 28c	116	19f–k, 20c, 20h–i, 21a– f/1f–h, 2i, 3a–f
47	29c/25c		
48–51	16a/8a	117	20m/21
52	16b/8b	118	20n/21
56	29e/25e	119	20d, 23i/2d, 5j
57–58	13c/22c	120	21a/3a
59	13d/22d	121	21b/3b
60	13f/22f	122	21c–e/3c–e
63	27b/27b	123	21f/3f
64	29d/25d	124	25a–c/7a–c
65	8a/17a	125	25d/7d–f
66	8b/17b	126–127	25e/7g, 7i–j

K 6
L 7
M 8
N 9

*References printed in red refer to the appropriate rules in the Benchmark Edition of *English Composition and Grammar, First Course*.